James Cook University Hospital

THE FIRST 25 YEARS

Hugh Sturzaker

BookPublishingWorld

A BookPublishingWorld Book

Cover design by Carole Reeve

ISBN: 978-1-90553-24-2 (pbk)

ISBN: 978-1-905553-25-9 (hbk)

Printed and bound in the UK for BookPublishingWorld

www.bookpublishingworld.co.uk

To my wife, Ann, children and grandchildren
who, sometimes, have taken second place
to my work for the hospital

"There is no true success without work"

Sir James Paget

Contents

Illustrations

Foreword

The year 2007 sees one of Great Yarmouth and Waveney's most important institutions, the James Paget University Hospital, begin celebrations for a quarter of a century of delivering acute hospital care to the local population. As a pivotal part of these anniversary celebrations, my good friend, Hugh Sturzaker, has written this history of the James Paget. As a Past Chairman of the hospital, I am delighted to have been given the opportunity to express my admiration of Hugh's efforts and to express the community's sincere appreciation for this most significant and readable volume.

This is the first time that the rich history of the James Paget has been captured in a book, telling the story of its continual evolution up to its current status as a fine University Hospital. *James Paget University Hospital – the First Twenty-Five Years* is the story of the James Paget's continual accomplishments. It follows a historical journey, not only filled with many medical advances and treatments, but also with the contributions of the individuals whose commitments to the James Paget and patient care are important, and sometimes crucial. They are, of course, the true heroes of this book and its recognition of their work is, in some cases, long overdue.

Hugh has given a narrative that gives a unique insight into the reasons why the James Paget University Hospital has a reputation of excellence and good practice throughout not only East Anglia but also nationally, and, in some cases, internationally. In accepting this task, Hugh has stepped outside of the role with which he is associated locally, i.e. a dedicated and accomplished surgeon, and has moved to be an authoritative author who has produced this excellent "human" volume. As a long-standing surgeon of the hospital, Hugh typifies everything that is best about the James Paget. I can best illustrate this point by referring to what I always called the "*esprit de James Paget*". I saw this every day that I walked around the Hospital, with Doctors, Nurses, Managers and

Board Members working as one for the good of the patients we serve. It was a great privilege and very humbling to be but one member of that team. I had always wondered how far back one would have to go to find the answer as to when this spirit was first engendered. Having now researched the matter, the answer is May 1844. I found this answer in a volume called *Memoirs and Letters of Sir James Paget,* which tells the story of the eminent surgeon from whom the hospital takes its name. In this book, Sir James Paget refers to the ethos of his hospital, St Bartholomew's, where he was a senior doctor, as being " ... the best managed in London; best, that is, in order and quietude, best in *esprit de corps,* in freedom from unnecessary interference of Hospital Governors or officials; best in the care ... ". That original spirit of Sir James Paget still drives our Hospital which has taken on his name.

Finally, I congratulate Hugh, whose vision and dedication have brought this project to fruition. In doing so, he has written a priceless account not only of the James Paget, but of the people and the community which it serves.

John Wells: Chairman
James Paget Healthcare NHS Trust (1993–2003)

Preface

Why write a history about a hospital that was built only twenty-five years ago? I have done it because this is a great story which needs to be told. I have tried to show the very poor health provision that the people of this part of East Anglia had for many years and the great fight that was necessary to obtain a new hospital. In the last twenty-five years there have been incredible changes and I want to show the changes which have occurred in so many diseases, how they are investigated and treated and how the management of the health service has altered. I want to explain how the hospital and the health service have evolved over the twenty-five years. We have new drugs, fantastic scanners and new operations. Laparoscopic procedures have replaced many open operations; stay time in hospital has been drastically cut and now 70–80% of operations are done as day cases. The population is becoming older, obesity is increasing in all age groups, bacteria are becoming resistant to antibiotics and epidemics of MRSA infection and Clostridium difficile are becoming more common. Diseases and people are changing, as are the way we manage them, so the health professionals have to adapt and this has been part of the success of the James Paget.

The population is becoming more knowledgeable and their expectations are higher. Lawyers advertise that they will sue for medical negligence with no cost to the individual. Fortunately, the local population has always been very supportive of its hospital and throughout its existence they have responded to various appeals. As a result, the hospital has many facilities which others do not have and the very act of raising money brings people together. The hospital has also been most fortunate in its managers, who have good relations with the clinicians and other staff. Since it became an NHS Trust in 1993, the hospital has always balanced its books and in 2006 it became a Foundation Trust and a University Hospital.

Central to the success of any organisation is the staff and repeated national staff surveys have shown that the job satisfaction here is in the top 10% in England. The staff get on well with each other and the design of the hospital is conducive to them seeing and talking to each other on their way round the corridors.

I want to explain the successes which have been achieved by the staff of this hospital and to look into the future. Will they be able to continue their successes; how will they cope with shorter working hours for junior medical staff, with increasing specialisation and with increasingly expensive technology? The population expects more and more from its health service. Will the staff be able to rise to the challenge? Will the buildings last another twenty-five years?

Why write the book now? Why not wait another twenty-five years? The main reason is that this is a great story and most of the people who have been involved in it are still around to recount parts of it. My research has shown that two people often have different memories of the same event which, no doubt, will become wider as time goes on. Unfortunately, as time passes, so does one's memory and papers are lost or are damaged. I hope that this book will stimulate the management of the hospital to record events as they happen, so that if someone wishes to write the history of the hospital's next twenty-five years it will be a little easier than it was to record the first twenty-five years. I hope you will learn from it and enjoy it.

Why should I write this book? In June 2005 I had just retired and was looking forward to spending more time with my wife and family and doing many of the things that I had not had time for over many years. On the other hand I have a great love for the hospital and thought that if someone did not record this story now it would not be done. But what qualifications do I have?

My first visit to East Anglia was when I came to apply for the post of Consultant General Surgeon with a special interest in surgery of the gastro-intestinal tract. At that time there were 120 Senior Surgical Registrars chasing after 20–25 jobs a year and only a few of those mentioned a gastro-intestinal interest. Added to that, my wife and I had decided that we did not want to live and work in London and she, who had been born and had spent all her life in Surrey, did not want to live north of the

Wash! Jobs, therefore, were in short supply and the competition was stiff.

It was with some trepidation that I ventured into East Anglia. The existing hospital buildings in Lowestoft and Great Yarmouth were not inspiring, but the concrete piles of the new hospital, being built on a green-field site at Gorleston, were starting to emerge. The most impressive memory was that of the people I met. There was a buffet luncheon which gave the Consultant Medical Staff the opportunity of meeting the half a dozen short-listed candidates the day prior to the interview. It was held in the Coastal Medical Education Centre at Northgate Hospital, Great Yarmouth, and afterwards Gerald Fayers, the Hospital Secretary, asked the candidates if we would like to look around the hospital. Two or three of us accepted his offer and I was struck by the wonderful relationship that he had with all the staff, knowing each of them by name. In spite of the buildings, it was a very happy hospital and there was the promise of a new hospital which was already being built. I was somewhat surprised, but delighted, to be appointed as the new Consultant Surgeon at the interview in Cambridge the next day and on my way back home by train I wrote an article about my experience of attending interviews for Consultant appointments. Very shortly afterwards, it was published in the *British Medical Journal.*

As a consequence of that appointment, I was around to see the hospital being built and was involved in some of the many preparations that were needed for it to be ready to receive its first patients. Since then, much of my life has been tied up with the hospital, so that I have seen it develop from the inside. In addition, as an examiner and Regional Advisor for the Royal College of Surgeons of Edinburgh and as an attendee at many meetings around the country, I have had the opportunity to see and discuss the hospital facilities in other parts of the country. In addition, I have been involved in establishing patient support groups and in raising money for several public appeals to provide new departments, buildings or equipment for the hospital, so I have had the opportunity of meeting many of the local inhabitants. They have been so supportive of "their hospital" that it has many features which other hospitals do not have. Consequently, I feel very privileged and fortunate to have obtained my job way back in 1979.

Since retiring I have continued to teach at the hospital and in Norwich and to examine around the country and occasionally abroad. Last year I was elected a Governor of the Hospital, so I continue a formal link with it.

As far as writing this book is concerned, I first set about it by drawing up an outline of the topics to be covered and approached David Hill, Chief Executive, and John Hemming, Chairman of the Trust, explaining my ideas and seeking their support. Next, I wrote to many people (Consultants, Heads of Departments, Managers, Executive and Non-Executive members of the Trust Board, Voluntary Organisations, Patient Support Groups, etc) explaining about the book, asking for their views and sending each of them a questionnaire. Some have been extremely helpful, but others have required repeated letters, phone calls, emails and visits. Even so, some have still failed to respond. I have emailed the whole hospital stating that if an individual or department had not heard from me to get in touch.

I have read many books and articles on the hospital and related issues; have read the local newspapers and spoken to many people. Finally, I have sent the relevant sections that I have written to each individual and department mentioned in the book asking for their comments and I have used these to correct the manuscript. In spite of this, I am aware that certain people, departments and events have been missed out and I trust that there are not too many inaccuracies. I take full responsibility and apologise, in advance, for all of them.

This exercise has brought back many memories. I hope that this book will do the same for you, that you learn something from it and, more especially, you will enjoy it.

Acknowledgements

This book would not have been written without the help and support of many people. Christine Eagle acted as my postmistress, directing many of the emails and letters between me and various people and departments in the hospital. She also gave me much valuable information gleaned from working for the health service for over thirty years. Anne Edwards, the Editor of the *Great Yarmouth Mercury*, and her staff allowed me access and the use of one of their offices to go through many years of old copies of the *Mercury* and to drink their tea and coffee. David Hill and Adrian Pennington have given me free access to many files and documents at the hospital and Elayne Guest was most helpful in her advice, support and in giving me her files.

Almost all the Consultant Medical staff and the two Nurse Consultants plus many of the present and past Executive and Non-Executive Directors gave me details from their *curriculum vitae*, for which I thank them. From these I have written up potted histories of each and, where I did not have a response from them, I have tried to extract the information from other sources. Some of the above, as well as many others in the hospital, have given me some information and even articles about their departments or organisations. I have used these to varying degrees and in most instances have made alterations and additions. Where an article is mainly based on what has been written by a contributor I have mentioned this at the beginning of each section. The length of an article bears no relationship to the importance of a department.

I would like to thank the following for their help: Sally Cockrell, John Corson, David Turner, Kingsley Branch, Peter Harrison (both of them), Gail Hunting, Sheila Howlett, Paul Aukland, John Studley, Gokarakonda Suresh, Prem Premachandra, Peter Black, Robert Jones, Robert Graham, David Wayne, Bernard Brett, Judith Dron, Pat

Nelson, Wolf Grabau, Graeme McLean, Julie Wash, Sarah McClintock, David Ellis, Peter Forster, John Ball, Barrie Dean, Chris Souter, Joe Ostrowski, Vinod Kumar, Frances Holly Archer, Susan Jones, Michelle Thompson, Willy Notcutt, Bob Mann, Pieter Bothma, Ajit Verma, Sarah Morris, Jenette Powell, Penny Cox, Jill King, Tina Dyble, T.C. Harry, Belinda Burroughes, Barrie Dean, Kathy Nobes, Kim Turner, Jim Small, Alan Price, June Northcott, Mike Pollard, Joyce Mowbray, Chris Souter, Madeleine Borg, Eileen Duckworth, David Todd, Chris Tom, Liz Brown, Brian Sweales, Iain Johnstone, Pat Mullen, Elaine Sparkes, Christine Thompson, Sue Barnes, Richard Allen, Mike Deavin, Liz Barber, David Adams, Donna Bilyard, Christine Eagle, Angie Benjafield, John Applegate, Janet Papworth, Tony Grice, Maggie Wright, Nichola Hicks, Irene Walker, Jerome Pereira, Anne Davis, Margaret Carver, Heather Cave, Mary Morris, Andrea Allen, Patrick Thompson, Paul Davies, Brian Callan, Arthur Harris, Denise Chapman, Tracy Moyse, Ann Filby, Vanessa Thompson, David Buddery and Alan Hunt.

I am indebted to Derek Rogers and Madeleine Borg for their help with the pictures and to Carole Reeve for the work she did in arranging the photographs in preparation for printing. I would like to thank Richard Chalmers, the Editor of Book Publishing World, for his great help and calm advice in converting my manuscript into a book. Having done all the typing myself, my typing skills are much improved, and it will be good to see the results in book form.

I thank the Wellcome Library for permission to use their lithograph portrait of Sir James Paget on the cover of this book, Anne Edwards and Archant Press for the use of their photograph of the unveiling of the board proclaiming the site of where the hospital was to be built and the James Paget University Hospitals NHS Foundation Trust for allowing me to use a number of its photographs.

There are bound to be a number of people whom I have forgotten to mention. I trust that they will accept my apologies.

I am most grateful to John Wells for kindly agreeing to write the foreword to this book. I have known him for twenty-seven years and I admired the time and energy he put into running the Trust while he was Chairman of it for over ten years. I was delighted when he accepted my request to write the foreword.

Finally, I would like to thank Ann, my children and grandchildren for their forbearance while I have been working on this book. I look forward to spending more time with them in the future.

~ 1 ~

Sir James Paget

Although Sir James Paget was one of the most famous and influential medical men in the latter half of Queen Victoria's reign, it proved difficult to name the new District General Hospital at Gorleston after him. Many names were suggested, even before the hospital was opened, such as Nelson, Lady Hamilton, Edith Cavell, Princess Diana, Prince William and Hugh McDonald, who had been a surgeon in Great Yarmouth since 1945. There was a competition in the local newspapers, with a fifteen pound prize for the name selected, which was Royal Jubilee. Dr. Wayne, Consultant Physician, had suggested Sir James Paget, but as he had been born in Great Yarmouth it was felt that this would not find favour with people living in Lowestoft. Dr. Wayne replied that, "he had been born between Winterton and Southwold". Eventually, the District Health Authority decided that the hospital could no longer be called the DGH and decided to call it the Prince William. People did not like the idea of visiting the 'Prince Willy' or the 'Willy Hospital'. The Consultant Medical Staff were in favour of James Paget and on 3rd September 1984, by a vote of 8 to 7, the Area Health Authority supported the idea.

James Paget was born at 59 South Quay, Great Yarmouth, on 11th January, 1814 and went on to become one of the best known and respected surgeons of the second half of the 19th Century as well as Surgeon to Queen Victoria for many years. His parents were Samuel and Sarah Elizabeth Paget and he was the twelfth of seventeen children born over twenty-six years. Only nine survived through to adulthood. His father was a wealthy ship owner, banker and brewer and at one time was mayor of Great Yarmouth. He supplied the Royal Naval North Sea Fleet with food and provisions and later went into partnership to own some breweries. With his wealth he built a mansion at 59 South Quay in 1813 and this is where James was born a year later.

By 1827, when James was aged 13, Samuel Paget was starting to suffer financial hardship and he could not afford to send James to public school at Charterhouse in London where his three elder brothers had been educated. Instead, he had to stay at the small school run by an ex-actor, Mr. Bowles, until he was sixteen years of age. From writings he made years later, it appears that he was not particularly impressed by the education he received there. He wanted to pursue a nautical career, but his parents did not want him to leave home and, eventually, on 9th March 1830, at the age of 16, he was apprenticed to Dr. Charles Costerton, who practised from a house in Hall Quay and was the medical practitioner to the Paget family. The apprenticeship was for five years and cost his father 100 guineas. During this time, he learnt to bandage ulcerated legs, bleed patients, prescribe medicines, treat colds and coughs and occasionally treat injuries. In his second year, he attended a course of lectures on bones given by a young surgeon from Acle which he thought were at least as equal to any of the lectures or demonstrations he subsequently had at St. Bartholomew's Hospital, London.

During the time of his apprenticeship he studied botany and, with his brother, Charles, he published a book resulting from their study of the fauna and flora around Great Yarmouth which was called 'Sketch of the Natural History of Yarmouth and its Neighbourhood, Containing Catalogues of the Species of Animals, Birds, Reptiles, Fish, Insects and Plants at Present Known'. This was a remarkable work in which they described 1,185 plants and 766 insects plus other animals, birds and fish. James later wrote, "I think it impossible to estimate too highly the influence of the study of Botany on the course of my life. It introduced me into the society of studious and observant men. It gave me an ambition for success. It educated me in habits of orderly arrangement. I can think of none among the reasons of my success – so far as I can judge of them – which may not be thought of as due in some degrees to this part of my apprentice life." Also, during these years he learnt French, Latin, Greek and later German, which enabled him to read papers in these languages and to travel in Europe.

Six months before his apprenticeship with Dr. Costerton finished, he moved to St. Bartholomew's Hospital, London, on 3rd October 1834, at the age of 20. (This is where Charles Costerton had started his medical training in 1810.) His fees were paid for by his brother, George. James was not very impressed with the standard of teaching, but he worked very hard, ending up with prizes in medicine, surgery, chemistry and botany. As a medical student, in 1835, he observed, and was the first to record, a nematode worm – later named Trichina spiralis – in the muscles of a patient who had died of tuberculosis. The following year, 1836, he passed the examination for the Membership of the Royal College of Surgeons of London. Intending to practise surgery, he put up his plate at 3 Serle Street, Lincoln's Inn. To supplement his income he wrote articles and reviews for a number of medical journals and taught some students for a fee of £10 monthly.

In spite of his brilliant student career, he failed to obtain a surgical training at that time and, in 1837, he became Curator of St. Bartholomew's Hospital Museum, which gave him an income of £40 yearly. In 1846 he published the Catalogue of the Pathological Specimens of St. Bartholomew's Hospital, three years after finishing as the Curator of the Museum. Previously, in 1839, at the age of 25, he became Administrator of Morbid Anatomy at the Hospital. By this time he was a popular teacher and, after requests by the students, he was appointed a lecturer in anatomy and pathology in 1841. He also had a small income from being warden of the students' residential college. His excellent work as Curator at St. Bartholomew's was noted and, in 1842, he was appointed to catalogue John Hunter's specimens which he had left to the Royal College of Surgeons of London. Between 1846 and 1849, he described and catalogued 3,520 specimens and published the details in five volumes called 'Pathological Catalogue of the College of Surgeons Museum', which ran to 1,218 pages.

In 1844, aged 30, he eventually married Lydia North, to whom he had been engaged for eight years, and they had four sons and two daughters. Their second son, Francis, became Bishop of Oxford, and another, Stephen, became a well-known surgeon and wrote *Confessio Medici.*

In 1843 he was one of the original 300 people to be elected a Fellow of the Royal College of Surgeons when it became "of England". (Prior to that it was known as the Royal College of Surgeons of London.) In 1847 he was appointed Professor of Anatomy and Surgery for the Royal College of Surgeons of England at St. Bartholomew's Hospital. Although he had had little training in surgery, he was appointed the hospital's dispensary surgeon in 1841, assistant surgeon in 1844 and full surgeon in 1861. He was very modest and his views on colleagues who tried to cover up their failings were encompassed in a lecture he gave to students on the calamities of surgery. Referring to those surgeons who said, "I did my best; but these things will happen", he remarked that, "there is no more miserable or false plea than this ... but there are some people who seem to have a happy art of forgetting all their failures, and remembering nothing but their successes, and, as I have watched such men in professional life, years have always made them worse instead of better surgeons. They seem to have a faculty of reckoning all failures as little, and all successes as big; they make their brains like sieves, and they run all the little things through, and retain all the big ones which they suppose to be their successes; and a mischievous heap of rubbish it is that they retain."

In 1847 he became Aries and Gale Professor of the Royal College of Surgeons of England at the young age of 33. This involved giving six lectures over a period of two weeks and he was re-elected to the Professorship for the following six years.

By this time his earnings were increasing, but his father's fortunes were declining, so James and his brothers agreed to pay off their father's debts. It took them until 1862 to do this.

In 1851 he entered consultant practice and rapidly became one of the most successful surgeons in London. At one time his annual earnings were £10,000. He was also developing an international reputation. He became Surgeon-in-Ordinary to Queen Victoria in 1858 and, five years later, he was appointed Surgeon-in-Ordinary to the Prince of Wales. In 1871 he resigned as surgeon to St. Bartholomew's Hospital and the same year Queen Victoria presented him with a Baronetcy and he had the Paget family motto 'Work Itself is a Pleasure' on his coat of arms. The occasion was noted in the *Lancet*, which said, "there are very few men who have done more to entitle them to special recognition at the hands of the sovereign than Sir James Paget, so there is probably no one on whom such a distinction could have been conferred with greater satisfaction; or who has more successfully laboured to elevate the character of the profession and enlarge its powers and usefulness. Of the high order of Sir James Paget's intellectual attributes, and of the unusually distinguished position that he has long occupied as a scientific surgeon, pathologist and physiologist there is no need to speak. It is not only that he has something good or original to say whenever he speaks or writes, but it is because he says it so well, that his writings and speeches are always interesting and suggestive."

In 1877 he was appointed Serjeant Surgeon to Queen Victoria, on the death of Sir William Ferguson, and the following year he stopped operating on major cases.

During his life he had many honours bestowed upon him: President of the Royal College of Surgeons of England (1875), member of the General Medical Council, Fellow of the Royal Society and Vice-Chancellor of London University. He was elected President of the Seventh International Congress of Medicine which was held in London in 1881 and which was attended by over 3,000 doctors and scientists, including Pasteur, Kock, Huxley, Darwin, Lister, Virchow and Osler. Apart from these medical and scientific people, he counted many others as his friends, including Charles Dickens, George Eliot, Lord Tennyson, Robert Browning, William Gladstone and members of the Royal Family.

Apart from the discovery of the parasite trichina spiralis, he was the first to recognise several other medical conditions. Paget's disease of the nipple is an eczema-like eruption around the nipple which indicates that either there is a cancer of the breast or that one will develop. He described "about fifteen cases ... in age from 40 to 60 or more years" in an article in St. Bartholomew's Hospital Reports entitled 'On Disease of the Mammary Areola preceding Cancer of the Mammary Gland' in 1874. In the article he also refers to "a persistent 'rawness' of the glans penis, like a long-enduring balanitis, followed after more than a year's duration by cancer of the substance of the glans". It is associated with large clear malignant cells in the epidermis as in Paget's disease of the nipple and similar features are seen in the skin around the anus. Paget's disease of bone he described as osteitis deformans in 1877. He noted the bowing and thickening of the long bones of the limbs, the increasing size of the skull and the development of malignant bone tumours.

Paget's name is also associated with axillary vein thrombosis, fibrosarcoma of the abdominal muscles, especially of the recti muscles (Paget's recurrent fibroid), recurrent abscesses (Paget's residual abscesses) and osteochondritis dessicans (Paget's quiet necrosis of bone). He was also the first to describe median nerve compression due to a fracture at the lower end of the radius and apophysitis of the tibial tubercle, which was later described by two radiologists, Drs. Osgood and Schlatter.

Sir James frequently came back to Great Yarmouth and, in 1886, he officially opened the new Yarmouth General Hospital. After one visit in 1891, when he was aged 77, he wrote to his brother George that "the town in its social and commercial aspects is indeed very sadly lowered; scarcely a house on the quay now appears as a private residence and the great ships and ship-building yards are gone. There are some changes for the better and especially the old Church which now surpasses any parish church that I have seen not only in size but in beauty and good order and the admirable method of its services." Sadly, the Parish Church of St. Nicholas was bombed in the 1940s but has since been re-built except for its spire.

Sir James was a deeply religious man and was an extremely hard worker and nowadays would be called a workaholic. The importance of the work ethic is noted in his family motto and on his coat of arms, 'Labor ipse voluptas' – work itself is pleasure. Although he thought little of the education that he received as a boy, his study of Botany, which led to his joint work with his brother on the flora and fauna of Great Yarmouth, was a great preparation for his future life. He was a great observer and questioned what he saw. He was a brilliant lecturer, gifted speaker and wrote well. He showed great humanity to his patients. Often he did not charge them and to some of the poor he was seen to offer them silver coins.

Infectious diseases were common and frequently lethal in his time and they were an occupational hazard for those carrying out postmortems. In 1839 he contracted spotted fever (typhus) after performing a postmortem and, in 1871, after another postmortem, he became seriously ill with abscesses in his arm and neck which required to be drained. Towards the end of his life he became frail but did survive to the age of 85, dying on 30th December 1899. His funeral service was held in Westminster Abbey and was led by his son, the Bishop of Oxford. Afterwards, he was buried in the grounds of Finchley Hospital, London.

Great Yarmouth should be very proud of its famous son and the hospital staff is very pleased that it was named after him. It is also grateful that his family continues to show an interest in it. Sir James Paget's second son, Francis, was Bishop of Oxford and his other son, the third Baronet, was General Sir Bernard Paget. He was Commander in Chief of Home Forces from 1941 to 1944. His son, Sir Julian Paget, was born on 11th July 1921 and was educated at Radley College and Christ Church, Oxford. He joined the Coldstream Guards in 1941 and served in North West Europe in 1944–1945. He retired from the army as a Lieutenant Colonel in 1968. He was appointed Gentleman Usher to the Queen in 1971 until 1991, when he became an Extra Gentleman Usher. He has written nine books on military history and Royal Ceremonial.

Sir Julian and Lady Paget have visited the hospital on many occasions in the last twelve years and their son, Henry, has visited several times, as has another relative, Dr. Oliver Paget from Switzerland. How fortunate the hospital is to continue this association with such a famous family.

~ 2 ~

Historical Aspects

The Health Services Prior to 1975

"The Health Service facilities in Great Yarmouth and Waveney tie with Weston-super-Mare as being the worst in England."

This was the view expressed by David Owen, the Health Minister, when he visited the District in 1975 and, as a result, permission was given to build a new hospital which opened to its first patients in December 1981. But why should this beautiful area of Great Britain have such an appalling health service? It can be put down to geography, the local population, politics and ultimately the lack of money.

Geographically the area lies on the East Coast of Norfolk and Suffolk and is the furthest point away from where the power and the money resided at the Regional Health Headquarters in Cambridge. It was almost "out of sight, out of mind". The population was insular, hard working and mainly poorly paid, accepting their lot. Many had never been outside their county; a trip to Norwich or Ipswich was a real expedition and there were some who had never been that far, so expectations were not high. Few people were involved in local politics and certainly not in health politics. The few Consultants on the coast worked hard looking after their patients and it was not in the interests of most of the visiting Consultants from Norwich to advocate building a new hospital on the coast, so it is unlikely that the state of the health provision in Great Yarmouth and Lowestoft was often brought to the attention of the Regional Health Board in Cambridge. The money was distributed from there to Ipswich, Peterborough, Norwich and other places, but only a trickle reached the coast. This is illustrated by the pounds per head of population distributed in the year1948: Cambridge £67, Bury St.

Edmunds £35, Kings Lynn £35, Peterborough £33, Ipswich £31, Norwich £31, and Great Yarmouth and Waveney a mere £9. The amounts did increase over the years, but the coast was always at the bottom of the money stakes. To appreciate the problems fully, it is necessary to look into the circumstances that existed prior to 1975.

The Great Yarmouth and Waveney Health District comprises the Eastern part of Norfolk and the Waveney District of Suffolk, extending from Winterton in the North to Southold in the South: a distance of 30 miles. Inland it extends 9 miles in the North to 15 miles in the South. Great Yarmouth and Lowestoft are the largest towns and there are several market towns or villages such as Acle, Caister, Gorleston, Beccles, Bungay, Halesworth, Harleston and Southwold. The countryside is mainly flat and undulating, providing good farming land, and the rivers, Broads and coast are popular attractions for holidays.

Great Yarmouth and Lowestoft had grown from the bounty of fish they obtained from the sea, particularly the herring which, when smoked, is known as the "Yarmouth bloater" – a name which is sometimes given to the folk of that town. Although smoked in the same way as a kipper, it is not slit open nor gutted prior to smoking, as is the case with kippers.

Great Yarmouth was built on a sandbank that did not exist when the Romans built their castles at Burgh Castle and Caister. The sand bank emerged in about 900, and by 1086 Yarmouth was already a small but flourishing royal borough with a population of 400. Permission was granted by King Henry III in 1261 to build a town wall, ditch and prison, all of which have survived largely intact. In 1334 the lay subsidy (taxation) rolls showed that Yarmouth raised more money than any other town apart from York, Bristol and Newcastle. The town's wealth was based almost entirely on the herring and this continued until well into the 20th Century. Many Scottish trawlers came down the coast each year fishing for herring. The fishermen's wives and girl friends would also come to gut the herring and put them into barrels before they were exported around the world. The ladies would stay in boarding houses in the Rows, which had been built in the 13th and 14th Centuries. The Rows were a gridiron of parallel, narrow passages leading up from the quayside and they were so narrow that special narrow carts (Troll carts) were built to carry possessions through them. Many of these rows were destroyed by enemy bombing in the Second World War and others were bulldozed when the war finished by an enthusiastic Council eager to provide new flats for its citizens.

In 1834 the Turnpike Act was passed which allowed the building of the Acle Straight across the marshes, so improving communications. In 1844 the railway between Norwich and Yarmouth was opened and there was a railway link between Norwich and Lowestoft. These measures allowed the development of the holiday industry in Lowestoft and Yarmouth and boarding houses and small hotels were built to cater for the increasing number of visitors who came to sample the air and sea. Both towns became fashionable holiday centres with the "bracing" sea air, great sandy beaches and boat trips on the Broads and in the North Sea. Royalty was also attracted and the Prince of Wales, the future Edward VII, spent much time in Yarmouth with one of his mistresses.

Both the fishing and holiday industries expanded in the first half of the 20th Century. In 1913, 1,163 boats used the port of Yarmouth and over 1.2 billion fish were caught. Holiday camps were being built along the coast and this brought more people to the area, but only for a few weeks in the height of summer. Unfortunately, in the 1950s the herring started to disappear from the North Sea and many fishing boats had to be sold or scrapped. Similarly, the holiday industry started to decline with the introduction of cheap holidays in Spain, France and other Mediterranean countries in the 1960s and 1970s. Fortunately, gas and then oil was found off the Norfolk coast in the 1960s and this brought construction work and supply vessels to both ports, but the great days of the herring and the holiday industry were rapidly declining, as did the economy of the area.

The economy depended not only on the fishing industry and tourism but on farming and also on manufacturing and light industry. The flat fertile fields of East Anglia are ideal for farming, but in the 1930s many farmers found it difficult to make a living. Conditions were even worse in the highlands of Scotland and farmers coming south found farming far easier in East Anglia. Some land owners were so grateful to have their land back in production they charged little or no rent. Farming was very labour intensive with much of the work being done by hand with the aid of horses and earnings were poor. There was some light industry manufacturing such goods as clothing and bandages and Lowestoft repaired and built boats. There were several breweries using the barley which was grown in East Anglia, but these were closing down as a result of mergers in the 1950s and 1960s. Similarly, Matthes, a bakery firm based in Yarmouth with branches throughout East Anglia, was forced to close after a merger with a larger national firm. As a result of all this, the average wage in the area was well below the national one and poverty was a big issue. This deprivation brought with it a lowered standard of living and poorer health, with the Regional Health Board doing little to help. A glimmer on the industrial front was the coming of the gas and oil industry and some light manufacturing industry such as Erie Resistors, which came to Yarmouth in the 1940s, Japanese television manufacturing in Lowestoft in the 1960s and Birds Eye Frozen Foods, which came to both towns after the war. The fish finger was 'invented' in Great Yarmouth in the 1950s!

Much of the housing in Lowestoft and Yarmouth was used as hoarding houses for holiday makers. They would produce bed and breakfast and often an evening meal for a small price, but this income lasted for only eight to ten weeks in the summer and, with the introduction of the cheap European holidays, people found that for nearly the same price or a little extra they could have more or less guaranteed sun abroad. As a result, boarding houses did not re-open and the popularity of the local cinemas and theatres, which had been filled with national stars throughout the summer months, declined and they started to close. Transport to and from the towns had also been affected by the Beeching Plan, which closed many of the railway lines which served the coast.

The people of the area had been isolated from the rest of the country for centuries. They were either self-sufficient on the land or eked out a poor wage on the land or in the towns. Most did not travel far, so were unaware of the changes taking place in other parts of the country. They accepted their lot.

As far as hospitals were concerned, it was not that there were not enough; there were too many. Most had been built by the Victorians, or even before that era, and many had changed little since that time. St. Nicholas Hospital in Great Yarmouth had been built as a naval hospital between 1800 and 1811. It was built in the form of a square around a large quadrangle, but was converted into a barracks in 1818. It was converted back to a hospital in 1855 to look after seamen who were mentally sick and after the 1940s became a civilian psychiatric hospital.

In the 1970s it had 193 beds. In 1993 it was sold for a pittance and this fine building has now been converted into elegant private homes. The psychiatric patients were moved into new accommodation built on the Northgate Hospital site.

A new Yarmouth Workhouse was built off the Northgate Road in 1838 and became Northgate Hospital at the start of the National Health Service in 1948. In the 1970s it probably did not look very different from when it was built, except for showing signs of age and neglect. The "Nightingale wards" had two rows of twelve beds with two to four beds at the ends of the wards. There were some modern buildings. These included the Matthes block, a two-storey building for acute medical patients containing fifty beds with a coronary care unit, built in 1963, and a Maternity Block with beds for 56 patients, labour wards, theatre complex and special care baby unit which opened in 1968. The Matthes block was named after Herbert Matthes, who was Chairman of the Local Hospital Management Committee. He had served the local hospitals for many years, was a member of the Regional Heath Board and had been a Mayor of Great Yarmouth. The Herbert Matthes Block was opened by Sir Stephen Lycett Green, Chairman of the East Anglian Regional Health Board. Within the grounds of the hospital were the chest clinic, a new District Pathology Department constructed in 1973 and a new Postgraduate Medical Education Centre, containing a Library, which was erected in 1975.

In the original Northgate buildings were wards for the acute geriatric patients and other wards for the chronic sick. Dr. Wayne recalls showing Dr. Owen, the Minister of Health, the geriatric wards and says, "They were truly unchanged structurally since they had been built in 1838 and were quite awful, with such high window-sills that even a standing person could see only sky – no flowers, no grass, no people, no world. He [Dr. Owen] was clearly appalled. … On such experiences did we get the promise of a new hospital."

Estcourt Hospital was built as an Isolation Hospital in 1875, just behind Northgate Hospital, and separated from it by a road. In the 1970s, Block A had 30 beds for patients undergoing pre- and postoperative care. Block B had 24 beds for patients requiring isolation or convalescence. In addition, there was a caravan where holidaymakers with renal failure could stay and have dialysis.

Great Yarmouth built its first major hospital at Deneside along the town walls and it was opened on 2nd April 1840. Less than fifty years later it was becoming too small and was replaced by Yarmouth General Hospital. The foundation stone was laid by the Prince of Wales on 18th May 1887 and the hospital was opened on 20th September 1888 by Sir James Paget, who was born in Great Yarmouth in 1814 and had gone on to be one of the most eminent surgeons of his day. In his speech at a luncheon in the Town Hall after the opening ceremony he said, "Yarmouth, 50 years ago, was one of the first places in the land for medical teaching and the present medical men had a reputation to maintain." Over the years there were a number of additions, including the children's ward in 1910. The accident and emergency department was at the back of the hospital and was enlarged into the maternity unit when this moved to Northgate Hospital in 1968. Previously, this had been a girls' school. Out Patient Clinics were held in a wooden building with each examination couch separated from the next by a curtain.

Following the move of Medical Patients to the Matthes Block at Northgate Hospital in 1964, almost all the patients were surgical ones: general surgical, gynaecological, emergency orthopaedic and ENT patients. In addition, there was the Paediatric Ward. There were 85 beds, two operating theatres (one for ENT), a minor operating theatre and a recovery room.

The hospital closed with the opening of the District General Hospital. It was eventually sold for £250,000 and, after being demolished, residential flats were built on the site.

Gorleston Hospital in Lowestoft Road, Gorleston, had been built as a private residence in 1887 for Dr. Collier and, after being owned by several people, it became a club; but, because of various irregularities, this was closed. In 1937 it was bought to replace the Gorleston Cottage Hospital. In fact, for several years before this the Governors of the Yarmouth General Hospital and the Governors of the Gorleston Cottage Hospital had had discussions about combining and building a new hospital as their respective hospitals were obsolete. Unfortunately, they could not agree on a site for this. In 1965 a new operating suite was built and the following year the hospital became the orthopaedic unit for the District with 23 beds. It did not deal with emergencies and these were done at either Lowestoft or Great Yarmouth. The hospital closed when the District General Hospital opened phase II and, in spite of many protests, it was razed to the ground several years later and the Newberry Clinic for Community Paediatrics was built.

Lowestoft and North Suffolk Hospital had begun life as Mutford and Lothingland General Dispensary. In 1840 an Infirmary was built on a site that is now known as St. Margaret's Plain, to give medical and surgical assistance to the poor. A Dispenser was appointed by the Management Committee to monitor and keep control of drugs and dressings and in 1866 surgeons were requested to shorten the length of stay of patients from two months to six weeks! A plot of land was purchased in 1879 and in 1882 the present Lowestoft Hospital was opened at a cost of £7,235.

Over the years various additions and improvements were made, such as the building of a children's ward, consulting and waiting rooms, a dispensary and a nurses' dormitory. Electric lighting and central heating were installed and X-ray equipment was purchased. In 1912 the hospital was renamed the Lowestoft and North Suffolk Hospital and in 1924 a new two-storey wing was added and a new operating theatre constructed.

With the establishment of the NHS in 1948, the hospital, along with all the others on the coast, came under the management of the Norwich, Lowestoft and Great Yarmouth Management Committee. In the next few years a new Physiotherapy Department and Administrative Offices were built. With the opening of the new Maternity Unit at Northgate Hospital in 1968, the Lowestoft Maternity Unit closed.

Up until the early 1980s, when the new District General Hospital opened at Gorleston, Lowestoft and North Suffolk was an acute hospital with 93 beds, 20 of which were medical. There were 14 children's beds, 2 single private wards and one double amenity ward. The 23 male surgical beds were shared by general surgery, orthopaedics and ENT and the 32 female surgical beds were shared by general surgery, gynaecology, orthopaedics and ENT. There was one operating theatre with diagnostic X-rays and outpatient clinics. From January 1982 it became a Community Hospital and since then there have been several changes in how it functions: it provided beds for GPs to look after their patients, it had facilities for early discharge of surgical patients, and in 1998, a 20-bedded Community Orthopaedic Rehabilitation Unit was opened, though a few years later this unit was transferred to the James Paget. Many Outpatients Clinics are held each week. The future of Lowestoft Hospital is still being discussed in 2007.

Southwold and District Hospital, Patrick Stead Hospital at Halesworth and Beccles and District War Memorial Hospital are cottage-type hospitals with 16, 21 and 26 beds respectively in the 1970s. Patrick Stead also had 10 Maternity beds. They continue to be run by the local GPs and some surgery is done there. Their great value is that they provide some nursing help for the local population.

Lothingland Hospital at Oulton was a hospital for mentally subnormal people and had 90 beds. In addition, there were a number of other hospitals in Norfolk and Suffolk providing facilities for mentally subnormal and chronic psychiatric patients.

Politics was the other reason for failure to improve the facilities on the coast. Until the early 1970s most of the hospital work was carried out by GPs with Consultants visiting from Norwich. The exception was in General Surgery, where Mr. McDonald had been appointed to Yarmouth General as Resident Surgical Officer in 1945 and was given the title of Consulting Surgeon at the start of the National Health Service in 1948. His opposite number in Lowestoft was Colin Craig, who had been appointed in 1953. Both were excellent surgeons, but they rarely communicated with each other and the only time that Mr. John Corson saw them in the same room together was at his appointment to become the third Consultant Surgeon in November 1969. The two Senior Surgeons ran two completely separate departments and Mr. Corson had to work in each. Much of his time was spent driving between the two towns and for many years the road was single carriage-way, which produced many delays in the summer months with holidaymakers on the roads.

Dr. Ronnie Gibbs was the only Consultant Physician resident on the coast for many years. He was a GP in Lowestoft and was appointed as Assistant Physician there for four sessions a week in 1956. A few years later he was upgraded to Consultant Physician. In 1967 he was given some additional sessions at Northgate Hospital with a commitment to looking after some of the Geriatric patients. All other Medical Consultant input was by visiting physicians from Norwich. Dr Gibbs shared the Acute Medicine work in the Matthes Block with Dr. Oliver, a cardiologist, and the Geriatric patients with Drs. Beattie and Adams. Drs. Campbell and Latter from Norwich did Outpatient Clinics. Unfortunately, there was no co-operation between the medical and geriatric departments as there was a clash of personalities among the visiting Consultants.

Anaesthetics had relied on GP Anaesthetists for many years, some of whom had been promoted to Consultant posts without any recognised Anaesthetic training. Dr. Neville Hicks, who had been trained in London Teaching Hospitals and was appointed Consultant Anaesthetist in 1961, found this particularly frustrating and communication between him and his Anaesthetic colleagues was not good. There was no anaesthetic office, most of the junior cover was by GP assistants and the anaesthetists had to cover many hospitals up and down the coast. His original appointment included a few sessions at the Norfolk and Norwich Hospital, but soon these were dropped. The situation did not improve until the appointment of Dr. David Turner as Consultant in 1969, as he had also received a proper, and up to date, training in anaesthetics. He was followed in another two years by Dr. Jesser Hind and Dr. Kingsley Branch.

The Orthopaedic Surgeons were Mr. Tony Ashford Hodges and Mr. David Burgess, who did the elective surgery at the small hospital in Gorleston and the emergencies at Yarmouth General and Lowestoft Hospitals. ENT Surgery was performed by Mr. Basil Adlington, who was also a GP, at Yarmouth General Hospital. When he retired in the early 1970s, he was replaced by first Mr. Tony Couldry and then, in 1975, by Mr. Khush Mangat. Both had joint appointments with the Norfolk and Norwich Hospital.

Most of the Obstetrics and Gynaecology was done by GPs, particularly Dr. Hugh Evans of Gorleston, with some backup from Norwich. An example of the difficulty in appointing Consultants to the coast is illustrated by the reluctance of some of the Norwich Consultants to give up their hold over the coast. At a meeting to discuss the appointment of a Consultant Obstetrician and Gynaecologist, Mr. Bulman, Consultant from Norwich, stated at the beginning of the meeting that he would tell them why they could not have a Consultant Obstetrician and Gynaecologist on the coast. At the time he was the only Gynaecologist in Norfolk and, like many of his Norwich colleagues, he had great power at Regional

Headquarters. Unfortunately, there were very few Consultants on the coast and they had little influence. Eventually, Miss Margaret Downs was appointed Consultant in Obstetrics and Gynaecology in 1958. She had been Registrar in Norwich and found the facilities on the coast appalling. In 1960 she set up a flying squad for obstetric emergencies occurring at home and worked hard to have a self-contained Obstetric Unit built on the Northgate site. This antagonised people in Lowestoft as they lost their local facilities and the insistence of developing this unit along with the Matthes Block at Northgate – vital though both were – was probably a factor in delaying the building of the new hospital.

By the early 1970s everyone realised the need for a new hospital, but the difficulty was where it should be built. Already there was the new Maternity Unit and an Acute Medical Unit on the Northgate site, but the site was too small for a District General Hospital and Lowestoft people would not countenance it being built in Great Yarmouth. Similarly, Yarmouth people would not support a hospital in Lowestoft. Eventually, a compromise was reached by Great Yarmouth Borough Council suggesting building it at Gorleston, which to all intents and purposes was half way between the two towns, though technically in Norfolk. However, it was not many years before then that Suffolk had extended to the River Yare and Gorleston had been in Suffolk!

John Corson took over as Chairman of the Medical Staff Committee from Dr. Clive Dowding in 1972, so was in a good position to see the politics involved in obtaining a new hospital. His position involved him attending meetings in Norwich and he reached the conclusion that, although many of their Consultants wished to keep their control on the coast, Mr. Alan Birt, Consultant Surgeon in Norwich, was wholly supportive of a new hospital and he thought that Sir Arthur South, who was Chairman of the District Medical Committee, held similar views.

In 1972 there was a joint meeting with representatives from the Ministry of Health, the Regional Health Authority, the District Health Authority and the Medical Staff Committee, who were represented by Dr. Neville Hicks and Mr. John Corson. Best wishes were received from the Lowestoft and Yarmouth MPs. There was a visit to the proposed site at Gorleston, but this was prime agricultural land and there was discussion as to whether the hospital should be built and if so should it be a 'Best Buy' or a 'Harness' design. The Harness design consisted of a spine into which various pods were plugged, so building could be stopped at any stage. The Best Buy made no economic or medical sense unless it was completely built, so the local team preferred this design. Unfortunately, no decision was made.

The reorganisation of the Health Service in 1974 established District Management Teams and one of the first tasks of the local DMT was to draw together the disparate parts of the service. There were the three small community hospitals in Southwold, Halesworth and Beccles; Lowestoft and North Suffolk Hospital, Gorleston Hospital, Northgate, Estcourt and Yarmouth General Hospitals. The Community services had been administered by the Great Yarmouth Borough Council and East Suffolk County Council. There was also the psychiatric service based at St. Nicholas Hospital in Yarmouth.

The District Management Team of Mr. Noel Johnson, Chairman; Mr. Rhodes, District Administrator; Brian Hall, District Finance Officer; Dr. Roger Newberry, Director of Public Health; and Bob Guest, District Nursing Officer, spent many long hours and many long meetings campaigning for finance and resources for a new hospital.

At the time, no building was allowed on farmland, but this was overcome by Great Yarmouth Borough Council putting a compulsory purchase order on the land just north of the land previously assessed and promptly giving permission for a new hospital to be built on it. The problem of funding was helped by a severe downturn in the building trade and the potential political crisis for the Government which it might bring about. This resulted in a visit by the Health Minister, Dr. David Owen. Among the people he met were Dr. John Ball, Dr. David Wayne and Mr. Noel Johnson, who was Chairman of the District Health Authority. Seeing the poor conditions of the hospitals at Northgate, Yarmouth General and Lowestoft, it was easy for Dr. Owen to be convinced of the need for a new hospital and, no doubt, he realised that such a decision would enhance his party's chances in the forthcoming election. The decision was that there would be a 'Best Buy' hospital and that it would be built in two phases.

On Thursday, 1st April 1976, a sign was unveiled beside the Lowestoft Road at Gorleston proclaiming that the Norfolk Area Health Authority had acquired the site for the erection of the District General Hospital to serve the Great Yarmouth and Waveney Health District. The unveiling was performed by Mr. Noel Johnson, Vice-Chairman of the Norfolk AHA, and Mr. Graham Sturrock, a member of the AHA. Also present were Sir Arthur South, Chairman of the AHA, Mr. Michael Cartiss (Future MP for Great Yarmouth) and Mrs. M. Reynolds, also of the AHA. The District Management Team were represented by Dr. Eric Back, Consultant Paediatrician; Dr. Graham Bracewell, a GP; Mr. Robert Guest, Chief Nursing Officer; Mr. Brian Hall, Treasurer; and Mr. A. E. Rhodes. Also there were Mr. D. G. Farrow, Chairman of the Yarmouth and Waveney Community Health Council; Dr. John Ball, Chairman of the Medical Staff Committee; and Dr. John Dawson, Chairman of the District GPs Forum. Mr. Johnson recollected that his father had suggested this site for a new hospital to the Minister of Health in 1948. This unveiling marked the end of many years of hard work by groups of people who had fought against national, local and medical politics and the indifference of others. It marked the promise of a new hospital with new people to staff it and the hope of a better health service for the people of Great Yarmouth and Waveney. Would the reality match the dream?

Building of District General Hospital 1976–1981

The Department of Health had agreed to a new hospital for the coast, but it would be over six years before it opened. It was agreed that the hospital would be of the 'Best Buy' design and would be built in two phases, with the first providing 248 beds, 20 day beds and 25 for geriatric patients. In addition, there would be an Accident and Emergency Department, an X-ray Department, Outpatient Clinics, a Pharmacy, Operating Theatres and some limited laboratory space for Pathology. The second phase would increase the number of beds to over 500, transfer the maternity services from Northgate and complete the Pathology Department. The conditions of the package were that there could be no alterations to the plans – although this type of hospital built elsewhere had shown design faults – and that Yarmouth General and Gorleston Hospitals would have to close.

The hospital was to be built on farmland owned by Yarmouth Borough Council and it had been farmed by Tom Cook, who had owned

Hobland Farm nearby for fifty years. He rented all the land between his farm and Gorleston from the Council and at one time this included the land along the cliffs east of the Lowestoft Road, where there are now houses. Apparently, when he came to sell his farm to R. G. Carter, the builder (who was to build the first phase of the hospital), in the 1950s, he told the Council that the next tenants for its land should be Bunns, the local fertiliser firm. So it was this firm which had to relinquish 40 acres for the building of the hospital. As it meant that their rental agreement with the Council was broken prematurely, they received £1,000 per acre compensation. The Council sold the land to the Area Health Authority for £37,000 an acre.

The hospital was one of the last of the Department of Health's 'Best Buy' hospitals to be built. The last was Hinchingbrooke Hospital at Huntingdon near Cambridge. The concept is a two-storey building in the form of a square containing courtyards to provide light and interest. The original building on the ground floor had at its centre the medical imaging department, the education area, Pharmacy and some offices. Around this is the main hospital 'street', outside of which are the Accident and Emergency Department, the main reception and Outpatient Clinics at the front; administration offices and some wards at the sides; and at the back the Pathology Department on the ground and first floor. Further behind this are the engineering departments, the Hospital Sterilising and Disinfectant Unit, the supplies department and many administrative offices. This block is built at a higher level than the ground floor of the main hospital and ramps run from it to the ground and first floor levels, making it easy for electrically motorised tugs to access the hospital.

On the first floor in the centre is the main theatre block, Special Care Baby Unit, Central Delivery Suite, Kitchens, Staff Canteen and originally the Intensive Care and Coronary Care Unit. The main corridor runs round this central block and leading off from this are the wards on three sides with the Pathology Department at the back. This sensible arrangement means that most in-patients are on the first floor with easy access to theatres and they need to use one of the two lifts only when they go to the Central Imaging Department or when they are admitted or are discharged.

The courtyards are a great asset to the hospital. Not only do they bring in light and air, but they are a joy to look at, are each separately designed and are well maintained. The corridors are not only a means of getting around, but their very nature means that staff frequently pass each other with a nod, a wave or even exchanging a few words, and this contributes to the hospital being a friendly place in which to work. It is very different from some of the tall, gloomy and unfriendly hospital buildings which have been erected in the last few decades.

A disadvantage of the 'Best Buy' design is that it was not possible to make alterations to it until after it had been built, although there were obvious design faults. Surprisingly, these had not been corrected previously as the design had been used for about ten years. Apparently, it was cheaper to build with the faults in place and rectify them later, as the cost of the architect's fees to make changes earlier would have been prohibitive! Such design faults were that the doorways between the Operating Theatre and the room in which trolleys were prepared with sterile instruments were too narrow to take the trolleys and the bidets in the Obstetric Unit were not fit for the purpose they were intended. The hospital is built with a flat roof and there have been many leaks and attempts to cure them. In some instances the only solution has been to allow the water to drain into a pipe below the ceiling and lead this internally through plastic pipes to the outside. A pitched roof would have been much cheaper in the long run and could have housed many of the services which are bare on the roofs or run above the ceiling panels which frequently need to be taken down for inserting new wiring or piping. Similarly, the cheap single- paned windows must have lost thousands of pounds in heating and many have had to be replaced. Unfortunately, the Department of Health's budgets for Capital and Revenue are run completely separately.

1977

In the week beginning 21st January 1977, Tilbury Constructions Ltd. started site works which involved providing roads, drains and car parks. The cost of this was £227,515. There had been five tenders for the job, the highest of which was £268,507. Tilbury had already started dealing with drainage work under a separate contract placed by Yarmouth Borough Council.

Already there was discussion about what the new hospital would be called and the *Yarmouth Mercury*, *Lowestoft Journal* and the *Beccles and Bungay Journal* announced a competition in April to find a name with a £15 prize for the winner and ten £1 prizes for the best 'bright ideas'. There were one hundred entries and on May 13th Mrs. Audrey Lay, of Westland Road, Oulton Broad, was declared the winner with the name 'Royal Jubilee'. However, it would be more than five years before James Paget was chosen and approved and it would involve a great deal of heated discussion.

The Prime Minister, Jim Callaghan, visited Yarmouth in May and noted the need for improved roads in Norfolk, especially the provision of a link to the Midlands. Unemployment in the area was above the average for East Anglia.

In June 1977 the contract for the building of the first phase was awarded to R. G. Carter of Drayton, north of Norwich. He had been a most successful builder and his son ran the firm in the 1970s. In addition, they had a building depot at Hobland Hall, less than a mile from the hospital site. The contract was for £6,542,432, although the actual bill was eventually double. In terms of money it was the largest contract that Carters had won. It was a three-year contract and work started in July. The building would use prefabricated concrete panels outside and dry-lined partitions inside, with a minimum of brick work and plastering. It was planned that there would be 80 supervisory and operative staff employed directly by Carters and an additional 200 specialist subcontractor employees. The Engineering Subcontractor was Hayden Young of Norwich and the Consultant Architects were McDonald, Hamilton and Montifiore.

June saw celebrations for the Queen's Silver Jubilee and in Great Yarmouth 75 skilled building workers were unemployed. Among them were 17 painters, 16 carpenters, 16 bricklayers, and 9 plasterers.

There was some discussion that there might be a third phase for the hospital which would include a new geriatric and psychiatric unit replacing Northgate and St. Nicholas Hospitals.

Miss Margaret Downes (by this time married to Mr. Clarke) retired on 20th June, having been appointed as Consultant Obstetrician and Gynaecologist in 1958. At that time the Obstetric Unit had consisted of 14 beds in a former girls' school behind Yarmouth General Hospital and a few beds in Lowestoft Hospital. The Hospital Confinement Rate was only 33% and was the second lowest in the country. In 1960 she had set up a 'flying squad' for dealing with obstetric emergencies occurring at home and had opened a new Maternity Unit at Northgate Hospital in 1968, which at the time of her retirement was delivering 1,700 births each year.

In a talk with Yarmouth Trades Council on 27th June, Sir Arthur South, Chairman of the Area Health Authority, said that Yarmouth people would have a say in what happens to their existing hospitals and that since reorganisation of the Health Service "there were too many administrators and too much duplication".

In September, six to ten trees on the Lowestoft Road were chopped down to make way for the entrance into the hospital grounds.

A movement was growing to save Gorleston Hospital for geriatric patients, but Mr. Robert Guest, District Nursing Officer, said that the only way they had got the district hospital off the ground was by promising to close Yarmouth General and Gorleston Hospitals, and that was not negotiable.

Towards the end of October, it was announced that Norfolk would be getting an extra seventeen and a half million pounds for hospital building, which could mean that the second phase of the District General Hospital could come sooner. There was a gross shortage of geriatric beds and the district had half what it should have.

Waiting lists for admission to hospital were getting longer:

June 1976	3,340 people were awaiting admission
December 1976	3,633 people were awaiting admission
June 1977	3,771 people were awaiting admission

A campaign to have a second river crossing at Great Yarmouth was gaining support.

Hospital Radio Yare was started on 23rd December to provide a service to hospital patients. It was the brainchild of Graham Gooda and was broadcast from a Portacabin at Northgate Hospital. It was officially opened by Harry Miller, Mayor of Yarmouth, on 9th February.

1978

In January Alan Price joined the Health District as Senior Nursing Officer for Planning and Commissioning. His main responsibilities were for those areas relating to patients and nursing staff.

On 20th January 1978, the East Anglia Regional Health Authority set aside £675,000 to build staff accommodation on the hospital site. There were to be 53 bed-sitting rooms, 12 two-roomed flats, 2 one-roomed flats and 12 two-bed-roomed flats. It was planned to start building in April 1979 in the hope that they might attract staff to take jobs at the new hospital.

30th February saw the Honourable Leo Russell, Chairman of the East Anglia Regional Health Authority, open the new Day Hospital for the elderly at Northgate Hospital. It was based on the new Day Hospital at Wisbech and had 25 places. It was a great day for Drs. Gibbs and Wayne, the Consultant Physicians/Geriatricians. It had cost £111,000, including equipment, and was the first of three which were planned for Yarmouth and Waveney. The next would be at the new District General Hospital and the third would be in the southern part of the District. At that time, the population was 175,000, of whom 28,500 were aged over 65 years.

The first of several industrial disputes hit the building site of the new hospital when thirty employees of R. G. Carter started a work to rule from 7th to 9th February. In the last few years of the Labour Government, there was an increasing number of industrial disputes and strikes throughout the country, some of which would disrupt the building of the hospital.

Canon Holt, Vicar of St. Nicholas, and a most popular figure in Great Yarmouth, retired in February.

The poor provision for the elderly (people over the age of 65 years) in the District was highlighted in the House of Commons by the Health Minister, Mr. Roland May, in a reply to Mr. Jim Prior, MP for Lowestoft, on 23rd February. Great Yarmouth and Waveney had 4.7 beds for the care and treatment of the elderly per thousand of the population of this age group. This compared with 6.8 in the Norfolk Area Health Authority, 11.5 in Suffolk Area Health Authority, 8.8 in East Anglia and 8.3 in England.

At the annual meeting between the Community Health Council and the Norfolk Area Health Authority, Dr. Newberry, the District Community Physician, said that he did not want to prejudice the new hospital by diverting funds to Gorleston Hospital to provide geriatric beds, but Alistair Roy, District Administrator, said he hoped to improve the situation by using 20–30 beds at Blythburgh. The Norfolk Area Health Authority planned to provide 7.3 beds per thousand in 1981–82 and 9.6 per thousand in 1985–86.

The debate about the poor provision for the elderly continued and on 7th July there was a letter in the local newspapers from Dr. John Dawson, Chairman of the District GP Forum, expressing concern over the lack of hospital beds for long-stay geriatric and acutely ill elderly medical patients. He said that the main reason was insufficient funds from the Department of Health and Social Security in the past and that a District of the size of Great Yarmouth and Waveney should have 285 geriatric beds instead of the 136 which it had.

In August, the expected total cost for building the hospital was estimated at £16 million and that building of the first phase would be completed by October 1980 at a cost of £11,087,000, which compared with the original budget of six and a half million pounds. It was hoped that the first patients would be admitted in mid-1981 and that the cost of the second phase would be five and a half million pounds and would provide a total of over 500 beds.

The Annual Report for the Yarmouth and Waveney Community Health Council for 1977 showed that 1,146 holidaymakers were admitted to the local hospitals and 8,960 were treated as Outpatients. The waiting times for surgery in the District were much greater than the rest of the Region, except for General Surgery. The worst was for ENT, where 42.7 people were waiting for each bed, which was 25 more than the Regional average. In Gynaecology 34.54 people were waiting per bed, compared with a Regional average of 10.48.

The number of people out of work in Yarmouth was nearly 3,000 in November.

In December, it was reported that the Norfolk, Lowestoft and Great Yarmouth area had only half as many eye surgeons as the rest of the Region and people were waiting two years for cataract operations. (In 2007 it is less than three months.) The only eye service on the coast was at clinics run by visiting Ophthalmic Surgeons and all eye surgery was done in Norwich.

1979

In late January 1979 there was a national strike in support of health workers having a minimum wage of £60 a week. It was not until towards the end of March that they voted to return to work.

Demolition work on the old open-air swimming pool in Great Yarmouth commenced in February 1979, in preparation for a Marina containing an indoor pool, gymnasium, bowls and other activities.

In March the number out of work in Great Yarmouth had reached 3,268.

At the end of March the hospital conditions for the elderly were reported as indescribable. Some had been moved temporarily for six months from Northgate to St. Nicholas Hospital, but were still there two years later. There was no day room and patients were sharing a room containing six beds. The next week there was support from Raymond Frostick, Chairman of Norfolk Area Health Authority, to set up a new geriatric unit.

The cost of a vasectomy was £41.

The National Election was on 3rd May, which the Conservatives won and Margaret Thatcher became the first female Prime

Minister. Mr. Jim Prior and Mr. Anthony Fell were elected MPs for Lowestoft and Great Yarmouth, respectively.

At its meeting on 24th May, the Norfolk Area Health Authority learned that the access road to the District General Hospital was neither large enough nor strong enough to take buses.

At the beginning of June there was a shortage of petrol nationally which continued for many weeks.

The Duke of Edinburgh opened the new pilot house on 15th June and the jobless in Great Yarmouth had fallen by 912 to its lowest level since 1975 and was 1,713.

The theatres for the Summer Season had such stars as Dick Emery, The Barron Knights, Paul Daniels, Bernie Winters, The Bachelors and Joe Brown.

From 6th August for 9 days there was an exhibition to recruit staff to the new hospital as it would need 700 staff. This was organised by Mr. Alan Price, Project Manager for the new Hospital.

For several years Dr. Wayne had been collecting funds for a renal dialysis unit, but in September it became apparent that there would be no such unit and this resulted in many letters in the local press decrying the decisions. Dr. Wayne responded that it was important to concentrate these facilities in Cambridge and Norwich and the money was being raised for a full emergency peritoneal dialysis service. This procedure would involve inserting a plastic catheter into the patient's abdomen through which liquids would be introduced into the peritoneal cavity. The impurities in the blood would transfer to this liquid, which would be removed.

The National Front held its Annual Conference at the Wellington Pier at the end of October. It was feared that there would be riots and all emergency services were on alert, as was Yarmouth General Hospital. Actually, there was no problem, but the Police bill came to £250,000, which could have been better spent on a number of health projects.

Mr. Peter Harrison was appointed to equip and commission the new building in December. He joined Mr. Alan Price, who had been working on the project since January 1979

At the end of the year one of the General Surgeons expressed his concern at the shortage of nurses. The Health District felt that this was not a serious issue and stated that there were 820 nurses in the District.

1980

At the end of January 1980 there were fears that the second phase of the new hospital would not be built, as dealing with the elderly in Norwich might move up in priority. This was in spite of the fact that even with the new hospital, when there would be eight beds per thousand people over the age of 65, the Yarmouth and Waveney Health District would still have the lowest provision for the elderly in the Region.

At the beginning of February, Dr. John Cowan, a GP in Gorleston, and his GP partner announced that they were to go ahead with purchasing the large YMCA Hostel in Lowestoft for £70,000 and turn it into a private hospital. For the previous few months he had been having discussions with Consultants in Norwich and on the coast and they had given him their support. About the same time, The Gables on the seafront in Gorleston came on the market. Previously this had been a hotel, but more recently had been a Nursing Home. Its attraction was that it was much closer to the District General Hospital which was being built, and had been converted to look after patients. A few Consultants decided to look into the feasibility of buying it while the rest decided to stay loyal to Dr. Cowan. In the end, Dr. Cowan decided not to proceed with the purchase of the Lowestoft property and a firm headed by Tim Barrett, who already owned at least one nursing home, bought The Gables. This was a big disappointment for the coastal Consultants and within the year BUPA was proposing to build a private hospital in Norwich. This was at Colney, near the University and close to where the Norfolk and Norwich University Hospital would be built 20 years later.

The North Sea Medical Centre opened its Mammography Unit in February. This was the brainchild of Dr. Chris Brookings, one of the GPs at the Central Surgery in Gorleston, who also worked at the North Sea Medical Centre. The Mammograms cost £21 and within a short time the

General Surgeons had made arrangements for selected NHS patients of theirs to have mammograms which would be paid for by raising money from various charity events.

Between 4th and 6th March, the Norfolk Area Health Authority and Great Yarmouth and Waveney Health Authority held an exhibition which was organised by Peter Harrison and Alan Price, who were in charge of commissioning and equipping the hospital. This was held at Ladbrokes Holiday Centre and was intended primarily for the hospital staff to see and assess equipment and instruments, but the general public were also allowed in. There were exhibits by 70 different firms.

The Great Yarmouth Book Club was celebrating the 200th Anniversary of its founding and at the time it thought it was the oldest Book Club in the country. Subsequent research suggested that another book club had been founded a few years before.

In May, Alistair Roy, Administrator of the District Health Authority, spoke to the Friends of Great Yarmouth and Gorleston Hospitals at their Annual Meeting and agreed that Administration was top heavy in the Region, Area and District. He thought that the Area Health Authority would go and he was proved correct.

On 30th May 1980, the topping-out ceremony of the District General Hospital was performed by Sir Arthur South, Chairman of the Regional Health Authority. He said, "Local people must press for the second phase of the hospital and, if they do, it will be built."

On 6th June a special supplement was published celebrating the hundredth anniversary of the starting of the Yarmouth Mercury. *There were articles about the newspaper, politics, entertainment, the railways, the port, fish, the World Wars and holidays.*

At a joint meeting in June between the Norfolk Area Health Authority, Yarmouth Borough Council and representatives of the oil companies, it was hoped that there would be a helicopter pad at the new hospital. Dr. Ian Anderson, senior partner at Central Surgery and the North Sea Medical Centre, played a big part in getting the oil companies to finance this, as it would be their employees who would be the principal users of this service.

In July, an editorial in the local press said that there was still uncertainty about whether phase two of the new hospital would be built and without it there would be no increase in beds. At the end of July it was announced that Area Health Authorities would probably be abolished.

Mick Ayers, the National Union of Public Employees area officer for North Norfolk and East Suffolk, warned that there would not be enough nurses for the new hospital. The hospital would need 800 staff and 200 of these would be nurses.

On 29th August there was a letter from Don Driver, who had had both legs amputated, informing the public of the formation of the Amputees Club, which was set up to support people who were about to or had had an amputation. This was followed by letters pointing out the importance of not smoking.

At the end of September a local surgeon, annoyed that beds and operating time were being wasted due to patients failing to come into the hospital, wrote to the *Great Yarmouth Mercury* suggesting that patients should put down a deposit when they were placed on the waiting list and lose it if they failed to come in. This hit the front page with the headline: 'Surgeon says that patients should pay'. There was a great deal of support for this from the local population, but the Yarmouth and Waveney Community Health decided against patients being made to pay a deposit.

The new hospital was under threat again with the news that the Regional Health Authority was overspent and the local area was £178,000 in the red. This was due to the fact that 70% of Health Service money went on wages and recent salary increases had been up to 25%, yet the Department of Health was funding only 14%.

The running of the Health Service was due to change yet again, but this time for the better. In October it was suggested that the Yarmouth and Waveney Health District Authority should be replaced by the Yarmouth and Waveney Health Authority, which would have responsibility for planning, development and management of health services within national and regional guidelines. Previously, the Health District only dealt with the day-to-day running of the Area Health Authority services. The Yarmouth and Waveney Health Authority came into being on 1st April 1982.

There was some optimism from Sir Arthur South, Chairman of the East Anglia Regional Health Authority, who said in November that, "all people in the high corridors of power have said you are going to have phase two [of the hospital]. You make them keep their word."

The jobless total in Great Yarmouth had risen to 3,984 by the end of November.

1981

Jim Prior, Lowestoft MP and now the Employment Secretary, met a delegation of six Trades Council members on 1st January 1981 to discuss the finances of the National Health Service and said that the Yarmouth and Waveney area had always been the Cinderella of the Health Service. Alistair Roy, Administrator of the Health District, reported that a 29-bedded ward was due to open at St. Nicholas Hospital in February and would be called the Mountbatten Ward. It would be for psychiatric patients and had cost £200,000. He also said that inflation and pay awards following the Clegg Report were likely to send the District half a million pounds into the red by the end of the financial year.

An anchor and some rocks were placed at the front of the hospital in January to symbolise the area's close contact with the sea. They had been trawled up from the bed of the North Sea and were found in Lowestoft Harbour.

Shortage of money and staff were leading to longer waits for clinic appointments and operations and letters were written to GPs and the local MPs pointing out the difficulties.

With the opening of the new Accident and Emergency Department in the District General Hospital, it had been planned that the small Casualty Departments at the Yarmouth General and Lowestoft Hospitals would close. However, campaigns to provide Casualty outposts in Lowestoft and Yarmouth started in February. Dr. Graham Bracewell, a GP member of the District Management Team, and John Cannell, a member of the Great Yarmouth Borough Council, Trades Council and the Area Health Authority, said that this was just a utopian dream if the money was not available. The Yarmouth and Waveney Community Health Council met on 2nd March and agreed by a small majority to support the idea of retaining Casualty Units in Lowestoft and Yarmouth and decided to make representations to Norfolk Area Health Authority. The discussion continued for several months and eventually it was realised that such a proposition was not feasible for manning and financial reasons.

The projected 12-bedded Eye Unit at the new hospital was under threat in March as the Area Health Authority did not have enough money to pay for the Consultant Eye Surgeon. Fortunately, this was eventually resolved, but it would have been a disaster if the unit had been postponed, as there was a two-year waiting list for eye operations and a fifteen-month wait for an Outpatient appointment. There were also fears that some of the wards may not open because of problems in recruiting doctors and nurses, but this was denied by Health District Administrator, Alistair Roy.

At the end of April there was a presentation of books worth £60 from Jarrolds Bookshop. This took place in the hospital and was the first presentation to take place there and the first of many which have been made through the generosity of the local population.

Annie Scarles, Sister of the Outpatients Department at Yarmouth General, retired in April after 42 years working in the same hospital.

In June, Drs. Jenny Jenkins and Eirlys Davies noted that there were no plans for a crèche at the District General Hospital and started canvassing opinions on the need for one. It was to be many years before there was a children's nursery on the hospital site to help staff return to work.

The commissioning officers for the hospital were collating equipment and objects needed for the hospital and these were itemised on 2,400 sheets of computer paper and cost £2,400,000. They included 2,500 bed sheets, 580 paper towels and 22 tons of pig manure for the gardens!

The question of a name for the hospital resurfaced in July and it was suggested that it should be named after Lady Diana the Princess of Wales and that she should be asked to open it.

Also in July, Jo Raven, who had organised a show at the Britannia Pier called "Face the Music and Dance", donated £2,000 to the Surgical Instrument Fund and to the newly established Mammography Fund which would enable ladies requiring mammography who were seen at

NHS Hospitals to have this done at the North Sea Medical Centre without cost to themselves. Mrs. Raven had had surgery for breast cancer and was aware of the value of mammography and wanted it to be more widely available.

At the beginning of September, the builders, R. G. Carter, handed over the new hospital to the Health Authority. The Commissioning Officer was Peter Harrison. It contained 248 beds in seven wards and an intensive-care ward and coronary care unit. With the completion of phase two there would be over 500 beds. In addition, there were two brick-built blocks providing short-term accommodation for staff who were moving to the area and were looking for homes of their own. There were five different types of accommodation, ranging from four bed-sit flats with kitchen and bathroom for student and pupil nurses (Yarmouth would be a student nurse training centre for the first time in 15 years) to two-bedroom self-contained flats for senior staff with families.

In September it was announced that Noel Johnson was to be the Chairman of the new Yarmouth and Waveney District Health Authority when it came into being on 1st April 1982. At the time, he was Deputy Chairman of the Norfolk Area Health Authority and he had been associated with the health service since 1953, serving on hospital house committees in both Lowestoft and Yarmouth before becoming Chairman of them. He was Vice-Chairman of the Hospital Management Committee before reorganisation in 1974. Among his many other public duties, he was Chairman of the Lowestoft Magistrates Bench and he was the ideal choice to lead the new District Health Authority.

Dr. Gerard Vaughan was Health Minister. He had been a Psychiatrist at the York Clinic, Guy's Hospital and his Consultant colleague was Dr. David Stafford Clark, who used to present 'Your Life in Their Hands' on Television in the 1960s. It was one of the first TV programmes to go into hospitals and show doctors and surgeons at work.

In November, Yarmouth's jobless total reached a record 5,052. This was the highest for 36 years, with 13.8% of the available workforce being out of work.

In the latter part of 1981, groups of people were being shown around the new hospital and, by the beginning of December, 3,000 had seen the inside of the new hospital. On 6th December, an open day was organised between 10 am and 4 pm and over 2,000 people went on organised tours of the hospital. After waiting so long to have a new hospital, the local population was very keen to see inside the building which they had witnessed being erected over the previous three years.

It was decided to move into the new hospital over Christmas and New Year to minimise disruption to normal hospital working. This was done with military-style planning. On Monday 21st December at 7 am, the Lowestoft and North Suffolk Hospital Casualty Department closed and the new Accident and Emergency Department opened for Waveney patients. The Casualty Department at the Yarmouth General Hospital closed on Sunday 3rd January 1982. Patients in Yarmouth and Lowestoft Hospitals were transferred to the new hospital between 21st December and 8th January. Outpatients' Clinics started at the District General Hospital on Monday 21st December and the final Clinic at Yarmouth General was on 31st December.

The WRVS (Women's Royal Volunteer Service) shop opened in the hospital foyer on 21st December, after Peter Harrison, Commissioning Officer, handed over the keys. The Mayor of Yarmouth made an official visit to the hospital the next day.

The following senior nursing appointments were made for the new hospital:

Miss J. Hall:	Nursing Officer for Accident and Emergency, Out Patients Department, Central Treatment and Day and Emergency Suite.
Mrs. I. Hursey	Nursing Officer (Night Duty) Surgical Unit
Mr. G. Ringwood:	Nursing Officer Surgical Unit
Mr. M. Kaloo:	Nursing Officer Medical Wards, Intensive Therapy Unit and Paediatric Unit
Mrs. J. Brown:	Nursing Officer (Night Duty) Medical Unit
Mrs. J. Idowu:	Nursing Officer, Theatres
Ward 1:	Sister Scarles
Ward 2:	Sister Pritt
Ward 3:	Sister Clements
Ward 5:	Charge Nurse Seeranj

Ward 5:	Charge Nurse Smith
Paediatric:	Charge Nurse Wilkinson
Stoma Care:	Sister Hunting
Operating Theatres:	Sister Bailey
	Sister Naish
	Sister Somers
	Sister Stanton
	Sister Fox
	Sister Stables
Recovery Area	Sister Taylor
Intensive Therapy Unit	Charge Nurse Yassin
	Sister Raper
Central Treatment	Staff Nurse Austin
Day and Emergency	Sister Murphy
Accident and Emergency	Sister Cheney
	Charge Nurse Watts
	Sister Catt
	Sister Hand
	Sister Gouldby
Out Patients Department.	Sister Richards
	Staff Nurse Truelove
Geriatric Day Hospital	Sister Duffield
Surgical Unit Night Duty	Sister Holton
	Sister Dade

Diary of Events 1982–2007

1982

But not everything was plain sailing. A nursing shortage delayed the opening of a 35-bedded Medical Ward by over a month. Recruitment for the Eye Ward was also proving difficult and special equipment for the Eye Department would not be ready until the middle of January. There was also a lack of car parking spaces, as the number had been calculated on the 250 beds in the first phase, whereas the rest of the services were geared up for the eventual 500 beds. Mr. Noel Johnson immediately ordered the construction of a new car park, which resolved the situation. However, these setbacks were small considering the size of the total project. It had cost £13million, which was over double the original price.

Nursing shortages affected the Intensive Care beds, allowing only 2 surgical beds and 3 coronary care beds to be used. This had consequences for operating lists, as people needing operations who were thought to require intensive care postoperatively had to have their operation postponed if a bed was not available. This was not only upsetting for the patient and relatives, but meant that some operating lists were underused.

On 11th February the helicopter pad was used for the first time when an RAF Coltishall helicopter airlifted a crewman with suspected meningitis from the Royal Navy Frigate HMS *Arethusa.* He was found to have a stomach complaint and made a good recovery.

Later in February there was more discussion about a name for the hospital. Among the suggestions were Lady Hamilton, Nelson, The Nightingale and Edith Cavell. There was also support for naming it after Hugh McDonald, who had served Great Yarmouth as Surgeon since 1945 until his retirement in 1979.

At the end of March the Citizen's Advice Bureau was set up in the new hospital for staff and patients, making it one of only a few hospitals in the country to have such a service. Advisors would visit the hospital on Tuesday and Friday afternoons and one of a panel of solicitors would visit once a month.

The Yarmouth and Waveney Health Authority came into being on 1st April 1982. It had a £21 million budget with 3,000 staff, making it the largest employer in the area. The Norfolk Area Health Authority was scrapped. From now on the Regional Health Authority would make policy decisions and monitor, but the Yarmouth and Waveney Health Authority would be in charge of its own patch. These were momentous changes and would bring decision-making much closer to the grass roots.

The new Health Authority would be overseeing not only the new hospital but also Northgate, Estcourt, St. Nicholas, Gorleston, Lowestoft and North Suffolk, Lothingland, Beccles, Patrick Stead at Halesworth and Southwold Hospitals. It would also have control over Community Clinics, Psychiatric Services, Speech Therapy and Health Education.

Brian Hall was the Treasurer, Dr. Roger Newberry was the Community Physician and Mr Bob Guest was the Nursing Officer for the Authority.

Mr. Noel Johnson was the Chairman of the Authority and the representatives of the District Councils were: Mr. Derrick Maddeys (Yarmouth), Mrs Jean Paul (Waveney) and Mrs. A. H. Sanderson (Broadland). Regional Health Authority appointed members were: Dr. E. H. Back, Dr. W. J. Wren, Mr. R. Mullins, Mr. A. G. Sturrock, Mrs. M. Reynolds, Mr. B. Walker, Mrs. J. Gibbs, Mr. R. Chase, Mrs. M. Chapman, Mr. R. M. A. Jones and Mr. J. A. Francis. Dr. D. J. Wayne was the Cambridge University Representative and Mr. P. E. Green represented Norfolk County Council, while Mrs. M. Kent represented Suffolk.

In April, an auction of the old Yarmouth General Hospital by Mr. John Blaxell of Howards Estate Agents failed to reach its reserve and was withdrawn at £215,000. It was going to be nearly another two years before it was sold.

Gerald Fayers, who had been Secretary of Northgate Hospital, became Secretary of the Yarmouth and Waveney Community Health Council, taking over from Ray Allen.

There was still industrial unrest throughout the country and in April 100 Health workers answered a call for a national hour of protest against low pay with a march from the District General Hospital to Middleton Gardens, Gorleston, where they held a rally. Later, the Yarmouth Trades Council backed the Yarmouth Health workers in their industrial action against the 6.4% pay offer in response to their Union's 12% claim.

Yarmouth Borough Council were considering in April whether to put in a bid for the old hospital and making a park and using some of the houses on the site for accommodation. The Regional Health Authority wanted at least £250,000.

In June, an altar table, candlesticks, altar cross and Bible were presented to the hospital's chapel. The furniture had been designed by Mr. Michael Griffith and Mr. Michael Olley, who were two nurses at St. Nicholas Hospital, and were made by former patient Mr. Ken Youngson. The furniture was made of solid mahogany and was paid for by money raised by Gorleston Toc H. The candlesticks and cross are copies of those in St. Nicholas, which are thought to be 300 years old. In

July, stained-glass windows were installed in the chapel and were paid for out of endowment funds.

The first strike by members of the hospital ancillary staff belonging to Cohse, NUPE and the TGWU was held on 4th June and another was held on 8th June. The consequences of this action was that admissions were restricted to urgent and emergency cases only: there were 60 empty beds and 83 patients had their operations cancelled. Dr. Kingsley Branch, Consultant Anaesthetist, said that the number of operations at the hospital had dropped by a third since industrial action started. There were 668 operations in May with only 491 in June. A third National Strike was called for 21st July, but the Yarmouth and Waveney Health Authority decided to go ahead with the official opening of the hospital, which had been arranged for that day. Health Service workers decided to strike during the official opening of the hospital.

In fact, there were to be three days of industrial action, on 19th to 21st July, and, as a result, only acute admissions were allowed from 15th July; beds were closed and only two operating theatres would be kept open. Outpatient clinics were also affected by the dispute, which was entirely separate from the national strike. This was a very sorrowful state of affairs for a hospital which was just six months old, but the situation in much of the rest of the country was even worse.

Wednesday, 21st July 1982 was the date set for the official opening of the hospital and should have been a happy one and one of celebration. In the event, the weather was gloomy and so was the atmosphere in the hospital, which was in the grips of a National Strike. The Mayor of Great Yarmouth refused to attend, as this would mean he would have to cross a picket line; the Health Authority had decided to spend not more than £250 on the event, but there was no evidence that any was spent. There were to be no refreshments for the dignitaries attending, but Dr. Back, Paediatrician and a member of the Yarmouth and Waveney Health Authority, made sure he had a kettle available in the children's ward to make a cup of tea for the very important person opening the hospital.

This person was Professor Dorothy Crowfoot Hodgkin, OM, FRS, who spent her early life near Beccles and went on to become one of the outstanding scientists of the century, discovering the structure of penicillin, vitamin B12 and insulin. But she was far more than a great scientist: she showed great compassion for others and was most modest. She was educated at the Sir John Leman School, Beccles, and at Somerville College, Oxford, where she became a tutor and fellow. Margaret Thatcher was one of her undergraduate students. Later, she was to become Wolfson Research Professor in Oxford and Chancellor of Bristol University. She was awarded the Gold Medal of the Royal Society in 1956, the Nobel Prize for Chemistry in 1964 and was made a member of the Order of Merit in 1965. When she was invited to Buckingham Palace to receive this honour, it is said that she walked there and approached one of the guards, saying, "I want to see the Queen". She took a deep interest in her students, especially the foreign ones, and did much to help those in South Africa at the time of apartheid. She suffered from severe rheumatoid arthritis, but this did not stop her travelling the world to attend meetings and to help others. She died on 29th July 1994, aged 84.

It was, indeed, a great honour to have such a distinguished scientist and such a caring individual to open the hospital. By her hard work and determination, she had not only discovered the structures of three vitally important substances in medicine (penicillin, vitamin B12 and insulin) and contributed to the knowledge of many others, but, by her compassion, she had helped many underprivileged people in this country and abroad. She was a truly great lady who had received the highest awards in this country and abroad, and it is unfortunate that many local people did not appreciate her greatness and others continued with their strike action. However, as a radical herself, no doubt she had sympathy for their cause.

It is interesting to note that her parents' home at Geldeston, near Beccles – which is where she grew up – was bought by Tony Couldry, retired ENT Surgeon, and his wife, and they still live there

Whitehall gave the green light in July for work to start on a second river crossing and Southtown bypass.

In the middle of July a number of walls at the back of the hospital were being taken down to connect with the second phase of the hospital.

Also in July, David Buddery and Phillip Freeman retired. They had been dentists in the area for many years and were given a reception at Piccolo's, a local restaurant. When the NHS was started in 1948, David Buddery was given the registration number GYR1. He had

lived in Yarmouth all his life, went to Yarmouth Grammar School and did his dental studies in Sheffield. After working as an Assistant Dentist for three months, he set up his own practice and for the last 20 years had worked part-time for the hospitals. With his retirement from dental practice, he worked full time at the hospital for many years and built up a small museum in a room adjacent to the library. He was one of the original members of the Amateur Radio Society and was President of the Waveney Light Opera Group in Beccles.

Frank Smith retired as Administrator of Staff Services at the District General Hospital. He had spent his early years in Burma and, after injury in World War Two, was transferred to the Ministry of Defence Accounting Team. Leaving the Army in 1971, he worked for the Health Service in Norwich, St. Andrews, Little Plumstead, Lothingland, Northgate and Yarmouth General Hospitals. As a pastime he wrote novels and had several published.

Evelyn Alexander celebrated her 90th birthday in August. She had been Matron of the Yarmouth General Hospital in the 1920s. It was run by four doctors, who were not paid, and about 25 nurses! She retired in 1931 when she married the Manager of Barclays Bank and spent much of her time making jam and other things for St. Nicholas Church, Great Yarmouth.

Unfortunately, national industrial disputes continued. Seven drivers and store men at Estcourt Road Stores were on strike. These stores served the whole of the District and the result was that over a hundred beds at the District General hospital were empty. John Corson, Consultant Surgeon, wrote to the local papers saying that many of the doctors and nurses had sympathy for the strikers but did not support strike action. The hospital had to use paper linen because of the dispute and only urgent and emergency cases were being admitted. On 22nd September, Alistair Roy and his team were locked out of their Health Authority offices by the strikers, who said that they had no dispute with the local management but with the Government.

The number of people out of work in Great Yarmouth in September was 4,328, which was 201 more than the previous month and 684 more than the same time in 1981.

Dr. Roger Newberry retired as District Community Physician at the end of September to be replaced by Dr. Elizabeth Ann Brown. He had worked in the District for many years and was responsible for the planning of Outpatients' clinics and operating lists for the new hospital. In 1983 he wrote 'Notes on the Hospitals of Great Yarmouth'. The building erected on the site of the old Gorleston Hospital which looks after Community Paediatrics was subsequently named after him. Ann Brown had trained at the Royal Free Hospital in London twenty years previously and took eight years to qualify as she kept having babies. Eventually, she had five children. She was interested in paediatrics and had held previous jobs as a School Doctor and Family Planning Doctor.

The industrial dispute continued in October and the Health Authority expressed its concern about the resulting increased waiting times. Dr. Back, a member of the Authority and a Paediatrician, said that hernias could become strangulated and abdominal pains could turn out to be cancer. The waiting times for patients to be seen in the Accident and Emergency Department could be up to 5–6 hours and was made worse by some people attending with minor conditions. 1,800 patients had been seen in that Department in January and in August (no doubt partly due to the influx of holidaymakers) the number was 4,280.

In October, Mr. Stanley Tuddenham, Joint Managing Director of R. G. Carter, who had built phase one, said that the hospital would have been completed by then if they had been allowed to continue the work, and their estimate for the work would have been cheaper. The Regional Health Authority admitted that costs had escalated since the first estimate, but it would have been improper not to have gone out to tender. In the end, the contract for the second phase went to another firm: Sindall Construction Ltd.

As a result of industrial disputes, the total number of people waiting to go into hospital had increased by 26% between the end of March and the end of September. Ironically, this and ward upgrading, which had reduced the number of admissions, enabled the Health Authority to stay in budget. During the year, £250,000 had been spent on telephone calls and £51,000 on postage.

Edna Plume retired on 31st December after nearly 30 years as a Medical Social Worker, and three days after her 60th birthday.

After spending three years as a policewoman, where she met her husband, Don, she joined as assistant to the Almoner in 1948. Four years later, she left to have her daughter and returned in 1957 as a medical social worker. She was one of the old school of medical social workers and always had time to talk through any problems a patient or a relative might have.

1983

Throughout most of 1983 there were discussions about the future of the old Yarmouth General Hospital. In January, Ryan Elizabeth Holdings of Ipswich submitted plans to redevelop it to produce 160 single-person flats, but its request for a council grant was deferred for six months. A few weeks later they pulled out of the negotiations because of a dispute with Howards Estate Agents, who were charged with selling the building, concerning a house in Lowestoft. In April, Quest Real Estate of Lowestoft produced plans to convert the Yarmouth General into about 100 flats, if they could purchase an adjoining car park from the council. They withdrew in September.

Valerie Howkins suggested a £1.25 million scheme to turn the old hospital into a centre for alternative medicine. She asked for 250 individuals or groups to donate £1,000 each and suggested calling it the Gordon Chapman Memorial Hospital in memory of the former Mayor of Great Yarmouth who had died tragically taking part in a pancake race for charity. This idea failed to gather sufficient support and, in the end, Badgecastle Homes of Norwich paid £250,000 for the building, which they demolished and then built 85 homes for people over the age of 55.

In January, the will of the late Mrs Lily Burrage was published in which she left £402,820 gross, £340,041 net. Her house at Hopton and the attached land was valued at £200,000 and she left this to the Health Service. The house and land were sold and the money from this largely financed the Education and Social Centre, which was built at the back of the hospital and was named after her.

Before the hospital opened it was hoped that the Friends of Lowestoft and of Yarmouth Hospitals would combine to form the Friends of the District General Hospital. Unfortunately, this was not to be and, at each meeting which was organised, only one of the Friends would attend. There were mutterings about the past and Roundheads (Yarmouth) and Cavaliers (Lowestoft). Eventually, it was decided to establish a separate Friends of the District General Hospital, whose Chairman was William Smith. In their first year they raised £8,000 and their membership increased from 17 to 29.

1984

John Cannell, Yarmouth Trades Council Chairman, claimed on 3rd January that Gorleston Hospital or Estcourt Hospital would close this year. Noel Johnson said that he knew of no plans for closure this year.

The District was employing 663 more full-time staff than it did four years previously.

> *The Government had encouraged the sale of Council homes, but Yarmouth Borough Council had sold only 492 of its 8,132 homes between April 1979 and September 1983. This was only 6% of the total compared with 20% by Breckland and 19% by Kings Lynn and West Norfolk District Councils.*

The Yarmouth and Waveney Coordinating Committee, which included Yarmouth Trades Council, organised a protest march from Northgate Hospital to the District General Hospital on 7th January to protest about the NHS cuts.

Eight months through the financial year, the Great Yarmouth and Waveney Health District was £103,000 overspent on a budget of just under £16 million. It was the only Health District in East Anglia to be overspent and was put down to high throughput and shorter stays, which were the best in East Anglia.

A cheque for £8,000 was presented to Dr. Wayne from Kidney Patients' Welfare of Great Yarmouth for the kidney dialysis fund. He said that they were a quarter of the way to the £100,000 needed to build a renal dialysis unit.

> *On 8th February, East Anglia's first private health screening unit was officially opened at the BUPA Hospital, Norwich. The hospital had opened at the end of 1983 and had cost £5,000,000.*

At the end of February, Great Yarmouth and Waveney Health Authority said that it would have a spending limit of £25,145,000, but £24,574,000 will be needed to maintain the present services. The budgets of the Regional Health Authority (RHA) allowed only 3% for pay rises and 5.3% for price increases. If inflation turned out to be higher than this, the RHA had not set aside further sums to cover it.

There were complaints that men and women had had to share the same bay at the DGH for a week. Mr. Bob Guest, District Nursing Officer, said it should not have happened and was due to pressure on beds combined with the ITU being closed.

There were talks to bring forward work on the Matthes Block at Northgate Hospital after it had been closed in April 1983 due to structural faults. It was planned to develop it into a 40-bed unit for geriatric patients.

Yarmouth and Waveney Health Authority received money from the RHA for development capital of £141,000 and revenue allocation of £96,000 for a child and family care centre at Northgate and other plans to help the elderly, mentally ill and handicapped.

At the beginning of May, Shell announced a £550m development project off Yarmouth which meant contracts for local firms.

In the first week of June, plans for a multi-million pound outer harbour at Great Yarmouth were given the green light by the Port and Haven Commissioners, telling consultants to carry on with surveys into its viability.

The College of Health published figures to show that the four areas having the longest waiting lists were General Surgery, Trauma and Orthopaedics, Oral Surgery and ENT.

In June, Dr Margaret Bean retired after 25 years working in the Great Yarmouth Family Planning Clinic, which she had helped to start. A presentation was made by Dr. Betty Scotter, who had played a similar part in starting the Lowestoft Clinic. Dr. Bean's husband was a former rector of Somerleyton.

Also in June, demolition of the old Yarmouth General Hospital started.

On 8th July, the Freedom of the Borough was presented to HMS Yarmouth, *which had fought in the Falklands. There was much celebration, with the crew marching through the town. Within a year it was announced that the ship was to be taken out of service.*

Cilla Black, Jimmy Cricket, Tom O'Connor, Dana, Jim Davison, Frankie Vaughan, Val Doonican, Danny La Rue, Ken Dodd and Vince Hill were just some of the stars playing in Great Yarmouth during the summer.

In August, there were reports that the District Health Authority (DHA) had suggested naming the District General Hospital the Prince William. The majority of hospital staff wanted it to be named after Sir James Paget, who had been born in Great Yarmouth and was one of the most famous surgeons of the previous century.

On 3rd September, the DHA decided to name the hospital after Sir James Paget. It was a very narrow victory, with only eight votes in favour and seven against. David Wayne had suggested the name five years previously. Major Pat Green had suggested naming the hospital after Prince William to avoid any rift between Lowestoft and Great Yarmouth and to get away from the name District General Hospital.

In September, unemployment in Great Yarmouth had dropped slightly to 4,673. This was 12.7% of the area's working population.

At the beginning of September, Anthony Ashford-Hodges and his wife returned from a 16-month, 15,000 miles sail aboard his 44ft steel yacht which he had built himself. The hull was made of steel as some years before his previous yacht had been wrecked on a reef. He said that on the present trip most of the equipment had failed and needed to be repaired.

On 15th September, the first patients were moved into phase 2 of the hospital. Since the hospital opened, the children had been temporarily accommodated in the maternity suite and they were transferred to their new purpose-built ward, which had 32 beds. Meanwhile, orthopaedic patients were moved from Gorleston Hospital, which had a maximum of 23 beds, to their new wards. Sindall Construction Ltd. was the builder of the second phase and the firm had completed the work ahead of schedule.

On 24th September, Frank Dobson, MP, Shadow spokesman on Health, criticised the DHA for having inadequate hospital facilities which left it with the worst care record in the country. He claimed this after visiting the James Paget Hospital. He told an open meeting of the Health Authority that it had a waiting list of 3,676 and of the 3,320 people needing non-urgent operations no less than half had been waiting for over a year. He knew of nowhere in Britain with worse waiting lists. ENT had 1,312 cases waiting. Dr. Ann Brown, District Medical Officer, said that his figures were out of date and March figures were in fact 3,525. She said that the hospital was already handling 14,000 in-patients instead of the intended 10,000. Productivity was very good, with 47.8 general surgical patients going through a bed each year, which was by far the highest in the Region, where the average was nearer 30 each year.

At the end of September the new endoscopy suite was opened and a cheque for £12,295 was handed over by WRVS, which paid for the fitting out of some little-used changing rooms at the end of Day and Emergency Ward.

On 17th October, the Hospital Cleaners went on strike to protest against privatisation. About thirty cleaners at the James Paget had voted on 15th October to strike. They were worried that privatisation which had happened in Cambridge would happen on the coast.

By the end of the year, 6,172 people in Great Yarmouth were out of work, which represented 15.3% of the workforce.

1985

In February, the College of Health Report produced figures for the previous year which showed that 41% of general surgical patients were awaiting admission for more than a year. It was 38% for oral surgery, 35% for ENT and more than half for Orthopaedic patients.

On 22nd February, the CT scanner appeal was launched. £500,000 was needed to buy and run it for the first one to two years. The Regional Health Authority had pledged £130,000. It would be the biggest fund raising effort in the area and it was expected to take two years. Within a week of the launch over £10,000 had been donated. Each week the amount raised was up to twenty thousand pounds and rarely was less than ten thousand pounds. Everyone was staggered by the rate at which the money came in.

There were 15 nurses short in theatre, which led to some restrictions in the amount of operating which could be done.

Mr. Noel Johnson wrote to the RHA asking for £180,000 for extra staff. Staffing levels were based on treating 10,000 patients a year, yet 14,700 had been treated.

A few years earlier, Aids had been discovered in America and so far no cases of AIDS had been detected in the District.

On 19th April, the Great Yarmouth and Waveney Health Authority appointed its first District General Manager. He was Mr. Alastair Roy, who was aged 35 and had been District Administrator since 1977. He had moved to Norfolk from Fife, Scotland, in 1971.

On 3rd May, it was announced that Debenhams Department Store in Great Yarmouth would be closed later in the year.

On 17th May, three months after it was launched, the Scanner Appeal was approaching £150,000 of the £370,000 required.

RHA agreed to give £180,000 to help the DHA pay for 20 extra nurses.

By 7th June, more than £190,000 had been raised for the scanner appeal and over £20,000 had been given in a week.

Towards the end of June, there was a threat of an IRA bomb in Great Yarmouth. There were fears that the news would cripple the holiday industry and put off the Queen's visit, which was booked for August.

On 5th July, there was a letter in the *Great Yarmouth Mercury* from Dr. David Hamilton, saying that he had been appointed Renal Physician from the beginning of June and the Renal Fund still needed money. It had been started by Dr. Wayne, nearly ten years before, and so far had raised £32,000. It is interesting to compare the support for this fund compared with the Scanner Appeal.

The tender from the Hospital Domestics was accepted after they agreed to a drop in wages and bonus payments. This meant a drop of about £8 weekly for a full-time domestic. The good news was that they had managed to beat off four private firms for the contract.

On 1st August, the Queen and Duke of Edinburgh visited Great Yarmouth. Afterwards they drove to Lowestoft, past the front of the hospital, but did not come in.

On 23rd August, the official order for the Scanner was signed and it was anticipated that it would be working before Christmas. It was bought from I.G.E. Medical Systems Ltd., based in Slough. Chairman Alleyn O'Malley and Appeal Secretary Ann Brown thanked the local population for their generosity and the support of the *Lowestoft Journal*, the *Great Yarmouth Mercury* and the *Beccles and Bungay Journal*. The £130,000 contribution from the RHA would not be available until 1988, so extra money needed to be raised. Extra money would also enable the creation of links between the James Paget and Addenbrooke's, which would enable pictures to be transferred for reading in Addenbrooke's.

By 13th September, the scanner appeal had reached £375,000 in just over 6 months.

Debenhams closed on 19th October.

In October, the DHA announced plans to close St. Nicholas Hospital in 1995 and to replace it with four purpose-built buildings in the District.

At the end of October, the scanner was delivered to the hospital.

The Power Station in Great Yarmouth closed on 31st October with the loss of a further 40 jobs. In the previous months, the 140 strong workforce had been halved. The Power Station was oil-fired and had been built 28 years earlier. Its chimney was the tallest structure in Norfolk.

Robert Guest retired as District Nursing Officer at the beginning of November after seven years in the job. He was aged 58. Alan Price, who was one of the hospital's Commissioning Officers, and was Deputy District Nursing Office, made a presentation.

On 20th November, the Scanner Committee disbanded itself. The same day, Joe Larter presented a cheque for £13,200, which was raised in a single gala night at Gunton Hall. It was the largest cheque received from a single event and, incidentally, was 14ft long.

1986

93 caterers at the James Paget retained their jobs after tendering against private firms for the contract to cater for the hospital.

17.3% of the workforce was out of work in Great Yarmouth. The figure of 6,540 was an increase of 650 on the same time last year.

In January, Robert Chase was appointed Chairman of Norwich City Football Club. He was aged 47 and was a member of the Great Yarmouth and Waveney Health Authority.

The Scanner was officially opened on 23rd January. An anonymous donation of £100,000 brought the total raised to over £530,000.

On 17th January the first exhibition of paintings held at the James Paget was opened by Mr. Noel Johnson.

At the end of February, Norwell Offshore Services crashed. Creditors were owed £2million, but later debts were found to be five million pounds. A number of local businesses collapsed as a result.

The site was agreed for the building of the Renal Dialysis Unit, which would cost £200,000. £75,000 had been raised already.

In spite of spending £1,200 on advertising, there were staff shortages in theatres, which led to the cutback in operations in General Surgery and Orthopaedics.

On 23rd March, Mr. Nicholas Ridley, the Transport Secretary, opened Yarmouth's Breydon Bridge while gales of 70 mph were raging. It had cost £7.4 million. The Haven Bridge, which was built 56 years previously, cost £169,773 and was opened by the Prince of Wales in 1930. Mr. Ridley promised to look at a third river crossing if the outer harbour went ahead.

In April, a group of MPs gave the go ahead for a Bill to provide an outer harbour for Great Yarmouth.

On 26*th April, Prince Charles visited Ladbroke's Holiday Camp, Caister, to see 300 youngsters on a course run by the Prince's Trust.*

The Round Table started its Annual Conference in Great Yarmouth on 7th May.

Also in May, an experimental bus service started between Belton and the Hospital every Thursday. The trial was to last for 9 weeks.

In June, Dr. Gibbs, Consultant Physician, retired.

Bird's Eye closed its factory in Great Yarmouth on 27th June. Three hundred of the staff transferred to Lowestoft, but 900 were made redundant, 280 of whom were part-time.

6,531 people were registered unemployed in the Yarmouth area, which was one-sixth of the workforce.

The proposed Gorleston bypass was being discussed and, although many people had opposed the idea, the majority of Gorleston people were in favour of the plans.

On 18th September, Sir Julian Paget, great grandson of Sir James, visited the hospital to unveil a bust of Sir James Paget. It had been made by Peter Knox and Barry Drake, who were lecturers at Yarmouth Art College, and was copied from the one in the possession of Sir Julian. He gave a talk about his great grandfather and there was a symposium on Paget's disease of bone.

At the beginning of October, Norfolk County Councillors agreed to meet planners involved with the Outer Harbour project to discuss having a third river crossing at Great Yarmouth.

In November, it was announced that the Hospital was overspent by £200,000 in the first six months of the year, as it had treated more patients than had been planned. The annual budget was £30m. Patients for oral surgery had to wait for 52 weeks before seeing a specialist.

21st November: The Marina complex in Great Yarmouth had cost the ratepayers £3m since it opened 5 years previously.

On 16th December, Gerald Fayers retired as Secretary to the Community Health Council, a post he had held for four years. Until 1982 he had been administrator of Northgate Hospital and he had worked for 45 years in the Health Service.

1987

In August, work started on the bypass around Acle. There had been pressure to build it for 25 years and it was expected to cost 5.2 million pounds.

Floors in the four-year-old nurses' home needed replacing at a cost of £50,000 as they were rotten. There was a dispute as to who would be responsible for paying the bill.

The prospect of the Outer Harbour in Great Yarmouth came closer in October when Norfolk Line said it was looking at investing in the project.

On 5th October at the Great Yarmouth and Waveney Health Authority meeting, it was announced that more nurses were leaving the hospital than joining it. Figures showed that the spending for the first six months of the year were more than £500,000 above budget. Most of the overspend was in the acute sector.

In October, the Kidney Fund reached its target of £300,000 with a £5,000 cheque from the local Kidney Patients' Welfare Group. The Fund had been raising money for ten years and it was hoped that building could start the following year.

Plans to knock down the former Gorleston Hospital and replace it with a new building for a community clinic were announced in December. Opposition to this was led by Mr. George Heyse Moore, Consultant Orthopaedic Surgeon.

1988

The possibility of charging for parking at the hospital was discussed in an effort to try and reduce the £500,000 overspend.

The jobless total in Great Yarmouth was 6,061, which represented 14.5% of the workforce.

On 9th May it was announced that on 17th July 60 beds would close to help meet the one million pounds overspending. Union officials warned that this closure could be a long-term measure. The cause of the problem was that the hospital had been funded to treat 19,197 patients, but had treated 2,514 more than this. Two weeks later, there was speculation that as well as closing beds, the hospital would have to reduce the number of operating sessions by seven a week. However, in early July, it was announced that the 60 beds would not be closed as the RHA had given a one million pound cash boost and allowed more time to pay back the borrowed money. Nevertheless, other schemes would suffer: namely, the extra £250,000 on day care for the mentally ill, £150,000 on growth in community services and £150,000 in community residences for the mentally handicapped.

In a national study, the Health District was in the top 10% in the country in terms of cost per acute case. Adjusting for a different mix of cases, it was the second lowest in East Anglia. The District was in the top 2% nationally for the number of general surgery in-patient cases dealt with. The number of orthopaedic cases treated as day cases was in the top 19%. The number of patients going through each general medical bed was in the top 3% in the country. In Paediatrics, it was in the top 12%.

In June, it was revealed that nursing auxiliaries would wear mauve dresses.

In July, the Health Authority announced a number of future developments:

The opening of a new Renal Dialysis Unit in 1990.

An Obstetric Day Unit would be built on top of the Renal Unit and the two together would cost one and a half million pounds.

A new, two million pound, 48-bed geriatric unit.

An acute psychiatric unit would be built in 1994 to replace St. Nicholas Hospital.

In August, the number of people out of work in Great Yarmouth had dropped to the lowest level since 1981 and the unemployment rate was 9.6%, compared with 13.3% the previous summer.

On 9th September, the new Pain Clinic was officially opened by Noel Johnson. It had been created by turning two offices into one room. It had cost nearly £40,000, and more than £18,000 had been raised by the WRVS. More than 500 patients with chronic pain were seen yearly and Dr. Notcutt said the James Paget was one of only a few hospitals in the country to have its own pain clinic.

At the end of September, staff shortages – due to holidays and sickness – resulted in the closure of 48 beds and only emergency patients being accepted. The following week, 10% of the nursing staff was off sick with diarrhoea and more beds were closed.

In October, 3,864 people were unemployed in Great Yarmouth, compared with 5,171 the previous year. This represented an unemployed rate of 9%.

The nursing crisis continued in November, with nurses leaving to take up jobs in hamburger chains, while others became car salesmen, rather than wait for the end of the dispute concerning pay and grading. The Urology Ward remained closed, with its nurses spread round the hospital, and Mr. Sansom, Consultant Surgeon, threatened to stop operating on his patients unless it was re-opened.

In an effort to cut down on overspending, it was decided to close 34 beds. This meant the closure of Ward 3, so that Ward 1, which dealt mainly with Urology, could be re-opened. Ward 2 would remain open for general surgery. Ward 9 would be re-designated to create 19 ENT and general surgical beds. Six beds on Ward 14 would house general surgery patients. This meant that at least 100 patients would have to wait longer each month. Hugh Sturzaker said that the health authority was being penalised, despite treating more patients per bed more cheaply than any other hospital in the area. In addition, despite treating more patients per surgeon than any other hospital in the area, 42% were still waiting more than a year for treatment. In a letter to the *Great Yarmouth Mercury*, he pointed out the inequality of resources:

"No doubt many of your readers were alarmed to see in the *Sunday Times* (13th November) that the only health authority in East Anglia to appear on the *Sunday Times* waiting list black spot was the Great Yarmouth and Waveney Health Authority.

This very clearly illustrated the inequality of health care throughout the country, but particularly in the East Anglia Health Region. It implied that perhaps our health authority is rather inefficient, whereas nothing could be further from the truth.

In East Anglia, this health district has one of the best bed occupancy and shortest turnover times, and the waiting time to be seen in outpatients is less than anywhere else in the region, and the number of patients seen per consultant is far greater. We do more day-case surgery than any other health district in the whole region, and yet we are one of the smallest districts.

All this is done without the benefit of any surgical registrar and the number of operations performed per surgeon in this health district is bettered by only two health districts in the whole of the country. In spite of this, the cost per patient is one of the cheapest in the whole of East Anglia.

Ever since the James Paget Hospital was opened, we have exceeded the number of patients we were expected to treat. Fortunately, each year the RHA has advanced us the extra money involved. Unfortunately, this was not the case this year, but, after much persuasion, we were granted overdraft facilities for the next two to three years at the expense of further developments. This was provided that the number of patients passing through the James Paget Hospital kept to the level of last year. Not surprisingly, the consultants here have increased the through-put even further and, as a result, over a third of general surgical beds are now closed and there are restrictions on operating time to try and keep us within the bounds set by the RHA.

Without further finance from the RHA or central government, I am afraid that the care for patients in this health district is going to get worse and the waiting time for routine surgery is going to get longer and longer. It would be a tragedy for the hard work done by all members of the health service in recent years and it is a tragedy for the local population.

However, I think it is important that the people of this District should know the full facts and perhaps they should be writing to their MPs and demanding that more money should be channelled to this health authority to enable the health professionals to continue their work properly."

The following week there were letters of support in the *Great Yarmouth Mercury*, and Mrs. Jane Dibden and Mrs. Marjorie Gilham started a petition which was taken up by the newspaper. It stated that, "the RHA forwards our petition to central Government asking for greater funding for the JPH to stop further bed closures, re-open those already closed and to ensure adequate future funding for the hospital." Thousands of people signed the petition, but it seemed to have little effect on the situation.

The Government finally agreed to dual the Acle Straight in December, but a major obstacle was to get the scheme on the Government's road spending schedule.

An ambitious £70m proposal to build a marina at Breydon was proposed.

23rd December: Lew Saunders, head porter at JPH, retired in December, after 40 years working for the NHS.

1989

In September, Yarmouth and Waveney Health Authority pledged to break even by the end of the year, despite a debt of half a million pounds. It planned to save more than £100,000 by closing the James Paget geriatric day hospital and by selling off some land and houses.

In September, waiting times were 8 weeks for routine X-rays and 6 weeks for ultrasound examinations, and an investigation was started to see how the service could be improved.

At the beginning of October, breast screening was started from a mobile van. This had been partly funded by Big C. The van would be placed in different sites around the District to make it easier for ladies to obtain their mammograms. Until Christmas, it was based in the grounds of the James Paget Hospital.

Project 2000 to train nurses started with half a million pounds from Government to cover the extra cost of training. It started on 2nd October in three centres: James Paget, St. Nicholas and Lothingland hospitals. Training would also take place at the specially formed Suffolk and Great Yarmouth Nursing and Midwifery College. All 33 student places had been taken.

Mrs. Margaret Banaeian, who was in charge of catering at the James Paget, won the Community Health Council's first ever Good Practice Award. She and her team had £1.34 each day to provide food for each patient.

Jobless in Great Yarmouth was down to 2,532, compared with 3,872 last year. This represented 6.9% of the labour force, compared with 7% nationally.

In November, longer waiting lists were expected as the Health Authority agreed to treat 20% fewer patients in an effort to balance its books. The hospital had treated 368 more patients than planned in the first six months of the year. There were discussions about whether the Authority should become self-governing within the NHS.

On 11th December, plans for a light industrial park around the James Paget went on display.

1990

On 8th May, the Charnwood Suite was opened by Noel Johnson. It provided six rooms for private patients and the conversion price from an antenatal unit had cost £60,000. The rooms cost £170 daily and the hospital hoped to make a surplus of £40,000 in the first year. The first patient arrived on 11th May.

1991

On 1st July, the Renal Unit opened with facilities for six patients to dialyse at any one time. The money to build the unit had been collected from the local population over 15 years following the launch of the Appeal by Dr. David Wayne and included a £50,000 donation from the British Kidney Patient Association. The total raised was £350,000 and prior to the opening of the unit patients had to travel to the West Norwich Hospital Renal Unit up to three times a week. Initially, 20 patients were dialysed weekly and Sister Judy Morrow was in charge of the unit.

In July, Richard Earland joined the staff as Resource Management Project Manager. Previously he had served in the Royal Navy as a diagnostic radiographer and had gone on to re-structuring the Naval Radiographic Service and doing research in survival and thermal medicine. He said that, "resource management used to be thought of as being to do with computers, but it is concerned with using the power of accurate, relevant and credible information to ensure that the best use is made of the facilities and equipment that the organisation has."

Pam Cushing became the first full-time Resuscitation Training Officer in East Anglia. The Consultant Medical Staff had campaigned for such a post for some time, but lack of money prevented its implementation. Her job involved not only training in the hospital but also in GP practices, dental surgeries, industrial areas and schools, and revenue from these posts helped to fund her appointment.

The hospital was the first in East Anglia to receive the new fire certificate to bring it in line with the new fire regulations and Tony Dickerson, Yarmouth and Waveney Health Authority Fire Officer, said it was a "credit to everyone involved".

In May, the Antenatal Clinic moved into the new wing housing the Renal Unit. It is on the first floor and consists of a purpose-built Obstetric Outpatient Department and Parent-craft Room.

Making Waves was first produced in December 1991 to improve communications among the staff and Elayne Guest was the editor until 2006, when Rebecca Driver took over the Editor's desk and it went into colour. It has usually come out four times yearly and is eagerly awaited by the staff.

1992

The Nursery opens. Lyn Farman, Theatre Support Manager, had done a project on setting up a hospital crèche for her College course and was asked by the hospital to develop the project into a permanent facility for the hospital. There were over 150 nursery staff applicants to work in the nursery.

An extension to Ward 17 was opened in January after a public appeal raised £500,000. The idea of providing separate facilities, including a sitting room, for haematology and oncology patients was suggested by Sandra Chapman, Deaconess for Hopton and Corton, while she was receiving treatment on Ward 17. Unfortunately, she did not live to see the building completed and it was opened officially by the Bishop of Norwich on 5th May.

Resource Management Initiative was raising its profile. The Health Authorities had regulations and directives concerning the purchase of health care systems and proper specifications needed to be produced before any order could be made. In addition, the European Commission had decided that there should be an open market across Europe, so, for larger orders, countries throughout the European Community could tender.

Discussions were starting about the best way of replacing the hospital's main computer, the Patient Administration System (PAS), which was nearly ten years old. Nearly every hospital in the District was connected to it, as well as the Regional Health Authority in Cambridge.

Chris Smith was promoted from Service Manager for General Surgery to Director of Patient Care. She took over from Vanessa Wood, who moved to Addenbrooke's Hospital.

Noel Johnson retired as Chairman of the Great Yarmouth and Waveney Health Authority at the end of March, having served the Local Health Service for 39 years.

A new digital switchboard was installed with each of the telephonists having their own TV-like monitor. This replaced the old system which required the telephonist to plug a cord into a hole on their consul to connect two phones together. The new system was much quicker and allowed people ringing in from outside the hospital to dial a number directly and not have to wait for a connection by the switchboard.

The Government brought out the White Paper 'Health of the Nation', which set targets for the reduction of the following diseases:

- Coronary heart disease/stroke
- Cancers
- HIV AIDS and sexual health
- Mental disease
- Accidents

One of the requirements on hospitals was to set an example as a healthy employer and suggestions at that time included banning staff smoking and prohibiting consumption of alcohol at functions. It was to be over ten years before a smoking ban was introduced.

The hospital installed a combined heat and power system which utilised the waste heat from a running engine to heat hot water and other mediums. The difficulty of installing such a system was the capital cost, but an arrangement was made with British Gas and Combined Power Systems, who supplied the unit, that there would be no capital or installation charges to the hospital. It was estimated that the savings would be in excess of £35,000 annually. The Combined Heat and Power Unit was computer-controlled from Combined Power Systems' head office in Manchester via a telephone line.

The Operating Department installed ORSOS – Operating Room Schedule Office System – as its new information technology system and it went "live" on 1st June. It supplied data on a variety of items, enabling the Department to utilise its resources more efficiently.

Margaret Banaeian moved to Chichester at the end of August after having been head of the Catering Department for many years, during which she did a great deal to improve the catering facilities for the staff, patients and visitors. She also oversaw the Portering Services. One of the innovations which was introduced during her time was the Gourmet Evening. The idea was to have a gourmet dinner for hospital staff and people from outside the hospital to give them the chance of mingling and enjoying good food and drink. The first few were held in the Sports Hall of the Burrage Centre and later were held in the hospital's coffee lounge until it was converted into the Broadland Suite, an outpatients' clinic. They were extremely popular, were held two to three times a year, and it would be worthwhile resurrecting them.

Barry Hunt, Chief Medical Laboratory Scientific Officer in the Department of Haematology and Blood Transfusion, was presented with a national prize by the Institute of Medical Laboratory Sciences on 22nd October. The prize of £500 was awarded every three years for the best medical laboratory computer software development.

The prize was awarded for developing the computer program which controlled and managed patient anti-coagulant therapy. The system automatically adjusted and prescribed Warfarin dosage and set and controlled clinic appointments, among other functions. Data confirmed that the quality of anti-coagulant dosage and control had increased significantly, patient waiting times had reduced and satisfaction with the service had increased.

The Burrage Centre Lottery, run by the James Paget Hospital Staff Social Club, held its first draw in December. Fifty per cent of the takings are prize money and the rest go to improving social club facilities and in the early years went towards paying for the building of the Celebration Suite, Pool Room and Kitchens. Since then there has been a draw each month with seven prizes, ranging from £500 to £25.

1993

On 1st April the James Paget became an NHS Trust. Mr. Garry Muter had been appointed as the prospective Chairman the previous October and, subsequently, five Non-Executive Directors were approved. However, towards the end of April, Mr. Muter resigned just before the Board's first meeting and Mr. John Wells, the Deputy Chairman, was appointed Acting Chairman. His position was ratified in October and he held the post for ten years, having been re-appointed on two subsequent occasions.

With the formation of the Trust it became the legal employer of its 2,000 staff. Previously, the Consultant Medical Staff contracts were administered by the Regional Health Authority and the rest of the staff were employed by the District Health Authority. The Human Resources Directorate was formed to take over those new responsibilities.

The management of the Occupational Health Service was transferred to the North Sea Medical Service, with Dr. Tom Pace in charge, although the clinic was retained on the James Paget site.

A new personnel computer system was installed.

Madeleine Borg, Chief Medical Illustrator and Manager of Medical Illustration Services, was appointed Honorary Secretary of the European Federation of Scientific Image after an election at a meeting in Gothenburg, Sweden.

During the May Bank Holiday, a group of individuals represented the hospital in the NHS Regatta sailing from Cowes. There were fifteen 35-foot yachts and the hospital was represented by David Hill, David Ellis, Peter Forster, Richard Earland, Helen Foulkes and Neil Duffield, who is in charge of the Great Yarmouth and Gorleston Lifeboat station. This was a great success and for the next ten years John Wells organised an annual hospital sailing weekend on the Solent with crews manning three to four yachts. It was a great opportunity for clinicians, managers and some non-hospital people to get together for a few days away from the hospital. John Wells' attention to detail was particularly apparent at the Saturday evening Dinners.

The Breast Care Unit Appeal was launched on 10th May with a target of raising £250,000 within the year.

Service Managers were appointed to support the Clinical Directors in running the Directorates and both embarked on a series of training events to help them run the patient services even more efficiently.

Brian Tate, who is responsible for the decorating schemes in the alterations and new building works throughout the hospital, won his age category in the British Triathlon Trials in May. He represented Great Britain in the 44–49 age group in the World Championships in Holland, where he finished ahead of the current veteran world champion. In June, he won the Bronze in Hungary for the European Masters Triathlon, despite having a heavy cold. These events involve a 1,500 metre swim, 40 kilometre bike ride and finishing with a 10 kilometre run.

Wendy Dwornik was appointed as the first Breast Care Nurse Specialist.

Considerable progress was made in reducing the hours worked by Junior Doctors. Pat Mullen played a large part in this and policies introduced at the James Paget were taken up by other hospitals in the Region.

The Domestic Services successfully fought off the challenge of competitive tendering and remained an in-house service forming part of the Hotel Services Department. Because of the colour of their dresses, they were known as the "Ladies in Lavender", and over the recent years had raised more than £10,000 for various appeals, such as the Scanner, the Sandra Chapman Centre and for equipment for the wards and departments.

Health Promotion Services joined the Trust on 1st August. Apart from providing leaflets, they had carried out 16 mail drops on information to schools, surgeries, libraries and hospitals; 14 public information campaigns; and nine Health Information Fayres in the community in the preceding year. They worked towards creating healthier working environments in the community by providing an advisory and training service to local industry and commerce.

Throughout the year negotiations proceeded on replacing the Patient Administration System (PAS) with a Hospital Information and Support System (HISS). PAS held details on many thousands of patients, booked appointments, managed waiting lists and automatically generated certain letters informing patients when they should come in for admission. HISS would do this and much more, such as collecting a great deal of information as a by-product of normal operational processes, enabling the hospital to be managed more effectively as well as passing results electronically from service departments, such as Pathology and Radiology, to clinical areas, e.g. the wards and outpatients. The search for a supplier of HISS was being done in association with Addenbrooke's, Norfolk and Norwich, West Suffolk and Hinchingbrooke Hospitals, and by the early part of 1993 the choice of suppliers had been reduced from 32 to a short list of four. It started to become operational in stages towards the end of 1994, and this continued for many months.

The new WRVS Shop was officially opened on Tuesday 19th October by Mrs Juliet Wornell, National Hospitals Co-ordinator for the WRVS. The new shop is much larger than its predecessor and is still in the Foyer of the Hospital.

John Wells was confirmed as Chairman of the Trust in October, having been Acting Chairman since April.

In November, the static racking for over 50,000 sets of notes were put on mobile bases to create a great deal more space. This involved the staff coming in on five consecutive weekends to re-file the notes.

1994

In April, the Great Yarmouth and Waveney Health Authority and the East Anglian Regional Health Authority were abolished. The Great Yarmouth Constituency and the Norwich Health Authority formed the East Norfolk Health Commission and the Waveney Constituency was incorporated into the Suffolk Health Authority. This meant that James Paget had to negotiate with two bodies rather than the single Great Yarmouth and Waveney Health Authority. This was a retrograde step and it would be another 12 years before it was reversed.

The East Anglian Regional Health Authority – which had existed in various forms since the birth of the NHS in 1948 – was replaced by a region incorporating Bedfordshire, Oxford and East Anglia. The area covered extended down to the West Country and its shape was reminiscent of a banana. Liaising with the Regional Health Authority in Cambridge, which is 85 miles away, had its difficulties; but this would be far worse with the new Authority. Fortunately – after much upheaval and job changes – it was abolished several years later.

On 1st April, the Breast Care Unit opened, having been funded by money raised from the local population. Central to it was the ability to perform mammography on-site, as well as ultrasound examinations of the breast. It was converted out of some old changing rooms and was magnificently designed and decorated. There was one problem, however: it was immediately below the kitchens and periodically fat and liquids escaped from the floor above, causing staining of the ceiling tiles. The Unit was officially opened by 91-years-young Renee Burgess, Chairperson of the BRAS, on 9th May. She had launched the appeal one year previously by donating £1,000.

At the start of April, the first part of the new computerised Hospital Information Support Services (HISS) became live. The Ophthalmology Outpatients Department was upgraded and there were improvements to the Day Care Ward.

From April, Ward 22 – which was built as a Day and Emergency Ward and subsequently stopped admitting emergency patients as they blocked the beds – was enlarged to provide another six beds which were to be used for short stays, i.e. the patient could stay over-night and in some cases for a couple of days. Another three beds became short stay as the Gynaecologists agreed to house their day cases on the gynaecological ward. This gave nine short stay beds, which greatly improved the throughput of the Surgical Department.

Dennis Manning, Senior Physiotherapist in Intensive Care and General Surgery, represented Great Britain as a helmsman in the second Blind Sailing Regatta in Fremantle, Western Australia.

Education Supervisors and individual training plans were introduced for Senior House Officers, and there was expansion of the Career Counselling Service for trainee doctors.

John Wells officially opened the Petanque pitch at the Burrage Centre in July and donated a silver challenge cup to the Petanque Club.

The Estates of the Trust, which consist of land, buildings, engineering plant and services, were valued at £31,888,000.

The Second National Prevalence Survey of Infection in Hospital was the first national survey to be undertaken over the previous 10 years and was co-ordinated by Professor A. Emmerson of Queen's Medical Centre, Nottingham. It showed that the James Paget, which participated in August 1994, had an overall prevalence of Hospital Acquired Infections of 5.5%, compared with a national figure of 9.0%.

In October, Mary O'Donnell commenced work as Quality Assurance Assistant along with Liz Barber, Patient Services Officer, using Q-Aid to assist them in monitoring standards throughout the hospital. Q-

Aid was a new computerised quality support system that helped the practice of quality assurance in the NHS by holding the hospital's quality standards and providing support for quality monitoring within the individual directorates. The initial pilot study was carried out within the Surgical Directorate, looking at Charter Standard 1 on Privacy, Dignity, Religious and Cultural Beliefs.

A new Gynaecological Theatre was constructed out of the old theatre storage areas and was officially opened by Dr. Kingsley Branch on Monday 17th October.

In October, Ken Rhodes was appointed the first Consultant Physician with an interest in the Care of the Elderly. Prior to this, each Consultant Physician had some responsibility for the care of the elderly.

In December, the Quality Improvement Steering Group, chaired by Mike Pollard, held its first meeting. Its terms of reference were:

- To drive/direct the Trust's Quality Improvement Programme and evaluate its effectiveness.
- To encourage and enable staff to undertake training in quality assurance and clinical audit.
- To assess the overcall achievement of the Hospital's Contract Quality Specification; to develop "benchmarks" of good performance within and outside the hospital.
- To share and publicise successful innovations within the Directorates.
- To remove obstacles, so allowing the service to improve.

From this Group a 'sub' group was formed – The Quality Link Group – which met monthly and was made up of a senior member of staff of each directorate, Liz Barber and Mary O'Donnell. Its duty was to set the Local Standards for the Trust and to publish them in a booklet that was available for all patients, staff and visitors. Liz Barber and Mary O'Donnell would work closely with the Link Group in monitoring standards.

A flexi-cystoscopy service was introduced. This involves the passage of a flexible instrument up the urethra to examine the inside of the bladder and is done under a local anaesthetic, so avoiding the need for a general anaesthetic and coming into hospital.

The total income of the Trust was £40,796,000, generating an operational surplus of £2,333,000 before interest and dividends payable. After paying net interest of £1,066,000 and a dividend payment to the NHS Executive of £295,000, the retained surplus taken to the reserves was £972,000.

In the year 1993/94 there had been 23,444 in-patients, 14,696 day cases and 148,593 outpatients. This was an increase on the previous year of 39% in day patients and 3.2% in outpatients. No patient was waiting longer than 18 months for treatment.

Other achievements in the year included:

- Appointment of a third Consultant Ophthalmologist and supporting team.
- Appointment of fourth Orthopaedic Consultant.

1995

The Rehabilitation Unit opened for its first patients on Saturday 1st April. Rehabilitation Services were transferred from Northgate and brought together Physiotherapy, Occupational Therapy and other services to help patients recover from strokes, major operations and debilitating illnesses. The idea of such a unit was conceived by Drs David Ellis and Peter Forster, and they convinced the District Health Authority of its need. The Unit was built on the ground floor adjacent to the Rehabilitation Department and had 24 beds. Arthur Harris and Brian Tate over-saw the design and the building work was carried out by Brocks Builders of Kessingland. The total cost of the project was £800,000. The Unit was officially opened by Sir Julian Paget, great grandson of Sir James Paget.

At the beginning of the year the construction of a new car park for staff was completed on the site previously occupied by the tennis courts in the north-east corner of the hospital grounds. In addition, close-circuit television was installed in all car parks to improve security and would be monitored by the security porters.

Mike Pollard wrote in the March issue of *Making Waves* about the importance of quality, and referred to work done in the United States and Japan to find the factors which led to successful companies. The study found that the successful United States companies were those which developed quality products. "Quality" in organisational terms was seen to derive from five factors, and successful organisations were those that were:

- Obsessively responsive to their customers.
- Sponsoring innovation that is encouraging and supporting new ideas being developed within their organisation.
- Constantly changing their shape.
- Emphasising the creativity of people working "smarter" rather than upon the so-called efficiencies derived from automation.
- High quality and competitive pricing went hand in hand.

The study showed that these values were not simply the preserve of senior managers, but were organisation-wide and were held dear by all grades and all groups of staff, regardless of seniority. Mike Pollard said that this spirit needed to be fostered at the James Paget if the hospital is to be a quality-driven institution.

New National Standards were published by the Government and from April patients had the right to expect:

- 90% of patients to be seen for their first outpatient appointment within 13 weeks and all within 26 weeks.
- All in-patient treatment should be carried out within 18 months and there would be a waiting time of less than 12 months for many procedures.
- Immediate assessment within the Accident and Emergency Department.
- Following admission through Accident and Emergency Department, a bed should be found as soon as possible and certainly within 3–4 hours.
- A qualified nurse or midwife would be responsible for the patient's nursing or midwifery care. The patient would be told their name.
- Except in emergencies, patients should be informed before admission whether it was planned to care for them in a mixed-sex ward. In all cases there would be separate washing and toilet facilities.
- There should be clear enquiry points and signposting in hospitals to help patients and visitors find their way around. The environment

should be clean and safe, and reasonable measures taken for the personal protection and safety of patients.

- Catering Services – Patients would expect to be given a written explanation of the hospital's food, nutrition and health policy and the catering standards they could expect during their stay. This meant that there would be a choice of dishes, including meals suitable for all dietary needs; ordering would be no more than two meals in advance; there would be a choice of the size of portions and patients would be given the name of the catering manager; help would be available, if necessary, to use catering services: for example, menus printed in other languages and large print.

It is interesting comparing the standards for the wait for outpatient clinics and treatment in 1995 with those expected now. There was also a great emphasis on bureaucracy, which would have resulted in the distribution of a great deal of paper. Was it really necessary for all patients to be told the name of the catering manager when most did not know the name of the doctors or nurses looking after them? The patients were being flooded with information, resulting in them not seeing the wood for the trees.

Prior to 1995, the linen for the hospital had been supplied through a contract with Anglian Harbours Trust and, although the James Paget had approximately two-thirds of the total linen usage, the hospital was frequently short of linen; so, in the summer of 1994, the James Paget decided to end its contract with Anglian Harbours and seek another directly with a laundry. The tender was won by Society Linen (Co-op Cleaners), and since then there was been no shortage of linen and the annual saving was £45,000.

In April, the Rehabilitation Services were transferred from Northgate to a new 24-bedded unit at the James Paget.

MRSA (Methicillin Resistant Staphylococcus Aureus) is a bacterium which is resistant to many antibiotics and causes severe wound infections and can be lethal when it gets into the blood stream. Over the previous decade, it had gradually come up the A12 and moved eastwards across East Anglia so that, by the summer of 1995, it was causing serious problems at the James Paget. Not only was it interfering with patients' recovery from illness and surgery, but it meant that beds were closed in an effort to combat it spreading. This affected elective operating lists and, in order to meet contracts, additional operating lists had to be arranged later in the year at extra cost to the Trust. Efforts at trying to overcome MRSA included swabbing staff and patients to see whether they were carriers of the bacterium and trying to isolate infected patients in side rooms – but there were not enough side rooms.

On 14th July, Dennis Waterman, the well-known actor, was present to unveil a bronze pig statue in the hospital foyer in memory of Aideen Wayne, who had been Dr. Wayne's wife. In 1975, she had founded PIGGY (People in Gorleston and Great Yarmouth) which, for many years, raised money for medical charities. The group commissioned local sculptor Barry Sutton to produce the statue.

During the financial year 1994/1995, the number of in-patient treatments increased by 13% and there was a 20% expansion in the Consultant Medical Staff numbers, which enabled the Trust to increase the number of outreach clinics: i.e. clinics in places additional to the James Paget. There had also been a reduction in the number of people on the waiting lists, especially in Orthopaedics and Ophthalmology, and only a small number of patients were waiting longer than 12 months.

One of the problems was the number of emergency admissions. Most of these were elderly medical patients who occupied the surgical beds, hence blocking routine surgical admissions. The consequence of this was that there was a rise in the number of patients who had their admissions blocked on the day they should have been admitted to hospital. This was extremely frustrating for all concerned, particularly for the patients and their relatives, and the Government insisted that these patients had to be offered another date for admission within the following month. An indication of the size of the problem was that there was a 13% rise in emergency medical admissions during 1994/1995, but there was a rise of 27% after January 1995.

During the financial year 1994/1995, the installation of the Hospital Information Support System (HISS), which replaced the old Patient Administration System (PAS), was completed on schedule and within budget. In addition, 1,200 members of staff were trained in how to use the new system.

Other projects completed and achievements made during the 1994/1995 financial year were:

- Appointment of nine additional Medical Consultants.
- The construction of an eighth operating theatre which was for the Department of Gynaecology.
- Creation of additional bed spaces in the Day Care Unit and its transition to a Short Stay Unit helped to reduce the cancellation rate for routine surgery.
- The establishment of a multi-specialist Breast Service which ensured patients received a diagnosis and treatment plan within 24 hours.
- Implementation of a District Bed Bureau which facilitated easier transfers to the Community Hospitals.
- Creation of a 6-bedded Adolescence Unit on the Paediatric Ward.
- Upgrading of the Mortuary facilities.
- Installation of a computerised fire alarm system.
- Implementation of a development plan for improving services for elderly people.
- The Health Promotion Services received the 'Investors in People' Award.

During the financial year 1994/1995, the Trust treated 17% more inpatients and day cases and saw 8% more outpatients than the previous year. The figures were: inpatients 28,778, Day Cases 11,968; Day Patients 6,311 and Outpatients 160,818. (Day Cases are those patients who are admitted and discharged the same day that they have their operation. Day Patients are people who are admitted regularly for procedures such as renal dialysis or chemotherapy.) The Trust met or exceeded all of the financial targets required by the NHS Management Executive. The total income for the year was £54,212,000, generating an operating surplus of £1,839,000 before interest and dividends payable. After paying net interest of £1,093,000 and a dividend payment to the NHS Executive of £235,000, the retained surplus taken to the reserve was £511,000. The total income was a rise of 33% on the previous year and the Trust achieved a 6.3% rate of return on assets, compared with a target rate set by the NHS Executive of 6%.

Management costs were divided into two parts: M1 and M2. M1 refers to the salary of only the more Senior Managers, together with the costs of Management Consultancy contracts, and that came to £1,631,000, which was 3.01% of total income. M2 added the salary costs of all other staff who worked in Corporate Management functions, and that represented 4.38% of total income or a total expenditure of £2,374,000. Thus, the management costs for the Trust were 7.39% of total income.

1996

A hospital is a stressful place not only for patients but also for the staff and in October 1995 a working party was set up to look at stress in the workplace and to suggest proposals for tackling it. In January, Brenda O'Neill was given a six-month contract as the project facilitator. Over the next few months, a questionnaire was sent to all staff and there was a positive response as to how to manage stress in the hospital. Subsequently, prospective mediators were interviewed, selected and training was given to them. In September the James Paget Hospital Support System was launched with 12 people from all parts of the hospital acting as mediators and working to a well laid down code of conduct.

The King's Fund Organisational Audit Report was the culmination of nine months of hard work headed by Sue Garwood, Project Manager. The surveyors commented on the standard of cleanliness throughout the hospital and the use of photographs to brighten otherwise dull corridors. The feedback on quality was that it was dealt with well centrally but needed further development at directorate and ward/departmental level. It was thought that the mission (Vision) statement could be updated and be more widely known. It was noted that not many work areas had an awareness of the statement and even fewer were using it as a basis for their own aims and objectives.

Areas which came in for particular praise were Medical Records, HSDU, Security arrangements and fire safety standards. There were commendations generally on the standards of patient care and the consideration for privacy and dignity. Infection Control and their team commitment was noted; also the improvements in the Accident and Emergency Department and in Theatres.

The British Red Cross set up a Home from Hospital Service at the Hospital. It was designed to help people settle back into their own homes comfortably and with as few worries as possible. The work is done by volunteers who receive training and out of pocket expenses. The tasks they do include shopping, collection of pensions and prescriptions, help with meals and relief for other carers. They encourage confidence and provide companionship.

On 22nd March, Kathy Nobes received the Henry Garnett award for her outstanding work as a Macmillan Nurse. Since she started as a Macmillan Palliative Care Nurse in the Great Yarmouth and Waveney area in 1986, she had been instrumental in developing a palliative care service that brings "hospice-type care" to the patient, both in hospitals and in the community. In 2007, Kathy Nobes continues to promote the ideals and principles of palliative care at all levels and has been in the forefront of developing educational programmes for all health care workers in all settings.

By March, no patient had waited more than 12 months for treatment and the waiting time for the first appointment to see a Consultant had been reduced to 13 weeks in 82% of cases. This was an improvement of 7% on the previous year, in spite of an increased number of outpatient attendances.

In March, the final phase of a new security system became operational within the Paediatric/Special Care Baby Unit/Maternity Unit. This followed a number of incidents nationally when babies had been abducted from hospitals. The security arrangements involved the installation of closed-circuit TV cameras and locking the entrances to these areas. Authorised staff are able to gain access by using a coded proximity card and other visitors must request access by operating a call button.

The new NHS Complaints Procedure came into force on 1st April and Stephen Cox, who had been the Medical Records Manager, became the Trust's designated Complaints Manager, with the title of Consumers' Relations Manager. The aims of the new Procedure were to speed up the process and to establish guidelines as to how complaints should be processed. It was hoped that the majority of complaints would be resolved by 'Local Resolution' and that where that failed the complainant had the right to an Independent Review. If the matter was not resolved, then it could be taken to the Ombudsman.

There had been 295 complaints (137 verbal and 158 written) during the previous year, which represented a rate of 0.15%, as there were approximately 200,000 patient contacts in the year.

During April and May, the James Paget Hospital Back Pain Service was formally launched with a series of Road shows for GPs. It was the original brainchild of Mr. George Heyse-Moore and Dr. William Notcutt who, while working together in theatre, used to lament about the inadequacies of the accepted back pain management. The main goal was to provide support and education for effective primary care of back pain with the emphasis on early and active management of acute patients to prevent chronic disability and future recurrence. When this failed, the service aimed to provide an integrated secondary referral service for back pain patients with a fast track for acute patients who are at an early stage in their disorder. The primary goal was prevention of long-term problems.

On 13th June, there was an open day for the Hyperbaric Chamber to mark the start of the service to treat patients under pressure. Initially, this was for treating divers who were suffering from "the bends" as a result of coming to the surface too quickly from a deep dive. For many years the service had been overseen by doctors from the North Sea Medical Centre using a chamber on the Harfreys Industrial Estate. The opening of the new chamber gave them the opportunity to carry out the work in the hospital with the help of a core of Anaesthetists. The Unit was officially opened by Dr. Nick McIver, GP at the Central Surgery, Director of the North Sea Medical Centre and a world expert on medical aspects of deep sea diving. In his honour the unit has been called the Nick McIver Unit.

The first Resuscitation Council Advanced Life Support Course at the James Paget was organised by Pam Cushing, Resuscitation Officer, and attended by 23 candidates from Norfolk, Suffolk, Bedfordshire, Staffordshire and Cambridgeshire. Their occupations included GPs, Ambulance personnel, Doctors and Nurses from Accident and Emergency Departments, Anaesthetists, Operating Department Practitioners and Nursing staff from ICU/HDU and Theatre Recovery. Since then this course has been held several times each year.

The new Coronary Care Unit opened to patients on Monday 8th July, having been officially opened by Mr. John Alston, Chairman of East Norfolk Health Authority on Friday 5th July. Until that time there was a combined Intensive Care Ward and Coronary Care Unit with four coronary beds. In addition, there was a six-bedded monitored bay on

Ward 5. The new unit had 10 beds which were managed by Coronary Care trained specialist nurses. A side room was specially designed to carry out specialised procedures on-site, such as the insertion of temporary pacemakers. Previously, patients had to be transferred to the X-ray Department for this procedure to be performed. The area vacated by the coronary care beds in the previous ITU/CCU became a High Dependency Unit which was opened by Joanna Spicer, Chairman of the Suffolk Health Authority on 30th August.

With the reconfiguration of the wards, 10 years later a new coronary care unit was built to be near the relocated medical wards. This was officially opened on 20th April 2007 by Dr. Wolf Grabau on the day he retired.

Four autoclaves in HSDU were replaced by three larger ones, each 28 cu.ft. in size, in February and March, and they were in service in April. Apart from their size, they had several advantages over the previous ones, which were developing a number of problems in the latter part of 1995, thus making it difficult for the Department to provide an adequate service.

Margaret Howard, Head of Midwifery Services, retired at the end of September. She began her nursing training at the London Hospital in 1953 and moved to East Anglia in 1961 to complete her Midwifery training.

John Wells, Chairman of the Trust, officially opened the new Medical Admissions Unit on what was Ward 5 on 17th October. It provided immediate assessment, investigation and diagnosis for all emergency medical admissions until the Emergency Assessment and Discharge Unit was opened in February 2005.

On Saturday 26th October, the 8-ton magnet which would be the centre of the MRI Scanner was lifted into place using a 250-ton specialised crane. This was needed as the only way into the scanner room for such a large piece of equipment was through one of the courtyards, and this necessitated lifting the magnet over the back of the hospital building.

The foyer of the hospital was refurbished during the year. This was done with wheelchairs in mind and gave a far better impression than the old design, which had lasted for 15 years. It is estimated that one million people pass through the foyer in a year.

Dr. Balakumar, Consultant in Genito-Urinary Medicine, died suddenly in October. He had helped to open the Bure Clinic in 1989 and was very popular with both staff and patients. A group of his friends and colleagues commissioned local artist Geoffrey Chatten to do a painting of orchids and it was unveiled in December by his widow and two daughters. This really beautiful painting hangs in the entrance to the hospital.

In December, the Children's Ward received the Charter Mark – an award for excellent service. It was one of the first children's wards in the country to receive this award.

Other achievements in the financial year 1995/1996 were:

- The Domestic and Catering Services had to go out to national tender, which the in-house teams won.
- Appointment of the Trust's first Consultant in Urology.
- Appointment of additional Consultants in Radiology.
- Completion of the Day Case Units on the ENT and Ophthalmic Wards.
- A Health and Safety Advisor was appointed.

The accounts for the Financial Year 1995/1996 showed the total income for the year was £57,830,000, which was a rise of 6.6% on the previous year. There was an operation surplus of £1,382,000. After paying net interest of £1,141,000 and a dividend payment to the NHS Executive of £222,000, the retained surplus taken to the reserves was £19,000.

The Trust treated 5% more in-patients and day cases (including day patients) than the previous year, with there being 29,915 In-patients, 12,320 Day Cases, 7,155 Day Patients and 161,426 Outpatients.

The M1 part of Management costs was £1,944,000, which represented 3.4% of total income. This increase on the previous year was due mainly to three major one-off projects:

- The undertaking of the King's Fund Organisational Audit.
- The Market Testing of the Catering and Domestic Services functions, which required the employment of temporary staff.
- The successful international recruitment of 8 additional Consultant Medical Staff.

The M2 part of Management costs (includes the salary costs of all other staff who work in Corporate Management functions) was £2,855,000, which represented 4.9% of total income. Thus, total management costs were 8.3% of total income.

1997

The new CT and MR Scanners were installed at the end of 1996 and the first patients were scanned in the first two weeks of January.

The Health Promotion Services ceased to exist in April as their contracts with the Health Authorities were not renewed. This was unfortunate, not only for the members of the team but also for the local population, for it lost the encouragement to participate in ill-health prevention and the promotion of healthy lifestyles. The Team had been commended by the Region in 1995 and had won the Oxford and Anglia Health Promoting Trust Award in the 500-bed Trust category in 1996. Pam Bell had been the Health Services Promotion Services Service Manager and had worked for the NHS for 40 years.

The James Paget took on the management of all the community services in Great Yarmouth and the running of Lowestoft Hospital after the collapse of the Anglian Harbours Trust. That was one of the reasons why the budget had risen from £33m when the Trust started in 1993 to £61m in September. The Trust had hoped to manage the community services in Waveney as well, but these went to the Allington Trust, based in Ipswich.

In June, the Trust was informed by the King's Fund that it had been awarded Full Accreditation for the following three years. This meant that the Trust had fully complied with the King's Fund Organisational Audit standards and criteria relating to legal and professional requirements, safety of patients, staff and visitors and patients' rights in terms of The Patients' Charter.

On the evening of 3rd November, a group of doctors, specialist nurses and managers from the James Paget met with support groups, voluntary services, fundraisers and trustees of the BIG 'C' Appeal. Dr. Jackson, Chairman of the Big 'C', explained that, since the charity had been launched in 1980, £4 million had been raised and had been used to help fund cancer units and to buy equipment for the Norfolk and

Norwich and James Paget Hospitals and to commission research. Mr. John Wells, Chairman of the James Paget Healthcare NHS Trust, agreed to co-ordinate a group of volunteers who would encourage and support fund-raising efforts for Big 'C'. The Beccles Friends of Cancer Research presented a cheque for £3,600, which went to the Mammography Mobile Screening Unit. The Unit cost £110,000 and Big 'C' had already contributed £75,000. The Trust was making a contribution and it was planned that money-raising activities from the newly formed group would go to the Big 'C' Appeal.

"The New NHS – modern, dependable." This was the title of the White Paper produced by the Labour Government in December following its landslide victory at the General Election earlier in the year. It sought to change organisational behaviour from a competitive to a collaborative endeavour. The new Government felt that the "internal market" caused fragmentation of the workings of the NHS. The White Paper stated that there was a need for co-operation between health authorities, trusts, GPs, social service departments and others. It introduced three new important concepts:

- Primary Care Groups (PCGs), which were collectives of GPs who in combination would serve a population of approximately 100,000. They would be accountable to the health authority and would have responsibility for commissioning all primary and secondary care services for the local population.
- The Health Improvement Programme (HIP) would be a local planning document which would identify the health needs of the local population and would describe the actions needed to deliver the plan.
- Clinical Governance, which was a means of putting clinical quality at the heart of the NHS. It was defined as "a new initiative to assure and improve clinical standards at local level, taking action to ensure that risks are avoided, adverse incidents detected rapidly, investigated, and lessons learned, good practice disseminated, and systems in place to ensure continuous improvement in care".

The ideas in this White Paper were going to have wide-ranging effects on the NHS in the next 10 years, and there was to be a vast injection of money. It would result in improvements in cancer management, shorter waiting lists for outpatient clinics and having treatment and the building of more new hospitals. However, there would be much discussion as to whether all the money was wisely spent.

On 1st September, the Trust changed its name to James Paget Healthcare NHS Trust to reflect its new status following the transfer of some of the Community Services from Anglian Harbours NHS Trust. These included the Northgate and Lowestoft Hospitals, the Children's Services and Community Services in the Great Yarmouth area.

The Tracheostomy Support Service received a Charter Mark Award at a ceremony in London on 1st December. The Right Honourable Frank Dobson, MP, Secretary of State for Health, made the presentation to Denise Smith.

A Pressure Sore Group was set up in the early 1990s. Pressure Sores are extremely painful and debilitating and when they occur can result in the patient spending many extra weeks or months in hospital. As a result of the work of the group the seriousness of pressure sores in the hospital had decreased, as demonstrated by audits undertaken in 1996 and 1997. Although the rate in the hospital increased from 11% to 12% in the two years (national average was 14%), the number of grade 4 scores was nil in 1997 compared with 8 in the previous year. The number of Grade 3 scores was 6 in 1997 compared with 14 in 1996. This reduction in the worst bedsores was achieved in spite of the number of high-risk patients increasing from 14.02% in 1996 to 18.13% in 1997. This work demonstrated the value of looking at a problem and instituting measures to overcome it.

Staff Nurse Olive Price retired on 31st November after working for the NHS for 40 years; the last six years on the Charnwood Suite.

1998

There were celebrations locally and nationally to celebrate the founding of the NHS fifty years ago. On 5th July, a special thanksgiving service was held in the chapel, a celebration cake was cut in the cafeteria by Trust Chairman, Mr. John Wells, and a number of departments were 'open' to the public. In addition, there was an Exhibition in the Board Room, an Art Exhibition in the Breydon Hall, organised by Julian Macey and Margaret Carver, and the League of Friends organised a Summer Fayre.

Ken Brewer, supervisor of the post room and transport, retired on 30th January after 22 years working for the Health Service.

Becki Ballard was appointed Project Manager for the Norfolk and Waveney Cancer Project, which was set up to co-ordinate and improve cancer services in the area along the recommendations in the Calman-Hine Report, which was published in 1995. The project was jointly funded by the Norfolk and Norwich Health Care NHS Trust, James Paget Healthcare NHS Trust and the Norwich Community Health Partnership. The steering group had key representatives from each Trust and included Dr. David Ellis, Medical Director from the James Paget, and representatives from primary care, oncology, palliative care and nursing.

Graeme McLean succeeded David Ellis as Medical Director.

The James Paget started its own Lymphoedema Service with the appointment in April of Sandra Westrop as a specialist physiotherapist. Lymphoedema is the build-up of fluid in an arm or leg, causing it to become swollen. It is seen most commonly in the arm after some operations or radiotherapy for breast cancer and early treatment and advice by the Lymphoedema Specialist can help in the management of this problem. Before 1998 patients had to be referred to the Priscilla Bacon Lodge in Norwich.

The East Norfolk and Waveney Research Consortium was established and as part of the closer links with the University of East Anglia five of the Trust's Consultants (Drs. David Ellis, Kang and Notcutt and Messrs Pereira and Premachandra) were appointed honorary senior lecturers to the School of Health, UEA.

The Bure Clinic website was launched in July to increase the public's awareness and knowledge about sexually transmittable infections. It is regularly updated and people can book appointments for the Clinic on-line.

On Sunday 13th September, the Chief Executive's Five Mile Fun Run was held on the Somerleyton Estate. It was organised by Linda Turner, Liz Barber and Wendy Burman and was started by Lady Somerleyton. The aim was to continue the National Health Service's 50th Anniversary celebrations, to promote healthy living and to raise funds for the Big 'C' Charity. Seventy-five people took part.

For some time it had been difficult to recruit nurses and on 16th August Andrew Fox, Medical Clinical Services Manager, and Alicia Hinton, Ward

Sister on the Day and Short Stay Unit, flew to Australia to spend an intensive six days interviewing qualified nurses to fill vacancies in key specialties. Twenty-five successful candidates were offered 6–12 month contracts, with the first nurses arriving in November. To further help recruitment, another "Back to Nursing" course was held in the autumn and the number of places for Nurse Training was increased. Unfortunately, not all the Australians came and none stayed for a long period.

On 2nd August, a group of porters led by Barry Wilkinson took part in the Gorleston Rotary Club's raft race, which was part of the cliff-top gala. Their raft, the 'Porters Pride', won The Mercury Challenge Cup and the team was second in the Rotary Challenge Cup, which was awarded to the team with the most sponsorship money. The £402 raised went to the JPH Digital Retinal Screening Camera Appeal. The Gorleston Chamber of Trade Challenge Cup went to 'Porters Pride' for the best-dressed raft – a hospital bed.

The Breast Care Nursing Team, led by Wendy Dwornik, Macmillan Breast Care Nurse Specialist, was awarded the 1998 Charter Mark and presented with the award at a ceremony at the Queen Elizabeth II Conference Centre in London.

The Burrage Centre Social Club Bowls Team won the Lothingland League and was runner-up in the Bob Whitely Cup.

The new Orthopaedic Rehabilitation Unit at Lowestoft Hospital was opened in August and named after Gwen Baker, who had worked for the Friends of the Hospital for nearly 50 years.

The General Practitioner Unit at Lowestoft Hospital was refurbished and named after the benefactor, Gertrude Barwood.

The Rehabilitation Unit organised a national meeting on Stroke Rehabilitation in the Burrage Centre in November, under the chairmanship of Dr. Peter Harrison. It had many speakers with a national reputation and was regarded as a great success. The meeting also made a profit, which was ploughed back into buying equipment for the Rehabilitation Unit.

On 5th November, the Linen and Sewing Room Services were presented with an award to mark their registration with the British Standards Institution. This followed a stringent audit of all policies and procedures. The official presentation was made by Nigel Wright, Sector Account Manager of the British Standards Institution.

The Women's Royal Voluntary Service presented the Trust with £25,000 worth of equipment on 19th November. This took the amount that they had given to the Trust since the hospital opened to over £200,000.

A new service for Chronic Fatigue Syndrome patients was developed whereby after assessment by the consultant the patient is referred to the Occupational Therapist for assessment and rehabilitation.

1999

The small group set up on 3rd November 1997, with John Wells as Chairman, to raise money to pay back the £75,000 which the Big 'C' had given towards the provision of a mobile mammography unit, had raised £35,000 in just over a year.

The Broadland Suite – a new outpatient suite – was opened on 4th January, having been converted from the old coffee lounge. The design and decoration were done to an extremely high standard, thanks to the work of Arthur Harris and Brian Tate. It was built adjacent to the Breast Imaging Department. Breast Clinics were transferred to the Broadland Suite and the proximity of the clinic to the Breast Imaging Department was beneficial to both. The Oncology Clinics were moved to this area along with some surgical clinics. Later in the year, two counselling rooms off the corridor going to the Breast Imaging Department were opened and this gave a much-needed facility to talk to patients and relatives in a quiet and relaxing atmosphere.

In January, the local health authorities and the Trusts were reaching agreements on their plans for the coming year when they learnt that they would have to contribute to the recent pay awards to health workers. In spite of this, various new services were introduced:

- Fast track clinics in Medicine.
- Increase in high dependency facilities.
- Increase in trained nurse levels on medical wards.
- Increase in Dermatology medical staffing.
- New Consultant Gastro-enterologist.
- Additional nurse in cancer services.

In March, the Trust attained level 2 compliance of the Clinical Negligence Scheme for Trusts. Only 8% of Trusts had reached that level. It had involved producing a Clinical Risk Analysis and Action Plan for every speciality and clinical support service within the Trust.

Room one in the X-ray Department had a new X-ray unit installed. It was the main accident and emergency X-ray room, so was used 24 hours a day, and the equipment was suffering breakdowns. The colour scheme was a shade of purple with room furniture to match.

The Government set four objectives:

- Coping with emergency admissions.
- Meeting cancer standards.
- Continuing to reduce waiting times.
- Control of infection.

The Norfolk and Waveney Cancer Network was established and was one of 34 cancer networks in England. It would be responsible for delivering the cancer agenda as set out in the NHS Cancer Plan and would work with the Norfolk and Norwich and James Paget Trusts, six Primary Care Trusts, Social Services and the voluntary sector.

The Hospital Intranet was started with Chris Thompson, Library Manager, as the Project Leader. It derived from a request from a Hospital Consultant to have a database of Clinical Guidelines and the desire of Chris Thompson to transmit the Library Bulletin, Catalogue, Holdings List and news from the Library around the Hospital quickly, continuously and without the need for 'bits of paper'. From this developed the idea of adding Hospital News, Educational Events, Department Information, the Telephone Book, etc. Kudos, a computer design company, was approached to bring this concept to reality.

On 20th May, Miss Helen McDermott from Anglia Television launched the Burrage Centre appeal to raise £1.8 million for a swimming pool and gymnasium. Unfortunately, for various reasons as mentioned in the section on the Burrage Centre, the Appeal failed to obtain a Lottery Grant from Sport England but did, eventually, manage to provide an excellent Gymnasium for the staff, some patients and the local community.

Stephanie Davis became Director of Finance in July.

On 3rd September, members of the Trust gathered in the Boardroom to wish Mike Pollard well in his new job as Chief Executive of Essex Rivers Healthcare NHS Trust in Colchester. He had been at the James Paget for nine years and in that time the Hospital had become an NHS Trust, had expanded to take over some parts of Anglian Harbours NHS Trust after it had failed, and throughout that time the Trust had always balanced its books. David Hill, Director of Finance and Deputy Chief Executive, was promoted to be the new Chief Executive.

The James Paget was one of only 24 Trusts in the country to be selected to participate in the National Booked Admissions Programme, which enabled GPs to directly book patients with hernias onto a special operating list according to strict guidelines. This was led by Paul Aukland, Consultant Surgeon, and Clare Rooney, Clinical Services Manager. The first patients had their operations in September.

The James Paget Domestics received a Gold Award for the Best Cleaned Premises by an in-house Cleaning Team for a Healthcare Trust.

Nurse prescribing for a limited number of drugs came into being on 1st November. At first, this was limited to those with a District Nursing or Health Visitor qualification who worked in the Primary Care setting and had successfully completed a nurse prescribing programme. In addition, they had to be registered with UKCC as a nurse prescriber and be authorised by their employer to prescribe. Since then, this practice has been extended to certain nurses working in the hospital.

With the Millennium approaching, there was a fear that computers world-wide might malfunction. Much work went into trying to prevent any problems in the Trust and over 750 personal computers were upgraded. Fortunately, the Millennium started with no adverse effects.

Transport for patients attending clinics and treatment at the hospital had increased by 5–14% each year for the five years leading up to late 1997, so the Trust Unit Management Team set up a small working group to look at the problem and come up with some proposals. The NHS Executive had stated that a patient's need for transport should be determined by a doctor, dentist or midwife. In practice, most decisions were made by clinic staff in the GP surgery and the Trust picked up the bill. After a number of meetings, criteria were established for patients who required transport to travel to Norfolk Trusts. This required that the patient filled in an application form and after it had been checked by the GP surgery it was forwarded to the clinic the patient would be attending. If approved, the transport would be booked. A new computer program was developed to facilitate this. Initial results showed that in the first nine months of 1999 there were 5,386 fewer requests for journeys compared with the same period the previous year, and the number of aborted journeys (those booked but, for some reason, not completed yet had been paid for) fell by 2,064 over the same period. The number of escorts also fell by 1,555. The transport bill for these journeys had been £786,000 annually and the number of journeys had been reduced by 6% in the first nine months.

Among the other achievements of the Financial Year 1998/1999 were:

- Waiting list reduced from 4,867 to 3,707.
- Only 139 patients were waiting over 9 months and only 10 waiting more than 12 months for treatment at the end of March 1999.
- Only a small percentage of patients waited for a bed more than two hours in the Accident and Emergency Department after the decision to admit them.
- The Linen and Sewing Room Services and the Medical Engineering Department successfully gained their BSI Registration to BS ENIS09002.
- Five additional Consultant posts were funded.
- Extra nursing posts were established.
- The number of written complaints was 125, a reduction of 22 on the previous year.
- The chamber in the McIver Hyperbaric Unit became a category 1 chamber, which meant that the hyperbaric facilities were capable of supporting the treatment of critically ill patients from any cause who might require hyperbaric intensive therapy.
- Attainment of CPA Accreditation by all four Pathology departments.
- The latest flexible video endoscopic equipment was bought for the Endoscopy Suite with money from a legacy from Mr. William Spencer, who had been a patient for 15 years. In his memory, the Endoscopic Unit was named the William Spencer Unit.
- Upgrading of the reception area in the X-ray Department.

- Appointment of additional Consultant Urologist and Consultant Ophthalmologist.
- Appointment of additional Consultant Physician with a special interest in Respiratory Medicine.
- Appointment of two additional Consultant Anaesthetists.
- Expansion of Palliative Care Service to include two additional specialist nurses and a specialist Physiotherapist.
- Development of draft standards for breast, lung and colorectal cancer by the Norfolk and Waveney Cancer Project to improve access to diagnostic services, reduce waiting times for treatment and ensure quality multi-disciplinary working.

The total income for the year was £67,573,000, generating an operating surplus of £2,194,000. After paying net interest of £754,000 and a dividend payment to the NHS Executive of £1,426,000, the retained surplus taken to the reserves was £14,000. The total income was a rise of 11% on the previous year and compares with 1993/1994 when it was £40,796.

The Trust treated 6.39% more in-patient and Day Cases (including Day Patients) compared with the previous year, and the numbers were: 30,158 In-patients, 14,445 Day Cases, 7,808 Day Patients and 158,257 Outpatients.

The total value of the Fixed Assets of the Trust as at 31st March 1999 was £45,901,000 and £599,000 had been received from donations from the public, legacies and invested income from the Charitable Funds.

The actual Management costs were £3,235,000, which was below the target set by the NHS Executive Regional Office.

On a typical day in 1999 the Trust cared for over 2,600 people:

- Over 440 were in-patients in both the acute and community hospitals.
- 134 patients attended the A and E Department (one every 11 minutes).
- 114 patients were treated as day patients.
- 630 attended outpatient clinics.
- 50 patients were seen at home by the Trust's Specialist Nurses.
- 300 X-rays were performed.

- 1,800 laboratory tests were performed.
- 50 people had speech and language therapy sessions.
- 180 patients had physiotherapy treatment.
- 54 people were seen by the occupational therapists.
- 71 people received advice from the dieticians and nutritionalists.
- 6 babies were born.
- 220 patients received care from the Trust's District Nurses.
- 85 families were visited by the Health Visitors.
- The Chiropodists treated 60 people.

The Trust employed 2,581 people at the end of March 1999.

2000

At midnight on 31st March, the James Paget Healthcare NHS Trust took over the running of Lowestoft's community and children's health services from the Local Health Partnerships NHS Trust. This involved about 140 staff such as District Nurses, Health Visitors, Physiotherapists, Dentists and Family Planning Doctors changing their employer.

Charter Marks for excellence in Public Service were awarded to the Ophthalmic Day Care Service and the Sandra Chapman Centre in February. The Ophthalmic Day Care Service had been set up in 1991 and allowed patients having surgery for cataract or glaucoma to have it done as a day case, whereas in the past they were usually in hospital for a week. The Sandra Chapman Centre was established to improve the facilities for patients undergoing chemotherapy or treatment for blood disorders. The Children's Service retained its Charter Mark.

The first phase of 'Southside' was built. This was to house the increasing number of people who were now working on the site. Initially it housed 30 people and the first floor temporarily housed some of the new training facilities.

The Government issued an NHS Plan for reform to "give the people of Britain a Health Service fit for the 21st Century". At last it recognised that there were insufficient resources in the NHS and the plan promised funding for new hospital beds, more equipment and more staff to deliver the services. The key targets included:

- Maximum wait for an outpatient appointment to be three months.
- Maximum wait for treatment to be six months.
- Improvements in patient satisfaction.
- Reduction in the mortality rate from cancer and heart disease.

The residential accommodation on the hospital site and the roads they are in were named after pioneers in the field of Medicine: Pasteur House, Nightingale House, McKee House, Lister House, Edith Cavell Place, Watson Farrer Place and Alexander Fleming Close.

Clinical Governance Day was held on 29th March with a display in the Boardroom giving a brief overview of Clinical Governance covering the following topics:

- Risk Management
- Complaints
- Health and Safety
- Audit and Effectiveness
- Quality
- Continued Professional Development.

At the same time, Chris Thompson and Liz Crowe launched the James Paget Intranet site.

The Cancer Information Centre opened in a room at the rear of the hospital near the Breast Imaging Unit. It was ideally situated for patients and relatives with breast cancer, but out of the way for most other patients, and in April 2005 it was relocated nearer the front of the hospital by taking over part of the Pharmacy waiting area. It is a drop-in centre manned by volunteers with Pat Utting as Cancer Information Centre Co-ordinator. It contains information books and leaflets as well as leaflets giving advice about financial benefits, beauty therapies and self-help groups. Access to the internet is also available here.

When the James Paget Healthcare NHS Trust took over the running of the Lowestoft Hospital in September 1997, it promised to make sure the hospital had a bright future. On 27th March, the Alfred Watson Unit was opened in the old Corton Ward by Lord Somerleyton. It offered slow stream rehabilitation, long-term care for some elderly patients and palliative care as appropriate. The ward had undergone a total redesign and refurbishment, creating a modern environment which afforded the patient greater privacy. Alfred John Goodrick Watson was a local man who had worked as an engine driver all his life and left a large legacy to the hospital in 1981/1982.

On 4th May, Gwen Baker received her MBE from the Right Honourable Lord Belstead, accompanied by his two Deputy Lieutenants, Lord Somerleyton and Noel Johnson. It was in recognition of the untiring work she had done for the League of Friends of the Hospital for the previous 50 years. The presentation was followed by a reception in the Gwen Baker Unit.

Mrs Ann Galey retired on 31st March after 25 years working for the NHS. She started in the Catering Department of Northgate Hospital in 1975 and transferred to the James Paget when it opened. She became Supervisor of the Sewing Room in 1988 and took on the Linen Room in 1994.

The Big ‘C’ Skills Laboratory was opened on Ward 16 by Dr. Ian Gibson, MP for Norwich North, in the presence of Tony Wright, MP for Great Yarmouth, Bob Blizzard, MP for Lowestoft, and Trustees from the Big ‘C’. The aim of the Laboratory was to teach skills such as inserting drips, resuscitation and laparoscopy. Later, it was transferred to the first floor of Southside, before taking up its permanent abode in the Teaching and Education Centre.

The Government approved the setting up of a new Medical School at the University of East Anglia. The joint venture came from the University of East Anglia, Norfolk and Norwich University Hospital NHS Trust, James Paget Healthcare NHS Trust, Norfolk Mental Healthcare and General Practitioners in the area.

In May, the Intensive Care Unit Appeal was launched to raise £600,000 to purchase equipment for the new unit. Among many functions which were held was the Hobland Ball on 15th July which raised £3,500. Subsequent functions included Antique Days, Fashion Shows, Football Matches, Fetes, etc.

David Ellis organised and hosted the MRCP (UK) Part 2 Examination in the James Paget for the first time on 19th to 21st June. This took place on Ward 3 and there were five guest examiners from different parts of the country.

The whole of the Accident and Emergency Department was redesigned and upgraded and this was funded by the Government’s

Modernisation Fund to the tune of £800,000 after the Trust successfully made a bid for capital funding. The work started in January and was completed in the autumn.

Twelve new staff houses were built on the north side of the hospital grounds and were ready for occupation in August.

Rosemary Thompson, Gynaecology Specialist Oncology Nurse, was selected to judge the World Championships in Artistic Roller Skating in Springfield, Massachusetts, in September. She was one of only seven judges in Great Britain who were eligible to judge at this level. She had been involved in roller skating most of her life and as a youngster had competed in artistic roller skating events at national level. She had played Roller Hockey at national and international level for several years, along with Christine Thompson, the Senior Hospital Librarian. She had been judging artistic roller skating for 15 years and became an international judge in 1994.

A Patient Process Redesign Workshop was held for the Radiology Department on 13th, 14th and 15th September. Representatives of the Department met up with a team of facilitators from Leicester and at the end of the three days an Action Plan was produced to develop the Main Radiology Department.

With nursing shortages still being a problem, Terri Yassin, Practice Development Nurse, Dawn Taylor, Senior Nurse in the Surgical Directorate, and Angela Wilson, Ward 7 Manager, flew to Manila in November to recruit nurses from the Philippines. 100 nurses were interviewed, 59 were offered contracts and the first group arrived at the James Paget in February 2001. It seemed wrong taking nurses from another country, but apparently the Philippines produce more nurses than they require and the nurses who take up positions abroad send back to their families in the Philippines a sizeable amount of the money they earn.

The Trust was awarded full accreditation from Health Quality Service in November, having achieved provisional accreditation in November 1999.

A Fracture Workshop was organised by Mr. John Petri, Consultant Orthopaedic Surgeon, assisted by Mr, Fanous, Associate Specialist, and Caroline Scarll, the Joint Review Nurse, on 25th November. Apart from lectures, the operating theatre staff and junior doctors who attended were able to try out fixation of fractures on plastic bones using real instruments and implants.

Among the other achievements for the year were:

- All waiting list targets were met. There were 3,852 patients waiting for admission at the end of March 2000.
- Reduced waiting time for outpatient appointments in all specialities.
- Purchased and installed a new pathology computer system.
- A fast-track diagnostic service for patients with suspected Deep Vein Thrombosis was commenced.
- The Cranbrook Unit opened as a therapeutic day centre at Northgate Hospital.
- Appointment of two Consultant Physicians with a special interest in Gastro-enterology.
- Appointment of Consultants in Obstetrics and Gynaecology, Paediatrics, Radiology and Haematology.

For the Financial Year 1999/2000, the total income for the Trust was £73,157,000, generating an operating surplus of £2,469,000. After paying net interest of £222,000 and a dividend payment to the NHS Executive of £2,191,000, the retained surplus taken to the reserves was £20,000. The total income was 8% more than the previous year.

The Trust treated more patients than in the previous year and there were 29,320 In-patients, 14,875 Day Cases and 8,285 Day Patients. 163,713 Outpatients were seen.

The total value of the Fixed Assets of the Trust at 31st March was £42,535,000. The Charitable Funds benefited in the year by £772,000 as a result of donations, legacies and investment income.

Management costs were £3,391,000.

2001

Professor Sam Leinster started work as the Inaugural Dean of the new Medical School on 1st January. In Liverpool he designed and implemented a new curriculum for undergraduate medicine and established the Breast Unit. At the time of his appointment, he was Chairman of the Association for the Study of Medical Education.

The Trust was one of 20 nationwide to be awarded the funding to pilot digital hearing aids for NHS patients. The project commenced in

February and was preceded by a re-organisation of the Audiology Department: additional staff, information technology and accommodation.

Lowestoft Primary Care Group became a Trust in April with Jane Hore as Chairman and Jana Burton the Chief Executive. It had an annual budget of £52 million. The Great Yarmouth Primary Care Group also became a Trust in April.

In January, some of the 59 Philippine Nurses started to arrive. Everyone noticed their high standards, their work commitment and the constant smile on their faces. Unlike their Australian predecessors, most of them stayed and some have married and have had babies. They started their three month Adaptation Programme on 12th February and all completed it within the minimum time required to be registered.

Further audits on the incidence of pressure sores in patients showed a decrease in the number. The incidence in 1998 was 2.3% and there was a slight increase in 1999 to 2.5%, although the severity of the bed sores was much less. The incidence for 2000 had fallen to 1.6%, which meant that 150 fewer patients suffered from this terrible complication. This was achieved in spite of fewer qualified nurses and the increased patient dependency and was helped by the increased frequency of patient assessment and the greater number of pressure-relieving equipment.

The National Booked Admissions Programme was launched in July 1998 and was introduced at the James Paget from January, starting with General Surgery Day Cases and minor operations. This was followed by ENT and Cataract Day cases in February and March. In fact, this was not a new concept for the hospital as a number of surgeons had been giving dates for operations to their patients in the outpatient clinics since before the hospital opened!

A stop smoking service started in February. GPs could refer patients or patients could telephone directly for an appointment.

A Partial Booking Scheme for outpatient clinics started in March. The aim of this was to try and reduce the number of people who failed to attend for their appointment. This was 15,000 a year or 8.8% of appointments. The scheme involved sending a letter to a patient acknowledging receipt of the referral letter from their GP and informing them that they would be contacted again approximately four weeks before the time to make an appointment. A further letter was then sent asking the patient to telephone the hospital to make an appointment. Patients failing to respond were referred back to their GP. This all seemed complicated, time consuming and expensive in the number of personnel involved and in the postage and telephone calls, but it did reduce the number of people who did not turn up for an appointment.

In the previous two to three years, 31 nurses had started work for the Trust after having being away from nursing for between 10 and 20 years and having attended Return to Practice courses held at the James Paget.

The Ophthalmic Outpatients' new Children's Play Area was opened by Mr. Bert Collins, Mayor of Great Yarmouth, on 9th March.

The Sandringham Unit at Northgate Hospital was named by Helen McDermott of Anglia Television on 29th March. It was formerly Ward 3 and had been extensively refurbished. It cost over £6,000 and most of that was raised through fund raising by the staff. It had 19 beds and accepted patients for non-acute medical care from the acute unit or the community. Patients were accepted for recovery care, palliative care and assessment for residential or nursing home placements, or if a complicated home care package was required. Unfortunately, it closed in 2006 and its functions were transferred to the Rehabilitation Unit at the James Paget after most of the staff from there had moved into the new Stroke Unit.

The Orthopaedic Joint Review Project started in line with similar projects throughout the country. Caroline Scarll, Joint Review Nurse, was in charge of the Project and arranged for the follow-up by nurses of all patients who had had joint replacements. There was, in addition, a retrospective review of joint replacements of the previous ten years. The clinic review started in June.

Arthur Watts from Great Yarmouth and Steve Cone from Lowestoft paddled in a kayak from Lowestoft to the Millennium Dome and then cycled back to Lowestoft to draw attention to Bowel Cancer and in the process raised £5,035.09.

Joanna Kingston, the first Infection Control Sister, retired at the end of March. She was devoted to her patients and staff and, with Dr. Anne Gerkin, Consultant Microbiologist, set high standards in the fight against infection.

The first Annual James Paget Audit Symposium was held on 7th June. There were 34 posters and the prize for the best one was awarded to Dr. Jenny Jenkins for her ongoing audit of Obstetric Anaesthetics showing how, after a period of education of both anaesthetists and pregnant ladies, the incidence of epidurals had increased yearly from below 10% to over 25% – equal to the country's average rate. In addition, the general anaesthetic rate for emergency caesareans had been reduced dramatically. There were five oral presentations and Nancy Dixon of Health Quality Quest gave the keynote address.

Dr. Katharine Kite was appointed as the Trust's first Nurse Consultant and commenced work in July as Nurse Consultant in Critical Care.

The Commission for Health Improvement (CHI) started its Clinical Governance Review on 19th November. The purpose was to:

- Identify good practice and areas for improvement.
- Independently assess systems to assure quality of care.
- Focus on the patients, clinical teams and corporate strategy.

The whole process lasted 24 weeks with a review visit for one week in March 2002. Prior to the first visit, the Trust collected data and information. This was forwarded to the Commission for Health Improvement to allow it to decide which Clinical Teams or patient pathway to review closely. CHI also consulted with local GPs, Primary Care Trusts, Social Services and the local public to seek their opinions of the Trust. The review team consisted of a Doctor, a Nurse, a Manager, an Allied Health Professional and a lay person, all led by a CHI review manager. It was amazing how the Commission had developed so quickly. The amount of money and time spent on these reviews was colossal, not only by CHI but also by the Trusts; but it made the Trusts look at the service they were providing to patients and hopefully it led to better care.

An extension to the Sandra Chapman Centre was opened on 20th June by Dr. Terry Mitchell, who had overseen the building of the original building which was opened in 1992. Work on the extension started in October 2000 and was completed in May 2001. It provided two new treatment rooms, counselling room and additional office accommodation.

Oncology Sister Maggie Boon left in September to pursue her love of music by undertaking a full-time Music in Therapy Degree Course.

Improving Working Lives was launched by the Government in October. Its aim was to ensure that working practices within the NHS made it easier for everyone who worked within it to achieve a healthy balance between their home and working life. Trusts needed to have certain policies and practices in place by April 2003 and future funding arrangements within Trusts would be linked to their success in achieving the standard.

The standard looked at seven distinct areas of work:

- Human Resources strategy and management.
- Equality and diversity.
- Communication and staff involvement.
- Flexible working.
- Healthy working.
- Training and development.
- Staff benefits and childcare.

The Trust set up a group representing a good cross-section of the staff to look into the various issues and to make plans for improving the lives of its staff.

The Waveney Suite was opened in October. It brought together the Subfertility Assessment and Treatment Area and the Early Pregnancy Assessment Unit.

In November, Julian Macey held a three-day Retrospective Art Exhibition of his work at the instigation of the Arts Committee. He had been painting for 40 years in a variety of mediums including oils, pastels and watercolours and he does superb detailed pencil sketches. He is a full Member of the Royal Miniature Society and has had work accepted for its Annual Exhibition since 1985. His miniatures have been included in two world exhibitions of miniatures and he is featured in the Royal Miniature Society's Centenary Book – a copy of which is held in the Queen's Library at Windsor. He had been an extremely active member of the Hospital's Art Committee since its foundation in 1985 and it was fitting that he should be given this honour of holding his own exhibition in the hospital.

The Catering Department was visited in December by a local Environmental Health Officer and was issued with the Award of Excellence for the fourth year running.

Chris Smith, Director of Patient Care for the previous eight years, retired on 19th December. Elayne Guest became the Acting Director of Patient Care, in addition to her many other duties.

Rev. Walter Currie, Hospital Chaplain, retired at the end of the year, having held his post since 1987. His successor was Vilda Steady.

In December, the National Cancer Plan introduced treatment waiting times, including the requirement that 100% of patients diagnosed with breast cancer should receive their first definitive treatment within 31 days of diagnosis. This target was met.

During the year the following projects were completed:

- The Renal Unit and Phase II of the Office Development were completed and operational.
- First phase of the ward upgrade was completed, including installation of a new nurse call system.
- The old Social Work Department on the back street of the hospital on the ground floor was converted into a specialist Pre-Operative Assessment Clinic.
- Updating the central heating boilers and bathrooms in residences continued.
- New vinyl sheeting replaced all existing carpets in the GP Unit at Northgate.
- Theatre lights in the operating theatres were upgraded.
- Alterations to three rooms in the Central Treatment Suite to allow the giving of general anaesthetics to Community Dental patients.
- Upgrade of three off-ward kitchens.

John Little, a much loved worker in the Operating Theatre Suite, died suddenly. He had a great love of gardening and a bench was dedicated to his memory and placed in one of the courtyard gardens.

During the Financial Year 2000/20001, the Primary Care groups of Lowestoft and Great Yarmouth became Primary Care Trusts and they took over the employment of Health Visitors, District Nurses and other Community Staff.

Other improvements in the Financial Year 2000/2001 were:

- The purchase of new and replacement medical equipment in excess of £800,000.
- Upgrading of different parts of the James Paget, such as roof replacement. Unfortunately, the hospital was built with flat roofs and has suffered repeatedly with leaks.

The total income for the year was £82,909,000, generating an operating surplus of £2,339,000. After paying net interest of £177,000 and making a dividend payment to the NHS Executive of £2,442,000, the retained surplus taken to the reserves was £13,000. The total income was a rise of 13% on the preceding year.

The income from Charitable Funds for the year was £1,061,000 and this was made up from donations, legacies and investment income.

The actual Management Costs were £3,471,000, which was below the target set by the NHS Executive Regional Office.

The Trust treated 28,428 In-patients, 14,527 Day Cases and 9,044 Day Patients. 172,197 Outpatients were seen.

2002

The whole hospital was shocked by the sudden death of Lou Lewis on Thursday 17th January. He had worked for the NHS for 20 years and was the Portering and Security Manager. He could be seen all over the hospital with his cheeky grin, was always willing to help and would frequently stop for a friendly chat. He managed to get things done by his gentle manner and was a friend to everyone he met. He had been an enthusiastic footballer and his two sons continued the tradition. A collection of £646 in his memory was used to purchase a Portable Pacemaker for the Coronary Care Unit and his wife, Hazel, purchased a painting of the Mediterranean which hangs outside his old office.

In February, Dr. Willy Notcutt organised the fourth annual healthcare weekend for sixth-form students who were thinking of having a career in healthcare. The weekends have become very popular and consist of talks and demonstrations by approximately 30 members of the hospital staff. Up to 60 students visit many parts of the hospital and are able to partake in hands-on activities. The feedback from the students has been very positive and very few finally decide that a healthcare career is not for them.

In March, the Assessor for the Clinical Negligence Scheme for Trusts spent two days examining the Risk Management System, meeting with key members of staff and visiting wards and departments to talk to staff.

Radiology services had improved as a result of a three-day workshop which had been held in September 2000 looking at Patient Process Design. By the beginning of 2002, the following had been achieved:

- On average, GP films reported in less than 36 hours.
- The maximum Radiographer shift had been reduced from 23 to 17 hours.
- 'Early Bird' Radiographer (0700-0900) introduced to provide pre-ward round service for the Medical Admissions Unit.
- 'Link Grade' Radiographer posts established.
- More radiographers undertaking extended role duties such as barium enemas, film reporting and intravenous injections.
- Out-of-hours Helper cover to assist with ward and Accident and Emergency patients.
- Improved facilities such as gowns, TV, etc.
- Regular Trust and GP Newsletters distributed.

The Early Warning Score (EWS) System became part of the hospital's standard observation chart. It was devised by Dr. Richard Morgan and Dr. Maggie Wright, Consultant Anaesthetists, in the late 1980s. It is based on information collected when observations are done on patients such as temperature, heart rate, systolic blood pressure, respiratory rate, urine output and neurological status. Observations in the normal range are scored as '0', but values outside this are given a number depending how far away the value is from normal. The individual scores are totalled to give the EWS. A figure of 3 indicates the patient is at risk of critical illness and those with 6 are seriously unwell. For some years it had been hospital policy that, when a patient triggered '3', the Senior House Officer or more senior doctor must be contacted and it was hoped that with the inclusion of the EWS on the observation charts it would help nursing and medical staff notice changes in it.

Other additions to the observation charts were put on the back, such as a cumulative fluid balance grid, a urinary analysis grid and a grid to record the patient's pain assessment.

Over the years it had become apparent that patients leaving the Intensive Care Unit (ITU) or High Dependency Unit (HDU) could deteriorate on returning to the ward where there were far fewer nurses, so making it more difficult to notice deterioration in a patient. The Early Warning Score helps in noticing these changes and allows appropriate actions to be taken. A further help was the introduction of the Outreach Team, suggested by Dr. Maggie Wright, Consultant Anaesthetist, which consists of senior nurses who have worked on the ITU, who are able to come to the ward at short notice to give advice and help. In addition, they make regular visits to patients recently discharged from the ITU and HDU. Over subsequent years this service has been overseen and improved by Katharine Kite, Consultant Nurse for Critical Care.

The increasing incidence of obesity in the community necessitated the Trust purchasing a heavy duty bed (the Huntleigh Model 1080 which has a capacity of 450kg/71stone and has inbuilt scales) and a Gantry Hoist System with a capacity of 400kg/63 stone. Later, the Operating Department had to invest in an operating table which was strong enough to take very obese patients.

The Patient Advocacy and Liaison Service (PALS) started on 1st April under the direction of Liz Barber. Its aim was to help patients and carers through the complicated and sometimes frustrating NHS maze and over the years its value has been increasingly recognised.

The Consumer Alliance had been going for a number of months and was a means of involving patients in the planning and decision making of local health provision. It met quarterly and was attended by the Trust Chairman, several Trust Directors, the Consumer Relations Manager, Patient Services Officer, Clinical Governance Co-ordinator, Chaplain and Social Services, among others. Members of the Group came from Age Concern, Citizens Advice Bureau, Pensioners Associations, Heartcare, CRUSE, Stroke Association, Disability Forums, Careers Forums and several other patient support groups.

The 2002 Patient Environment Assessment Visit secured a mark of 97%, which was a great tribute to all members of staff.

Nigel Crisp, NHS Chief Executive, visited the James Paget for a day after requesting a visit to a hospital in the Region which was highly regarded and would give him a good feel as to what was going right in the NHS. On 21st April, after a reporter had spent a day in the hospital, the *Sunday Express* said, "The James Paget Hospital is staffed by a resilient 3,000-strong team of Doctors, Nurses and Ancillary Staff, whose dedication to their patients goes way beyond the call of duty." In addition, Bob Blizzard, Waveney MP, paid tribute in Parliament to the James Paget and this was echoed by the Prime Minister in his reply.

The JPH Healthy Lifestyle Supporters' Club celebrated its first anniversary on 18th April. Members had lost over 150 lbs (10 stone 10 lbs) between them and the ITU Appeal had benefited by £415. Meetings were held at 5 pm each Wednesday in the Gynaecology Department and there was a small library from which books and videos could be borrowed.

The NHS Plan gave guidance about strengthening the role of ward sisters/charge nurses and introducing senior sisters/modern matrons. By 1st May, several modern matrons were in post.

The Trust became an Accredited Testing Centre for the European Computer Driving Licence (ECDL) which encourages staff to become more computer-literate. Seven modules have to be passed to obtain the qualification:

- Basic Concepts of Information Technology.
- Using the Computer and Managing Files.
- Word Processing.
- Spreadsheets.
- Databases.
- PowerPoint Presentations.
- Information and Communication.

Sue Coote, Stoma Care Sister, died on 24th June after a courageous fight against cancer. She qualified as an Enrolled Nurse in 1990, studied further and worked as a Staff Nurse on Ward 1 and in the Central Treatment Suite. She joined the Stoma Care Nursing Team in 1999. The following year she completed her Diploma in Higher Education Nursing and continued studying for the Specialist Stoma Care Nursing Course, in spite of undergoing chemotherapy. She was delighted to be appointed a Sister in stoma care. Her friends and colleagues will remember her sense of humour and her infectious smile. In spite of having to face her own disease and the chemotherapy, she was a source of inspiration not only to her patients but also to her colleagues and friends. From money raised in her memory, a painting of Greece was commissioned and it now hangs outside the Stoma Care Office.

In July, the Trust received 3 stars based on the 2001/2002 performance tables. It was one of only three Trusts in East Anglia to reach this status. The ratings were based on nine key targets which covered clinical quality, access times for diagnosis and treatment, patient and staff satisfaction, personnel and financial management. The Trust's performance was above average on several of the targets and the only significant problem area was the number of cancelled operations, which was associated with the pressure on beds.

On Monday 1st July, a new trolley snack service started. Sarah Jordan, who was the backbone behind the service, started at 8 am by making sandwiches and rolls. From 9 am to just after midday, she toured the hospital selling refreshments to many staff. The new service was very popular.

The new Endoscopy Suite opened to its first patients on 8th July. It had been constructed out of the old Ward 16 and comprises a reception and waiting area, three fully equipped treatment rooms and rooms for cleaning and sterilising the equipment, staff changing, a small kitchen, offices, etc. Big 'C' contributed £154,000 for equipment, enabling the third treatment room to be fully utilised.

The Endoscopy Suite was officially opened by Lynn Faulds Wood, the well-known TV presenter, who had travelled by car from Reading in the afternoon and travelled back to London that evening. Ten years previously, she had had an operation for bowel cancer and had set up a charity to raise awareness of the disease and to collect money for its investigation and treatment and for research.

Paul and Pauline Aukland had donated a flight in their plane to the ITU appeal and the lucky winners were Sue Meacham from the Pathology Department and Jean Eccleston. The flight took off from Seething Airport on 15th July and took them over parts of Suffolk, the James Paget, Great Yarmouth and their own homes.

Val Field, Anaesthetics Department Administrator, retired on 6th August, having worked for the Anaesthetic Department for 26 years. She started working at the Yarmouth General Hospital in 1973 on the children's ward, but within a few years was coerced into working for the Anaesthetic Department. She had great organising ability and her gentle manner persuaded many people to do a task that they did not really want to do. She was the central hub of the Department, but fortunately over the years she had trained up a group of dedicated secretaries to take over her work.

In September, the first students started their medical training at the University of East Anglia.

The new Day Unit was opened in October and is on the first floor of an extension built on the north side of the hospital. It has easy access to theatres and consists of three bays and two single-bedded rooms, giving a total of 32 beds. In addition, there is a pleasant reception and waiting area with toilets, rest room, storage areas, etc. Mr. Noel Johnson performed the official opening.

From November, the Trust started training four Radiography students. They receive academic training at Suffolk College in Ipswich and attend the James Paget for clinical training on block release.

The Hospital Occupational Physiotherapy Service started. It provided a musculoskeletal physiotherapy service solely for staff on a daily basis, aiming to see urgent cases the same day and non-urgent ones within one to two weeks.

Dr. Crawford Jamieson started using a small capsule containing a miniature video camera to visualise the small bowel. The capsule is swallowed by the patient and images from the camera are stored on a small computer worn on the patient's belt during the examination. Later, the images are studied to see if there is an abnormality which could explain the patient's problem. There were only a few of these systems in the United Kingdom and none in East Anglia.

The Trust was selected as one of 12 Early Implementer sites for the Agenda for Change which was the Government's title for the new pay and terms and conditions system to be introduced across the NHS. The implementation of this involved a number of people in an enormous amount of work and, although most staff did benefit from the scheme, several were unhappy with the outcome.

The first medical students from the University of East Anglia attended for teaching sessions in December.

The James Paget Healthcare NHS Trust Older Person Mental Health Steering Group was formed in December. It is a multi-professional and multi-agency group and includes members from the Great Yarmouth and Lowestoft and Waveney Alzheimer's Societies, nurses from Northgate Hospital and Carlton Court representing Norfolk Mental Healthcare Trust, nursing staff from all three hospitals within the James Paget Healthcare Trust, including representation from the Nursing Education Department, staff from Great Yarmouth Social Services, Great Yarmouth Teaching Primary Care Trust and Waveney Primary Care Trust, a member of the Great Yarmouth Teaching Primary Care Trust Public and Patient Involvement Group, a Practice Nurse representing the community hospitals in Waveney, and a carer. The aim of the Group was to improve the care received by patients with mental health problems and their relatives/carers during their visits or admission to the James Paget.

On 13th December, all members of staff who had worked for the NHS for 20 years or more were invited to a special luncheon in the Celebration Suite of the Burrage Centre. In addition, they were presented with a certificate commemorating the 20 years service. This idea had come from the Improving Working Lives Group and the event was hosted by John Wells, Trust Chairman.

Anne Loy, Clinical Coding Supervisor, passed the National Clinical Coding examination with distinction and was awarded the prize for the highest marks achieved nationally in the 2003 examinations. Her job involves translating medical terminology written by a clinician to describe the patients' diagnosis, symptoms and treatment into a coded format which is recognised both nationally and internationally. With the Department of Health's new "Payment by Results" guidelines, the level of income the Trust received was determined by the accuracy of the coding. This information also provides a sound basis for audit and research, for monitoring trends in morbidity and for the planning and commissioning of new services locally and nationally.

As a result of achieving 3 Star Trust Status, the Trust was awarded an additional £500,000 of capital to spend at its own discretion. As the award was the result of the efforts of the whole staff of the Trust, the Board and Unit Management Teams decided to seek suggestions from the staff on how to spend the money. Eventually, it was decided to buy new electrically operated beds for the patients on many of the wards.

These beds had the advantage of being much more comfortable for the patients and made nursing easier.

In the Financial year 2001/2002, the total income was £85,885,000, generating an operating surplus of £2,182,000. After receiving net interest of £129,000 and making a dividend payment to the NHS Executive of £2,311,000, the retained surplus taken to reserve was £8,000. The total income was a rise of 4% on the previous year.

The Trust treated 28,464 In-patients, 10,274 Day Cases, 10,014 Day Patients and saw 166,198 Outpatients. It invested over £900,000 on new and replacement medical equipment and the Charitable Funds benefited by £857,000 from donations, legacies and investment income. Actual Management Costs were £3,612,000.

2003

In January, the new Dermatology Department was opened. It is housed on the ground floor in an extension from the north side of the hospital. It is palatial and self-contained, providing outpatient clinics, minor operating theatres and teaching facilities.

The New Opportunities Fund awarded £800,000 for the enhancement of home-based palliative care for patients with cancer and other life-limiting illnesses in Great Yarmouth and Waveney. This was the result of a joint bid by James Paget Healthcare NHS Trust, with the Great Yarmouth and Waveney PCTs and Norfolk and Suffolk Social Care Services. The grant funded the following staff:

- 1 Hospice at Home Co-ordinator.
- 1 Family Support Worker.
- 2 Macmillan/Specialist Palliative Care Nurses.
- Secretarial support.
- A team of professional Carers.
- Designated Consultant time for palliative care.

Barry Nash, who had been Chairman and a tireless worker for the League of Friends for many years, died after a short illness. He and his wife had devoted many hours to raising money for the benefit of patients and the hospital, and their work was much appreciated.

The new Operating Theatre and Day Case Unit, especially for eye surgery, was officially opened on Friday 25th April by Sir Patrick Holmes-Sellors. The new Unit was named the Windsor Suite as its completion in 2002 coincided with the Queen's Golden Jubilee and it was fitting that Sir Patrick had been Ophthalmic Surgeon to the Queen.

Eight Spanish nurses joined the Trust at the end of April. They had trained in Spain, were required to pass an English test and had a six week induction course before being allowed to work in the hospital.

The Hospital hosted the Intercollegiate MRCS Examination for the Royal College of Surgeons of Edinburgh on 15th and 16th May. The examination was held in the new Day Care Unit and all seven external examiners and the organiser from the College commented on the excellence of the venue. One examiner remarked that the attitude of the patients indicated that they must be well looked after at the James Paget!

Tony Harvey, Clinical Skills/Medical Devices Trainer, led the James Paget contribution to the NHS stand for the Norfolk Show and for the second year running it won the "Best Stand" in the Show. He took an ITU bed with a manikin, ventilator and other equipment and was assisted by a number of staff from the James Paget.

In June, five new electric tow tractors were purchased to replace the old ones which were no longer working satisfactorily. Like their predecessors, which roam round the hospital corridors towing a variety of trucks, they are coloured red.

In July, the Trust achieved three star status for the second year running.

Julie Cadman died suddenly and unexpectedly on 24th August at the age of 26 years. She had been a Physiotherapist for the Trust since 1998 and between September 2002 and March 2003 she worked in a voluntary capacity as a physiotherapist at St. Francis Hospital, Katete, Zambia. She played the cornet for the Waveney Valley Brass Band, competed for the Norwich Rowing club and was a keen cyclist. At the time of her death she was training for the Jungfrau Marathon. She will be remembered by her many friends at work for her generous, supportive and cheerful nature and was always ready to offer help.

The Cadet Nurse Programme commenced on 8th September and, in conjunction with Great Yarmouth College, the ten cadets undertook a two-year BTec National Diploma in Health. Successful completion of this gave them entry into the second year of pre-registration nurse training at the University of East Anglia.

Her Royal Highness the Princess Royal opened the new Intensive Care Unit on 10th September. Although the weather was miserable and wet, the helicopter bringing the Princess arrived on time. Apart from visiting the Unit, she toured parts of the hospital which were lined with members of staff and eventually came to the Boardroom, where she met various people who had been involved with the planning and building of the unit, as well as some of the many people who had raised money for the Appeal over the previous three years. John Wells made a speech of welcome and presented the Princess with a James Paget Hospital paperweight. The Princess then made a speech – without any notes – referring to her own family's experience of intensive-care facilities and said, "in spite of the technology it is the people who make the difference". Finally, she unveiled a plaque commemorating her visit and the opening of the unit.

In October, Mr. Medhat Hassanaien held the hospital's first MRCOG OSCE Course in the Burrage Centre. Doctors attending the course came from Hong Kong, Saudi Arabia, Ireland and the United Kingdom.

John Wells retired as Trust Chairman on Friday 31st October after over 10 years in the post and being the longest serving NHS Trust Chairman in the whole of England. He showed great commitment to the welfare of both patients and staff and worked tirelessly for so many causes, especially the ITU Appeal and the small group he chaired which raised nearly £100,000 for the Big 'C' Charity in just three years. John Henning took over as Chairman on 1st November. At the time, he had been a Non-Executive Director of the Trust for three years and the Managing Director of UK Operations for the Scientific Instrument Division of Thermo Electron.

A new Modernisation Programme Board was established to realise the vision that "by 2010 we will be delivering the NHS Plan vision of high quality, effective and responsive services, and that this will be achieved through a combination of highly trained and committed staff and the best of modern technology". Achievement of this vision will require looking at whole services, at the experience of patients from the onset of symptoms, through the acute unit and back to their home. In addition, it will involve working in partnership with Primary Care Trusts, Social

Services, voluntary and other services. It needs to put the patients at the centre of the process and redesigning services around their needs. The Board would:

- Oversee the challenging programme of change.
- Prioritise and authorise new projects.
- Commit resources.

The Modernisation Programme Board consisted of:

- David Hill, Chief Executive.
- Wendy Slaney, Medical Director.
- Stephanie Davis, Director of Finance and Performance.
- Roy Haynes, Director of Human Resources and Operations.
- Nick Coveney, Director of Nursing and Patient Care (Chair).
- Elayne Guest, Director of Corporate Services.
- Linda Clarke, Service Improvements Facilitator.

Initially, the Board identified 12 areas to focus upon, which together were known as The Next Big Step:

- Clinical Care
- Infection Control
- Risk and Clinical Governance
- Communications and Documentation
- Discharge Planning
- Theatres
- Trauma Pathway
- Primary/Social Care
- Human Resources-skill mix, training and development and workforce planning
- Physical Space
- Organisational Structure
- Bed and Site Management.

Each of these areas would be the responsibility of a separate hospital manager who, with Nick Coveney, would make up the Programme

Assurance Team, which would be responsible for publicising the work and achievements of the Team. In addition, a Service Support Forum was established for those leading service improvement projects to meet every six weeks to provide a forum for discussion, support and shared learning.

The Trust appointed Christine Ames as Falls Project Manager to implement a risk assessment tool to assess all patients over the age of 21 years of their risk of falling and to establish a comprehensive therapeutic care-plan to assist nursing staff with an improved clinical management of their patients. Christine Ames quoted some interesting statistics:

- 1,336 patients fell whilst in the care of the hospital in 2002.
- A fifth of all 999 responses are directly related to a fall.
- 27,000 people fell in East Anglia in 2002, of which 13,000 were transported to hospital and 1,851 came to the James Paget.
- Hip fractures cost the NHS £1.7 billion each year.
- Up to a third of patients who fracture their hips die within a year and 23% die within 90 days of their operation.
- It can take up to 2 years to completely rehabilitate a 'faller', at a potential cost to the NHS of £25,000 within that period.

It was hoped that this project would reduce the number of falls in the hospital, would save many patients a great deal of pain and increased time spent in hospital and, eventually, would save the Trust money.

The Norfolk and Waveney Cancer Network had been in existence for four years and had David Ellis, Consultant Physician, as the Lead Clinician. The Management Team was based in the Community Hospital on Bowthorpe Road, Norwich, and was responsible in a facilitating role to work with clinical teams involved with cancer across the whole patient-care pathway, from prevention to referral, hospital, community and palliative care. All decisions in the Network were approved through the Network Management Board, which had senior representation from Trust and Primary Care Trusts at Chief Executive Level.

In the Financial Year 2002/2003, the bed occupancy rate was a staggering 98% and all targets set out in the NHS Plan were met by March 2003. Among the achievements were:

- The Accident and Emergency Department sustained the target of 'see and treat' within four hours in 90% of cases throughout the year.
- Only one patient waited for more than 12 months for a routine operation and the majority were treated within six to nine months. The one patient was missed due to an administrative error and, when discovered, admission was speedily arranged.
- Majority of outpatients were seen within 13 weeks of referral by their GP. 253 waited more than 13 weeks, compared with 463 the previous year. No patient waited more than 21 weeks to be seen.
- 99.5% of patients suspected of having cancer were seen within two weeks of referral.
- There were 248 complaints, which was a 16.8% reduction on 298 received the previous year.
- The James Paget Healthcare became the first Trust in Norfolk, Suffolk and Cambridgeshire to fully implement an e-mail system available to all staff in the Trust.

Other achievements in the year 2002/2003 were:

- Refurbishment of the Doctors Mess.
- Appointment of a Skills Laboratory Technician for the Education Department.
- Central Delivery Suite was refurbished and altered to create a self-contained suite for parents experiencing a difficult time around childbirth or the loss of a baby.
- Upgrade of the maternity wards to create more single rooms and a more secure environment.
- Upgrading of Pathology Waiting Area.
- Investment in new and replacement medical equipment was in excess of £950,000.

In the Financial Year 2002/2003, the total income for the year was £93,408,000 (9% more than the previous year), generating an operating surplus of £2,558,000. After receiving net interest of £57,000 and making a dividend payment to the Department of Health of £2,582,000, the retained surplus taken to the reserves was £11,000. The actual management costs were £3,699,000, which was below the target set by the NHS for the Trust.

The total value of the Fixed Assets of the Trust as at 31st March 2003 was £53,565,000.

The charitable funds benefited from donations, legacies and investment income to the tune of £1,057,000.

The total number of patients treated was: 31,043 In-patients, 11,178 Day Cases, 11,487 Day Patients and 166,573 Outpatients were seen.

2004

Mr. Hassanaien organised the MRCOG written course on 31st January and 1st February in the Burrage Centre and planned to organise future courses.

Two ladies celebrated working for the hospital as volunteers for over 20 years. Vivien Burgess joined the hospital when it opened and her first placements were on the Main Information Desk, the Diabetic Clinic and the Pathology Laboratory, working two days a week until 1985, when she joined the Pain Relief Clinic. She trained as a nurse and was a Justice of the Peace. Mary Farrell started working for the hospital in 1983 and initially worked on the Main Information Desk before moving to the Antenatal Clinic. She started work as a school teacher in Stowmarket before becoming Head of English and subsequently Deputy Head at Harris Middle School in Lowestoft.

Increasingly, the Hospital seems to run on Committee Meetings and, to address the issue, the Improving Working Lives Project produced an Effective Meetings Skills Behaviour Charter:

- Confirm that the meeting is necessary, has clearly stated objectives and has participants who can effectively contribute.
- Prioritise time for meetings, arrive prepared and ready to contribute.
- Start on time; keep interruptions to a minimum; end on time.
- Do not take other work into a meeting, either physically or mentally.
- Participants to respect one another; only one person to speak at a time and allow others to express their views.
- Do not be selfish; put aside personal agenda.

Princess Anne meeting Intensive Care Unit staff

Target for Intensive Care Unit Appeal reached at John Wells retirement

The Right Reverend Peter Nott, Bishop of Norwich, opening the Sandra Chapman Centre

Presentation of PIGGY.
David Wayne, Dennis Waterman and sculptor Barry Sutton

Proposed Palliative Care Unit
(copyright LSI Architects, LLP)

Rene Burgess cutting the cake after opening the Breast Care Unit

Lynn Faulds Wood opening new Endoscopy Suite

League of Friends

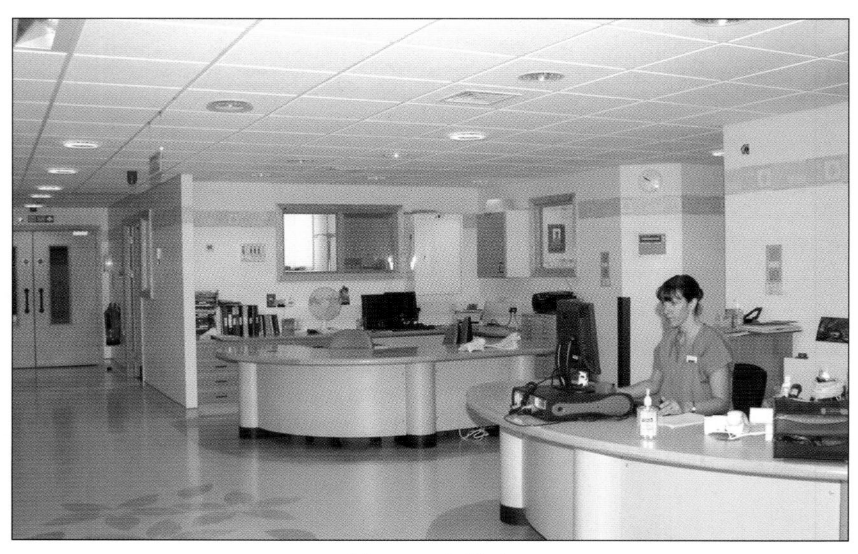

Neonatal Unit

Hospital Chapel

John Hemming, Chairman and Bob Blizzard, MP launching the Trust as a smoke free zone

Delivery of MRI scanner

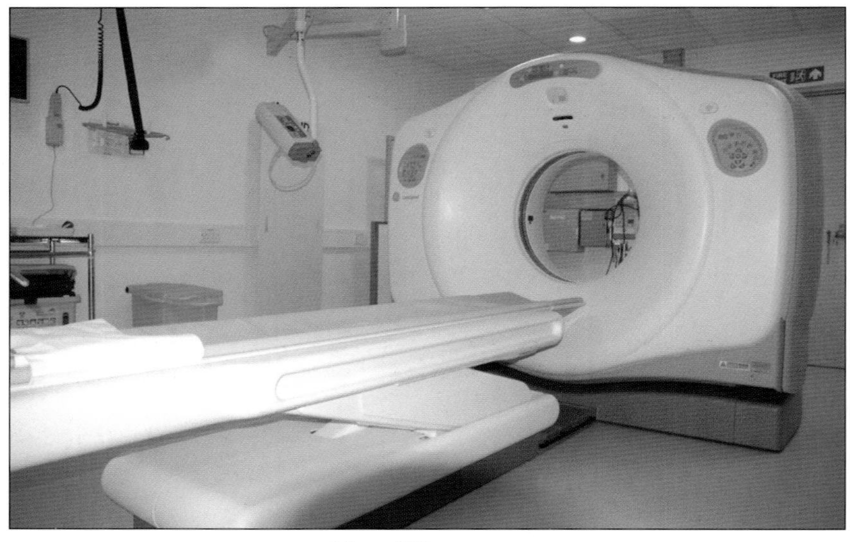

New CT scanner

A hospital courtyard

Renal Unit and Ante-natal Unit

Aubergine - refurbished staff restaurant

Original hospital switchboard

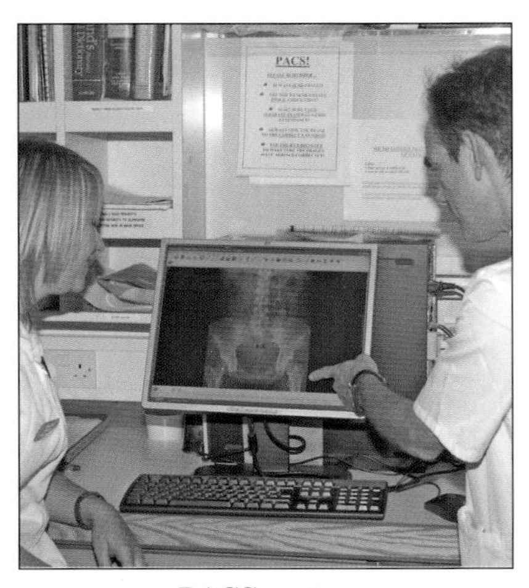

PACS system

- The chairperson should use "effective" skills to manage the meeting.
- Prepare and distribute timely and informative Agenda, Minutes and Action Lists.
- If you are unable to attend a meeting, let the organiser know – send apologies.

In April, Katharine Kite secured £40,000 from the Norfolk, Suffolk and Cambridgeshire Workforce Development Confederation for the development of a course aimed at ward-based staff to help them develop and enhance the critical care skills required by a range of ward patients. It was called the Practitioners' Acute Care Course (PACS) and was developed in association with Kate Allen, the Critical Care Course Tutor at the University of East Anglia, and Jo Sumptom, Consultant Nurse for Critical Care at Ipswich Hospitals.

Sheila Harrison retired as evening Domestic Assistant in April, having worked at the hospital since it opened.

The results of the NHS National Staff Survey, which was carried out in October 2003, showed that the Trust received more positive results in all categories than the majority of Trusts. The exceptions were opportunities for flexible working and work pressure felt by the staff, where the James Paget's results were the same as most other Trusts.

In the previous year, there was an enormous increase in the number of patients seen in the Accident and Emergency Department, which was partly explained by GPs' new working arrangements. In spite of this, the Department achieved the target of seeing and treating 98% of patients within four hours and, as a result, was rewarded by the Department of Health with £100,000 for compliance.

Teresa Cook was elected Vice-President of the Chartered Society of Physiotherapy, which has 45,000 members and is involved in professional, educational and trade union activities. She had represented the Eastern Region on CSP Council from 1999–2003. In addition, at the University of East London she had run the only post-graduate course for physiotherapists specialising in continence rehabilitation and had written a chapter in the second edition of 'Physiotherapy in Obstetrics and Gynaecology'.

The Changing Workforce Programme of the Modernisation Agency chose the James Paget as one of eight pilot sites in England to investigate new ways of working in the Emergency Assessment and Discharge Unit. A grant of £100,000 was made to assess the role of highly trained nurses or Allied Health Professionals in the admitting, clerking and initiating of investigations on some patients. The project involved the development of outcome measures, with subsequent data collection and analysis.

The Trust lost one of its three stars in July. It was a big disappointment to everyone and apparently was due to a minor administrative error.

The European Working Time Directive decreed that Junior Doctors should work no more than 56 hours weekly, and this was achieved by 1st August. It was made possible by employing more Junior Doctors. The introduction of the planned 'Hospital at Night' project, when specially trained nurses will take over some of the doctors' duties, will also help in this. The next reduction in hours will be in 2009, when the target will be 48 hours per week.

In September, the Modernisation Agency produced 10 high-impact Changes for Service Improvement, which were:

- Increasing the number and types of operations which are done as day cases.
- Improving access to diagnostic tests.
- Robust management of the discharge process and reduction in length of stay.
- Better management of the admission process.
- Avoiding unnecessary follow-up in outpatient clinics.
- Examining therapeutic interventions.
- Applying a systematic approach to care for people with chronic conditions.
- Improving access.
- Streamlining the patient journey.
- Redesigning and extending roles in order to attract and retain an effective workforce.

A Service Improvement Team was established in April to lead the increasing number of major projects and to take responsibility for the co-ordination, support and implementation of the modernisation programme. Among the programmes being planned or being introduced were:

- Choose and Book, which enables patients to book an outpatient appointment in the GP's surgery at the time of referral.
- Hospital at Night, which enables 24-hour clinical cover with fewer junior doctors.
- New ways of working, expanding, changing roles and creating a more flexible and generic workforce.
- Designing a new diagnostic and treatment centre. Later, this was downscaled and a decision was made to divert the money to improving the wards.

Providing safer care for the patient had received much attention over recent years with such initiatives as Clinical Governance, Risk Management, Clinical Audit and Effectiveness and Health and Safety. Many of these overlapped each other and they were eventually merged under the umbrella of Healthcare Governance. A Healthcare Governance Committee was formed to provide the Trust Board with a co-ordinated view about patient safety. All this works within the Framework of Standards for Better Health issued in July 2004 and monitored by external bodies such as the Healthcare Commission, NHS Litigation Authority, the National Patient Safety Agency and the Health and Safety Executive. The Committee produces the strategies, policies and procedures required to set, implement and maintain the requisite standards. It monitors action plans created to deliver the integrated management of risk and governance. This includes compilation and continuous updating of the Corporate Risk Register. Healthcare Governance is led by the Medical Director and the Director of Nursing and Patient Care.

John Petri received an award at the Medical Futures Innovation Awards ceremony in London on 3rd November for the work he had done showing the benefit of Dual Operating. This involves him having the use of two operating theatres, which enables the anaesthetist and operating room staff to prepare the next patient on the operating list in the adjoining theatre while he is still operating on the previous patient. This enables him to perform more operations on an operating list and to reduce the number waiting to have an operation.

In the week beginning 22nd November, the Norfolk and Waveney Cancer Network was the first Cancer Network in the country to be peer reviewed by an external team. This involved meetings with cancer clinical teams and visits to departments to assess the Network's compliance with the newly published Manual for Cancer Services and to consider the experience of patients with cancer and carers.

A Bone Mineral Density Scanner was installed within the Cranbrook Centre at Northgate Hospital and assessed its first patient on 6th December. It assesses the bone mineral content of a patient's bones and indicates if they are osteoporotic (thinned) or normal. Previously, this assessment was made using the CT scanner, but limited access meant that the waiting list was 18 months. The new scanner is dedicated to measuring bone density and within a few months the waiting list was down to a matter of a few weeks. The Great Yarmouth Primary Care Trust provided the funds for the purchase of the machine and the Waveney Primary Care Trust supported the initiative to ensure that patients throughout the area had access to this service.

A brand new in-patient CT Scanning Suite, complete with bed wait areas, reading rooms and a splendid reception area, was opened in December. The new machine produces images much faster and in greater detail than the last CT scanner, which was decommissioned and was replaced by a further CT Scanner in 2006, along with a new MR Scanner.

Patients requiring a GP-requested X-ray were allowed to choose and book appointments and the appointments section extended its hours to facilitate this.

In the Financial Year 2003/2004:

- The overall bed occupancy was 98% throughout the whole year and the shortage of beds led to the Trust declaring a 'Red Alert' on many occasions.
- The Accident and Emergency attendance rose by 2,748.
- No patient was waiting for an outpatient appointment for longer than 17 weeks and the majority were seen within 13 weeks. At 31st March 2004, there were 136 patients waiting longer than 13 weeks, compared with 253 the year before.
- There were more cancelled operations due to the high pressure on the beds and only five patients were not re-appointed for admission within 28 days.
- The number of patients waiting to be admitted reduced by 10 per cent to 3,825, compared with the previous year.

- A Risk Register was established and the top ten risks are presented to the Board for discussion at the monthly public meetings.
- There were 246 formal complaints, which was two less than the previous year.
- New computer system installed in Accident and Emergency Department, allowing all patients' details to be recorded electronically, so doing away with handwritten notes.
- Operating theatres had a new computer system which is used to record operation notes and the timing of the various stages of an operation.
- Three-bedded observation/overnight ward in the Accident and Emergency Ward was opened.
- Upgrading of two X-ray rooms.
- Extra land was purchased to build a new car park.

The total income for 2003/2004 was £102,703,000 and management costs were £3,910,000, which represented 3.8% of income. The value of the Trust's fixed assets was £55,806,000 at the end of March 2004 and it had invested £9,182,000 in fixed assets during the year. Over one million pounds had been spent on upgrading and replacing medical equipment.

The total income for charitable funds from donations, legacies and investment income was £1,395,000 for the year.

2005

In January, the James Paget became a Clean Hands Partner Hospital and the official launch of the Campaign was on Friday 3rd June. Its aim was to make people aware of the importance of washing hands in reducing the incidence of infection. Apart from notices throughout the hospital bottles of hand gel were available at each bedside. This scheme was particularly important as the incidence of MRSA (Methicillin Resistant Staphylococcus Aureus, which is resistant to most antibiotics) was increasing not only in the James Paget but nationwide.

In January, people throughout the hospital were shocked to learn that Glenn Fransham had been drowned after his car had been shunted by another vehicle into a dyke beside the Acle Straight. He was only 38 years old. He had worked at the James Paget for nearly 20 years as an

Operating Department Assistant, rising to be deputy in charge of the Emergency Theatre. He worked hard, set high standards and had a puckish sense of humour. Unfortunately for the James Paget, he moved to the theatres at the Norfolk and Norwich University Hospital nearly two years before he died, but still kept in touch with his friends at the James Paget. He learnt to play the guitar and formed a band, which played for various charity events. His favourite poem was 'Risks' and in his memory this was carved on a slab of Cumbrian slate in the courtyard below the Staff Dining Room and was unveiled on 14th December 2005.

The Education and Training Centre was officially opened by Professor Shirley Pearce, Director of the Institute of Health Studies at the University of East Anglia on Tuesday 18th January. It is housed on the first floor of a new building, with Medical Records on the ground floor. The centre cost £1,250,000 and was designed by Integrated Building Services Design Partnership plc and built by the building contractor R. G. Carter in eighteen weeks. (R. G. Carter had built the first phase of the hospital in the late 1970s and early 1980s.) The architects were LSI Architects of Norwich. The driving force behind the project was Arthur Harris, Capital Planning Manager.

The centre is for all staff, doctors, nurses, midwives, therapists and support services and comprises three sections:

- Nursing Education and Practice Development.
- Postgraduate Medical Education.
- Undergraduate Medical Teaching.

The previous twelve months had been particularly difficult for elective surgical admissions, as so often the surgical beds were occupied by medical patients who had been admitted as emergencies. Consequently, every evening patients were telephoned the night prior to admission to be told that their bed booked for the next day might not be available. This was time consuming for the bed bureau and distressing for the patients and their families, but fortunately beds were found for the majority of the patients. This was achieved by putting some of the emergency medical admissions into the Day Ward over-night. In fact, there was a sort of 'musical chairs' moving patients around the wards to try and get everyone in. This was totally unsatisfactory and the main reason for bringing forward the plans to have an Emergency Assessment and Discharge Unit. Another means of making better use of the beds was admitting more patients on the day of operation rather than the day before, and this was helped by the Pre-Assessment Clinic, where patients due for admission are assessed a week or two prior to admission.

The Emergency and Assessment Discharge Unit opened on 21st February and the Medical Admissions Unit closed. It was officially opened by former Chairman of the Trust, Mr. John Wells. M. S. Oakes Ltd, the builders for the project, won first prize in the Norfolk Architect Association Craftsmanship Awards under the class of Restorations and Alterations. The unit provides 36 beds and a focus for the multi-professional assessment of patients admitted as emergencies to the hospital. Its aim is to increase the number of patients discharged within 24 hours, reduce overall length of stay and the number of medical patients in non-medical beds.

On 9th March the Trust became a smoke-free site. It was one of the first Trusts in the country to attempt such an initiative. Some heavily addicted smokers found it hard and could be seen moving to the outskirts of the hospital grounds to have a smoke. This resulted in complaints from some people living on the neighbouring housing estate. The Burrage Centre had voted to allow smoking in an area in the bar and this was frequented by some smokers each day. The Trust gave extra help through the Occupational Health Service by providing counselling and nicotine patches.

As at 31st March, the Trust employed 3,030 staff, 50.4% being full-time and 49.6% being part-time. 79.6% were female. Ten per cent were Medical, 45% were Nurses and Midwives, 12% were Other Clinical and 33% were Non-Clinical, which included Hotel Services, Estates and Administration. It was pleasing to note that the Trust's retention rate for staff was the best in East Anglia. During the year the Trust had recruited 50 nurses from India.

The National Staff Attitude Survey showed considerable improvement on the excellent results of previous years in almost all areas studied and for many the levels of staff satisfaction were in the upper quartile, compared with other Trusts on a national basis.

By March, no patient was waiting longer than nine months for treatment and the Trust achieved the national target of having no patient waiting for an outpatient attendance for more than 17 weeks. In fact, there were only two patients waiting longer than 13 weeks.

The move of Cellular Pathology from the James Paget to the Cotman Centre (named after the well-known Norfolk watercolour artist, James Sell Cotman) in Norwich occurred over the weekend of 9th and 10th July. It was brought about by the fact that histopathogy was becoming more and more specialised, so that hospitals needed extra Pathologists and these were not available in the country. The Pathologists in Norwich found that their laboratories in the new hospital were inadequate; so, after a great deal of discussion, the two Trusts decided to amalgamate their Cellular Pathology Services in a vacant building near the Norfolk and Norwich University Hospital. The new unit consists of 15 Consultant Pathologists, 23 Biomedical Scientists and 20 Support Staff.

From August, newly qualified doctors had to do two years in posts equivalent to the old pre-registration house jobs, except that the posts would be for four months each and there would be protected training time which the Trust had to provide along nationally agreed lines. For the first year – Foundation 1 (F1) – there was a shared rotation with the Norfolk and Norwich University Hospital and the second Foundation year involved some jobs in General Practice and in mental health.

The scheme did not get off to a good start as it had been agreed that many of the F1s would come from the London Teaching Hospitals as they thought they would have a surplus. Unfortunately, they did not, and at the last moment many Trusts in East Anglia had to take doctors from Europe, some of whom spoke little English and their knowledge of medicine was below standard. Fortunately, in recent years the James Paget had been testing their junior doctors and this proved invaluable in assessing these new doctors. It resulted in a number being taken off medical duties while they were retrained and had further tests of their competence. In addition, locums had to be employed to maintain the service, which was a further expense.

Elayne Guest was presented with the national award for Excellence in the Supervision of Midwives at a ceremony at the Royal Aeronautical Society, Hyde Park, London. In addition to all her many duties for the Trust, she was the Midwifery Officer for East Anglia.

The Healthcare Commission requires Trusts to carry out patients' surveys and three were conducted in the year. The stroke survey had a

68.4% response rate, which amounted to 39 patients. 82% felt that their stroke had been diagnosed quickly and nearly all patients felt confident with the care they had received. In the Outpatient Survey there was a 63% response from the 850 questionnaires sent out. A minority felt they needed more information about medication and where to go if they had anxieties, but 96% were satisfied with the way they had been managed.

Out of 850 questionnaires sent to patients in the Accident and Emergency Department, there was a response rate of 47.3%. Two areas which had received low scores in the survey two years ago (more information about medication and better pain control while waiting to be seen) had greatly improved. 86% felt that their treatment was excellent, very good or good.

The Trust received 313 complaints during 2004/2005, which was an increase of 57 on the previous year. This represented an increase of 27.2% but, taking into account the increased activity, it represented an increase of only 0.073%.

In April, the Cancer Information Centre moved from the back of the hospital to an area which was part of the Pharmacy waiting area, and in the first six months it had as many enquiries as it normally had in a year. The Centre was officially opened by Bryan Gunn, the ex-Norwich City goalkeeper, on 8th September.

Andrew Turner, who was a kitchen porter at the hospital for 19 years, died on 8th September after a valiant fight against cancer and months of treatment in Norwich and in London. Frequently, he was referred to as a “gentle giant”. He was very fond of his pet dogs and after holidays would frequently bring back presents for his colleagues.

Throughout the year, work had been going on to establish the Picture Archiving and Communications System (PACS). This is a computer-based, digital image capture system that saves images to a dedicated computer server rather than to X-ray film. These images can then be viewed across a wide network within and outside the Trust. On 13th October, the Radiology Consultants started reporting directly from the online “soft copies” and from the middle of November the Department ceased printing images for all GP requests.

On Wednesday 14th December, a memorial to Glenn Fransham, who had died in January, was unveiled in the courtyard below the Staff Dining Room. It consisted of a wooden bench and a slab of Cumbrian slate (Glenn was an enthusiastic climber) on which was engraved his favourite poem, 'Risks', which he discovered at the top of the Honister Pass in the Lake District. It was hoped that people might wish to sit, chat and reflect in this very peaceful courtyard. No-one seems to know who wrote it, but the poem is worth quoting:

RISKS

To laugh is to risk appearing the fool.
To weep is to risk being called sentimental.
To reach out to another is to risk involvement.
To expose feelings is to risk showing your true self.
To place your ideas and your dreams before
the crowd is to risk being called naïve.
To love is to risk not being loved in return.
To live is to risk dying.

To hope is to risk despair, to try is to risk failure.
But risks must be taken because the greatest risk
in life is to risk nothing.
The person who risks nothing does nothing, has nothing,
is nothing and becomes nothing.
He may avoid suffering and sorrow, but he simply
cannot learn, feel, change, or love.
Chained by his certitude he is a slave;
he has forfeited his freedom.
Only the person that risks is truly free.

On Boxing Day, Rosie Winterton, Minister of Health, visited the Accident and Emergency Department, the Emergency Assessment and Discharge Unit and an orthopaedic ward.

For the Financial Year 2004/2005 the total income for the Trust was £116,636,000 and management costs were £4,448,000, which was 3.8% of total income. The total value of the fixed assets was £66,428,000. The income from charitable sources in the form of donations, legacies and interest on investments was £1,395,000.

2006

Rosie Winterton returned to the James Paget on 20th February to officially open the enlarged Renal Unit and then the new Scanning Suite with its new CT and MRI Scanners.

In the early part of the year, staff from the Sandringham Unit at Northgate and the Gwen Baker Unit at Lowestoft moved to the James Paget. The services delivered are medical rehabilitation and orthopaedic rehabilitation, respectively. The Sandringham Unit staff moved into the Rehabilitation Unit while the majority of staff from there moved across the corridor into the new Stroke Unit, which had been established in Ward 15. The 15 orthopaedic beds on the Gwen Baker Unit were absorbed into the Orthopaedic Wards at the James Paget so that Orthopaedic Rehabilitation continued where the original surgery was done. This stopped the need to transfer patients to Lowestoft a few days after their surgery and was far better for relatives living in the north of the District.

The results of the third national in-patient survey which was carried out in 2005 were released. There was a 62% response rate and 87.3% rated their overall care as excellent, very good or good and 87.6% said that they would recommend the James Paget to their family and friends.

The National Staff Survey showed a 60% return from the Trust. For the sixth year running, the staff reported improved satisfaction levels on a range of questions and showed significantly better results than the national average for other acute Trusts.

The Trust met all three cancer targets, which were:

- Patients suspected of having a malignancy to be seen in clinic within two weeks of referral.
- Treatment to commence within 31 days of the diagnosis being discussed with the patient.
- Treatment to commence within 62 days of the patient being referred by their GP.

In preparation for Foundation Status, an election was held in March for Governors: 17 to represent the community and seven staff representatives.

The existing playroom and paediatric area in the Accident and Emergency Department were completely refurbished and an extended 'see and treat' area developed. This was financed through the Alexander legacy.

In April, the Trust transferred the management of the GP beds at Northgate to the Great Yarmouth Teaching Primary Care Trust.

The Stress Management Group started a new scheme with BWell Health Club for staff who might be experiencing stress or depression. (BWell runs the Gymnasium in the Burrage Centre.) Members of staff with these problems could be referred by the Occupational Health Department for a 10-session programme of exercise and the pilot scheme would be assessed after six months. It is hoped that exercise, which is known to increase the sense of well-being, will result in an earlier return to work for these people.

The Trust became a Foundation Trust on 1st August and to celebrate the occasion a new sign was unveiled in front of the hospital. The following day, David Hill, Chief Executive, informed the Chairman, John Hemming, that he had been appointed Chief Executive of the healthcare system in Bermuda. The whole hospital was shocked by the news when this was announced on 11th August and a search for a successor was begun.

A Foundation Trust consists of three parts: the Membership Community, the Governors' Council and the Board of Directors. Membership is open to anyone working in the hospital who has been a patient or lives in a defined catchment area. The Governors represent the views of those who elect or appoint them. Seventeen are elected from the community, seven are elected from among the staff and nine are appointed from various bodies such as the University of East Anglia, Great Yarmouth Borough Council, Waveney District Council, Norfolk and Suffolk County Councils, the Great Yarmouth and Waveney Primary Care Trust and a Voluntary Sector Representative.

The Board of Directors includes the Executive and Non-Executive Directors and was previously known as the Trust Board. The purpose of a Foundation Trust is to make it more responsive to local opinion and to be more independent of the Department of Health, so allowing it to make decisions, act upon them and to have greater financial freedom.

The first Council Meeting of the Governors was held on 11th August and the seven staff-elected Governors were: Paul Smith, Allison Bester, Les Wilson, Frank Grinnell, Peter Harrison, Rachel Hulse and Katharine Kite. The 17 Governors elected by the public were: Elizabeth Harrison, Colin Denny, Victoria Mason, Richard Morling, Gillian Pope, Russell Allen, Mary Shillabeer, Eirlys McLean, Peter Gordon, Iain Ferguson, Paul Foulger, Susan Meecham, Neville Sanderson, Hugh Sturzaker, Ian Fox, Christine Smith and Wulf Forsythe-York.

There were nine appointed Governors, who were:

- Brian Howard from Great Yarmouth Borough Council.
- David Wright from Norfolk and Norwich University Hospital NHS Trust.
- Dennis Cave from the Voluntary Sector.
- Christine Mowle from Norfolk County Council.
- David Edwards from University of East Anglia.
- Wendy Mawer from Suffolk County Council.
- Sue Allen from Waveney District Council.
- Two to be appointed by Great Yarmouth and Waveney PCT.

In September, the Hospital held the first National Nurses' Ophthalmic Study Day in the Celebration Suite at the Burrage Centre.

Refurbishment of the Staff Dining Room was completed in September.

The East Coast Palliative Care Centre Appeal was launched at a promotional evening in October in the Burrage Centre Celebration Suite and was hosted by Tony Mallion of Radio Norfolk.

The Trust achieved the 'Practice Plus Standard' for good staff management. Roy Haynes, Director of Human Resources and Operations, said that it "has given us national recognition for the investment the Trust has made in staff facilities and the way the staff is managed".

Senior Enrolled Nurse Sheila Perry retired as the longest-serving nurse on the Intensive Care Ward. She commenced her nurse training at Lowestoft Hospital in 1976 and completed her pupil nurse training in September 1978. She continued working at Lowestoft Hospital until she transferred to the Intensive Care Ward at the new District General Hospital when it opened. At that time it was a combined unit with the Coronary Care Unit until a separate one was opened in 1996.

The Government published "Commissioning a patient-led NHS", which suggested merging some of the 28 Strategic Health Authorities to form 10 throughout England and making the Primary Care Trusts coterminous with county boundaries. This led to a concerted campaign by the local population around the James Paget which straddles the Norfolk/Suffolk border and eventually Health Secretary, Patricia Hewitt, ruled in favour of there being a separate Great Yarmouth and Waveney PCT. This is reminiscent of the Great Yarmouth and Waveney Health Authority which existed at the time the hospital opened. The new PCTs would be purely commissioners of services and would manage the contracts and budget on behalf of the GP practices that would commission and negotiate the services they need for their patients. The new organisations went into shadow form on 1st April 2006 (the Great Yarmouth and Waveney PCT was launched on 1st October 2006) and became fully established on 1st April 2007.

The Chairman of the Great Yarmouth and Waveney PCT is Bernard Williamson and the Chief Executive is Mike Stonard. The Trust has an annual budget of £300,000,000 and employs more than 700 staff serving a population of 220,000. It has taken over the headquarters of the old Waveney PCT in Beccles. The new PCT will own and manage the community hospitals in Beccles, Halesworth and Southwold and employ healthcare professionals such as District Nurses, Health Visitors and School Nurses. It will work closely with the 27 GP practices in the area, with Community Pharmacists, NHS Dentists, local authorities and the voluntary sector.

The PCT uses its budget to "commission" (buy) services on behalf of its population from providers such as the James Paget University Hospitals NHS Foundation Trust, Norfolk and Norwich University Hospital NHS Trust, Norfolk and Waveney Mental Health Partnership NHS Trust and the East of England Ambulance Service NHS Trust.

A new birthing pool was christened on 1st October. Although water births were available in the expectant mother's home, this was the first time such a birth had taken place in the hospital. The pool was paid for by 10 Midwives and their families raising over £500 by a sponsored cycle ride in September.

On Wednesday 15th November, there was a farewell party in the Burrage Centre Celebration Suite for David Hill.

The National In-patient Survey results for 2006 showed:

- Food and cleaning scores were well above the national average and were better than 2005.
- Confidence and trust in doctors and nursing staff was high.
- Most patients felt they were treated with dignity and respect when they were in hospital and was 80% compared with 72% in 2005.
- Most patients rated the care they received as excellent or very good.
- The hospital had more emergency admissions than most acute hospitals in both 2005 and 2006.
- Patient information and discharge procedures needed more attention.

Some of the achievements of the 2005/2006 year were:

- The Trust was the only hospital in East Anglia to receive three stars.
- Reduction of waiting times for routine operations to well below six months, ahead of the national requirement.
- Reduced waits for outpatient consultations to a maximum of 13 weeks.
- Over 98% of patients in the Accident and Emergency Department were seen and treated within four hours.
- The Trust broke even financially.

2007

Aubergine, the staff restaurant, was officially opened on Monday 29th January by Celebrity Chef Richard Hughes. The refurbishment had taken place over six months and included replacement windows, radiators, flooring, ceiling and lighting. The old furniture was replaced with new tables, chairs and leather sofas. Richard Hughes offered to come back with three of his chefs to cook up, alongside the hospital chefs, a specialty themed lunch for staff.

The new intranet went live on Monday 15th January.

The Hospital at Night project was piloted at the James Paget in January. It is a national project which has been trialled elsewhere and introduced into several hospitals. The idea stemmed from the realisation that Junior Doctors' shorter working hours made it difficult to maintain an adequate service to the patients throughout the 24 hours without looking at different ways of working. The Hospital at Night Team at the James Paget will consist of:

- Night Site Co-ordinator.
- Clinical Support Practitioner (CSP).
- Clinical Support Assistant (CSA).
- Specialist Registrar in Medicine.
- Specialist Registrar in Surgery.
- 3 Foundation Year 2 (FY2)/Senior House Officers, made up from medicine, surgery and other surgical specialities, rotating in the night shift.

Anaesthesia and Paediatrics will continue to have their own dedicated teams.

On Friday 30th March, a Press Conference was called to announce that over recent months there had been an outbreak of a virulent strain of Clostridium difficile and it had been associated with the deaths of 17 patients. This received widespread national coverage in the papers and on radio and television. Clostridium difficile is found in the intestines and most people who have it show no symptoms. In people who are frail or who have been treated with certain types of antibiotics, this bacterium can multiply and cause profuse diarrhoea, abdominal pains, dehydration, organ failure and further problems from the toxins released.

The Trust had been aware of the problem since the start of the year and had instituted increased cleaning measures and new ones using steam and bleach, as the spores of the bacterium are resistant to traditional cleaning measures. It had also used a vacant ward for isolating patients who had the infection. Further enquiries showed that many other Trusts had similar or worse problems. Fortunately, the new measures, including new antibiotic policies, rapidly brought the outbreak under control, but it is a situation which will need constant vigilance.

Adrian Pennington, the new Chief Executive, was due to start on 1st April, but he was in the Hospital on Friday 30th March, so it was a memorable first day for him.

Since being appointed, Adrian Pennington had made several visits to the hospital and sat in on Board and Executive meetings. From April onwards, he is frequently seen around the hospital and holds weekly sessions which any member of staff can attend and ask questions.

The new Coronary Care Unit was officially opened by Dr. Wolf Grabau on the day he retired, April 20th.

During the Financial Year 2006/2007 the following have been achieved:

- National targets were met for cancer patients to start treatment within 31 days of being informed of the diagnosis and starting treatment within 62 days of being referred by their GP. All patients referred with a possible diagnosis were seen within two weeks.
- Patients were admitted within 20 weeks for in-patient and day case treatment.
- The number of patients with MRSA in their bloodstream was reduced from 50 to 27 cases in the last two years.
- Length of stay for minimally invasive hip surgery was reduced to four/five days.
- Opening of a new children's area in the Accident and Emergency Department.
- No patient waited longer than 11 weeks to be seen in an outpatient clinic.
- No patient waited longer than 13 weeks for a diagnostic appointment.
- Patients were seen in the Genito-Urinary Medicine Clinics within 48 hours of requesting an appointment.
- Systems in place to allow Patient Choice and Booking.
- A financial surplus.

The Trust generated an income from PCTs of £117m for the provision of healthcare to NHS patients. Other income came from private patients (0.7% of the total patient related income), education and training, staff accommodation and car parking. The Trust achieved a surplus of £2,200,000 for the eight-month period ending on 31st March 2007. In the four month period leading up to Foundation status, the Trust made a small surplus of £25,000. The total net book value of Trust assets was £69,500,000 at the end of March 2007. The costs for management and administration were £5,517,000, which was 4.2% of income.

An enhanced recovery programme which speeds up the recovery from operation and results in patients staying in hospital for less time has been trialled on patients having colorectal surgery and is to be extended to patients having other types of surgery.

During the year, the Trust received 268 complaints. (A complaint is defined as anything which requires a formal report.) This compared with 335 the previous year, which was a reduction of 15%.

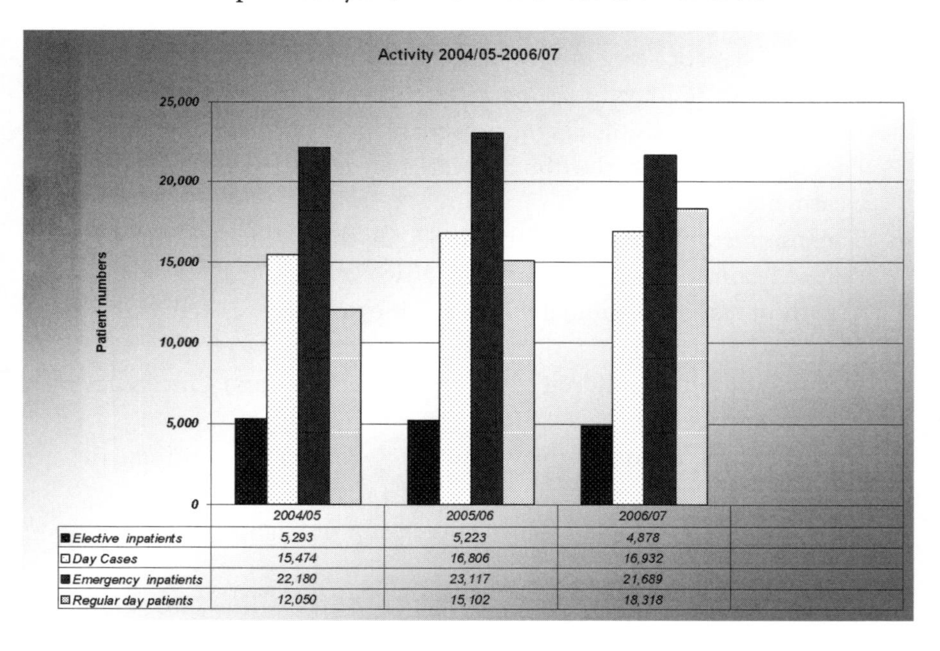

	2004/05	2005/06	2006/07
Elective inpatients	5,293	5,223	4,878
Day Cases	15,474	16,806	16,932
Emergency inpatients	22,180	23,117	21,689
Regular day patients	12,050	15,102	18,318

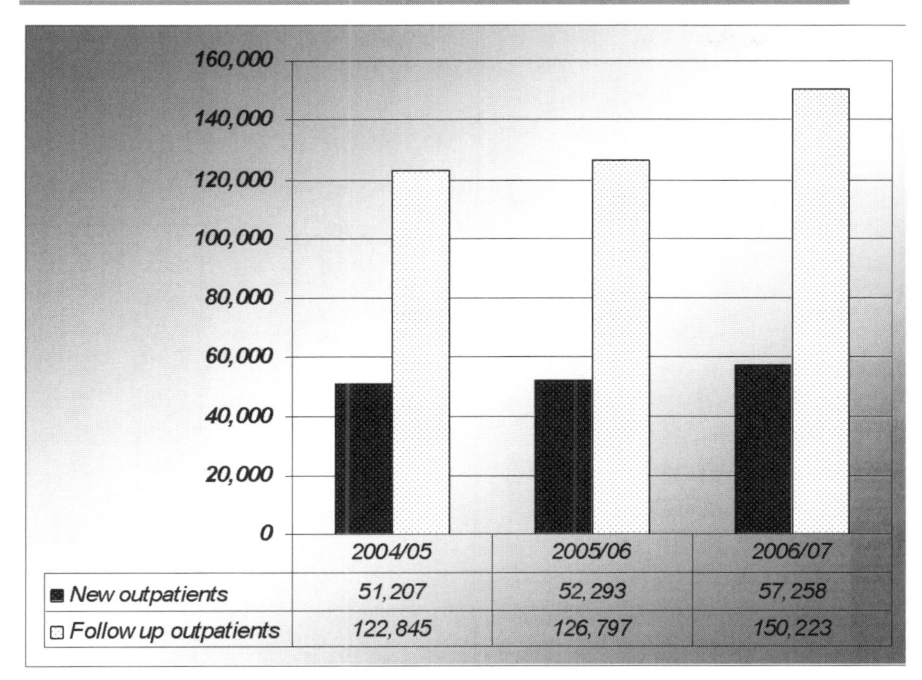
160,000
140,000
120,000
100,000
80,000
60,000
40,000
20,000
0
2004/05
2005/06
2006/07
New outpatients 51,207 52,293 57,258
Follow up outpatients 122,845 126,797 150,223

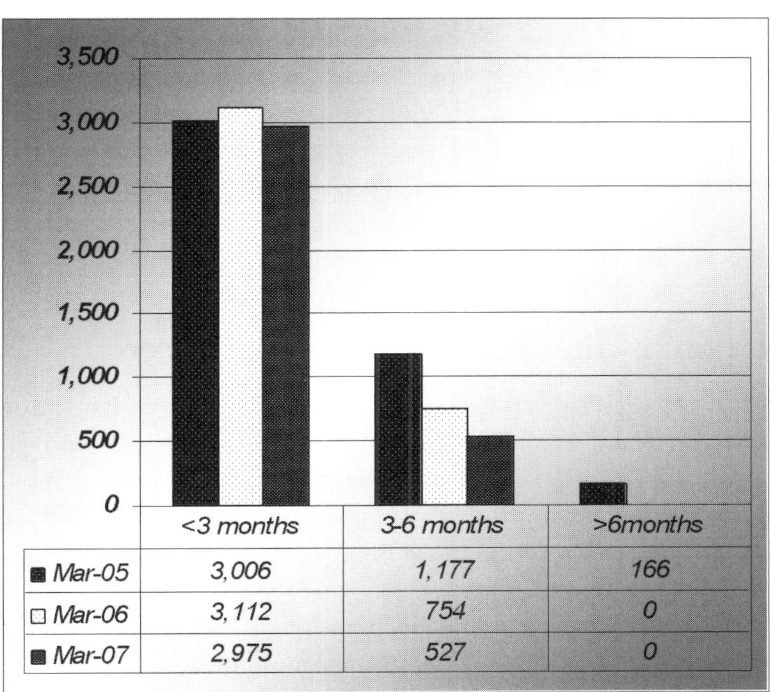
3,500
3,000
2,500
2,000
1,500
1,000
500
0
<3 months
3-6 months
>6months
Mar-05 3,006 1,177 166
Mar-06 3,112 754 0
Mar-07 2,975 527 0

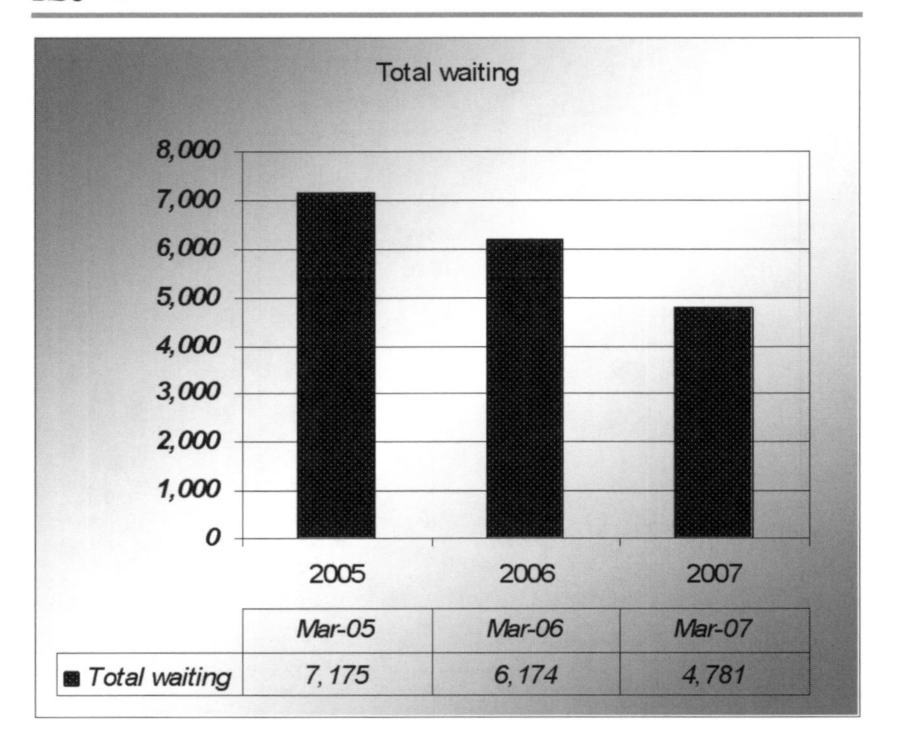

On 29th May, it was announced that the Outer Harbour at Great Yarmouth would go ahead and that construction would commence the following week. The cost would be £50 million. There was concern that the infrastructure of road and railway links to the harbour would be inadequate, but the prospect of new jobs and trade for the town and surrounding area was welcomed.

Reflections by the first Senior Nursing Officer

The history of the last 25 years has been outlined and at this stage it might be interesting to go back to when the hospital first opened and see it through the eyes of Sally Cockrell, the Senior Nursing Officer for the first five years. It is fascinating to note how the hospital was run by her and two or three others and compare it with the vast number of managers who exist now, preparing figures, reports, statistics, etc. Undoubtedly there have been enormous improvements in the quality of the service, the reduction in the waiting times for outpatient clinics and for admission; also in the technology, which has revolutionised investigations and treatment. However, more time is spent in attending committees and filling in details on a computer rather than attending to patients. Sally Cockrell was not only a first-rate leader of her nurses, but she took the peaks and troughs in her stride. Her account of the first five years makes interesting reading.

"I arrived in Great Yarmouth as Senior Nursing Officer of the Great Yarmouth General and Lowestoft Hospitals in August 1980. I took very little notice of the building of the District General Hospital, as my post on its opening was to be in charge of the southern community hospitals and Lowestoft.

One day, in October 1981, I was called in to see Bob Guest, Chief Nursing Officer for the Great Yarmouth and Waveney Health District, at his office in Havenbridge House. Much to my surprise, he told me that I was to be the Senior Nursing Officer of the new hospital and from the next day I should go and sort out recruitment for it. At that point I had not even set foot on the site.

At 8 am the next day, I arrived at a room in the residence, which was in use as a temporary office. It was filled with sacks of application forms. At 9 am, an agency secretary arrived who had been sending out forms in answer to the national advertising campaign, so together we started sorting. Next door was Peter Harrison, the Administrator. We were the only two senior managers on site.

I had been given by Mr. Guest the staff establishment of 311 whole-time equivalent (wte) nursing staff with a list of the wards and the designated sisters who had been appointed from the closing hospitals; a list of other staff who stated they wanted to move to the District General Hospital with their specialty preference which totalled 90 wte, leaving me with the task of recruiting 222 wte before the end of January1982! And sorting out where they would be allocated. Later that day, I had my first tour of what was now my hospital.

In almost solitary isolation, I short-listed then went on to interview. Night duty was the most difficult to fill. In the months that followed, my selection proved to be sound, with only a couple of mistakes – and thankfully they left fairly soon!

On 21st December, the Accident and Emergency Department and the Day and Emergency Ward opened with staff from Great Yarmouth and Lowestoft. I remember visiting on Christmas Day and thinking that, if there was a major accident in the District, how would we cope with the in-patient beds so far from Accident and Emergency.

During January 1982, the wards of the Great Yarmouth General closed and I have a group photograph of all the staff working there. At this time, Lowestoft Hospital changed its function to Elderly Care, which was another challenge! When the Yarmouth General was closed, a grand party was held.

During January 1982, the wards from Great Yarmouth General Hospital and the acute wards at Northgate were transferred. I remember that month as continual induction courses for transferred and new staff. There were a few minor fallings out amongst the staff who transferred if they were not allocated to work with their favourite ward sister or friend, but they soon settled.

Although the District had a nursing procedure committee, it was soon obvious a local group was needed to agree practice and procedures for the District General Hospital. The mix of this group had to be diplomatically picked, using staff previously of Yarmouth and Lowestoft with a sprinkling of new staff. After some initial "this is how we did it where I worked", the group worked well together and acted as a role model for bringing all staff together.

In January1982, Peter Harrison, myself and our secretaries moved into temporary offices in what is now the gynaecological clinic, where we remained until the administration block was built.

During the months that followed, the day-to-day decisions on policy and procedure were made by Peter Harrison, the Administrator, and myself. It was a unique experience; for several months there was little senior management involvement. The NHS was going through another reorganisation. By 1st April 1982, the Area Health Authority had been disbanded and all staff working at District level and senior management level had to apply for a post in the new structure. Districts remained the same, but at operational level hospitals would be managed by Unit Management Teams. I applied for the post of Director of Nursing at the District General Hospital. The interview took place on 3rd November. Thankfully, I got the post, and from 1st January 1983 the Unit Management Team came into being. My colleagues were Mr. John Corson, General Surgeon, and Mr. Tony Wilson (previously of Northgate) as Administrator. It proved to be one of the best groups I have ever worked with. We met every Wednesday morning for around one hour and decisions were made and problems tackled in a very civilised way. It was disbanded in December 1985 when another NHS reorganisation, resulting from the Griffiths Report, introduced General Managers. Once again it was apply-for-a-job time. Tony Wilson was appointed to look after the north of the district and our last meeting was 19th March 1986.

I remember one rather dramatic moment. The Queen was scheduled to visit Great Yarmouth on 1st July 1985. It was at the time the IRA were very active, so the police asked that, in the event of there being a bomb situation, a small team should be available to treat casualties at the site. We were warned that un-detonated bombs may be *in situ,* with a likelihood of going off. At UMT it was decided that Mr. Corson and myself would form the team, as neither of us had young dependants and we preferred not to ask a staff member to be put at risk. I had a month to get my clinical skills up to date. The staff was highly amused when I asked to be taught stitching and was reminded how to put up intravenous lines. Thankfully, the visit passed off with only happy memories for the people of Great Yarmouth.

My day at work usually started around 8 am, so I could be available for the night staff. I would then tour the hospital. It was very easy due to the open plan and there were only six in-patient wards; one Gynaecology, two Surgical, two Medical and Orthopaedics. For each shift there was a Nursing Officer who carried the bleep for sorting staff problems and doing clinical procedures when the staff in charge lacked the skill. On rare occasions, and most Christmas mornings, I took it. The staff was always very amused. One diary entry states, 'had bleep this a.m. Staff ran my little legs off.'

During one January, the overnight snow was very heavy, so I set off early. When I got to the start of the dual-carriageway between Lowestoft and Gorleston, the police were just turning traffic back. After pleading with them, I was allowed through. It was the first and only time I have ever had a police escort. When I got to work, my fears of no staff and chaos were totally unfounded. The hospital community spirit was at its best. Day staff had got husbands to bring them in early. The night staff who could not get home were found beds in the residences. In-patients ran normally, but there was hardly an outpatient to be seen. The appointment staff did a sterling job, ringing outpatients and offering alternative dates.

Budgets and staffing ruled much of my time. I note from my diary at UMT on 7th August 1985 the nursing budget was sixty-four thousand pounds overspent but, thankfully, on 29th January 1986 at UMT I learned it was now breaking even!

Although open, the hospital remained a building site as the two wings were added. This phase was completed in July 1985 so, at the UMT on 31st July, we invited the commissioning team for a glass of wine.

Another branch of my work was with the School of Nursing. Although the District had trained enrolled nurses for some years, the DGH was designated to train State-registered nurses and had classroom facilities. I was involved in setting up the practical experience and preparing for the General Nursing Council's inspectors. We passed, although there was a long list of priority work to be undertaken. I helped interview candidates and the school attracted mainly local people, in particular the more mature student. From a rocky start, the numbers grew, which meant learners on most wards, which is always a bonus for morale and the maintenance of across-the-board standards and procedures. It was really a proud moment for Nursing when the first students qualified and started working as trained nurses wearing the hospital badge.

One person who figured large throughout my time at the JPH was Noel Johnson, Chairman of the Health Authority. He was my rock. Almost daily he toured the hospital. Every member of staff was able to approach him. For him there was no closed door. I would be in my office and the door would be pushed open and there would stand Noel – no knock, no thought of interrupting. He would come to tell me nurse so-and-so was unhappy due to being moved or because of her shift pattern. What was I going to do about it? I had to kindly, but firmly, tell him he could not get involved.

I obviously worked closely with the Medical Staff. On the whole, we had a good working relationship, but there were a few battles over their urge to treat patients, which caused high bed occupancy. This helped to keep the waiting list down, but occasionally put strains on the nursing levels and the patients' environment.

The new General Manager, Andrew Butcher, arrived in April 1986, and in September announced his new structure for the hospital. During the winter I felt I needed a new challenge, so my New Year's resolution on 1st January 1987 was to look for a new post. Most surprisingly, the Director of Nursing post for the Ipswich hospital was advertised. I applied and was offered the job. I was given a grand party on my last day at James Paget Hospital, which was 15th April 1987.

I have two other memories of James Paget when I was on the receiving side. I was a patient myself in 1983 and my mother was in and out from 1982 till her death in the hospital in 1985. On all occasions, I witnessed towards all patients the caring attitude of the nursing staff. More recently, since 2004, I have been once again in and out as a patient and know the care remains something to be proud of."

Reflections by Arthur Harris

Arthur Harris has been involved in the building and design of the hospital from 1975, so knows more about its structure and workings than anyone else. He has been involved in the planning of every project – from minor alterations to the building of all the extensions which have sprung from the core of the original building. He is known for his attention to detail and the hospital has been most fortunate in having such a person in charge of all the works which have been done over the years. Here he gives his views of what has happened to the structure of the building since 1975.

"Having joined the Health Service in 1972, I was appointed as District Building Officer in 1975 for the Great Yarmouth & Waveney Health District, together with Malcolm Brooke, District Works Officer, and George Tarlton, District Engineer. The Havenbridge office block had only just been built in Great Yarmouth and the Health Authority, as the only occupier, had leased the seventh floor, which had panoramic views. The major talking point in the office from day one was the hospital to be built at Gorleston, but there was still a considerable amount of scepticism on whether the new hospital would materialise.

Finally, the big day came and the Health Authority received confirmation that the hospital had been approved and land had been purchased. My first involvement in the project was to arrange for the Development Display Boards to be erected on-site, but very much kept under close wraps. We erected the boards, still with their wrappings on, which made it extremely difficult, particularly in the winter and with the high winds. Everything was set for the formal opening and all dignitaries were invited. Unfortunately, a few days earlier, we had a considerable amount of rain and many of the invited guests had forgotten that the Unveiling Ceremony was to be in the middle of a ploughed field. Nevertheless, the Unveiling Ceremony went ahead with great success; ladies in high-heeled shoes disappeared into the mud and the suits worn by the men probably had to be sent to the cleaners.

The initial building was constructed in three phases: firstly, the construction of the roads and car parks commenced in September 1976 and was completed within a few months by Tilbury Construction Limited. The next phase was the construction of the three-storey nurses' homes, nicknamed the 'barrack blocks'. This development caused a lot of disquiet with the neighbouring properties, due to their size in relation to the adjacent bungalows.

Construction of the main hospital commenced in 1977 and was completed in August 1981 by R. G. Carter Limited of Great Yarmouth. The design of the hospital was known as a 'Best Buy' hospital and had been developed by architects, MacDonald Hamilton and Montefiore of London, in conjunction with the Department of Health. The mechanical and electrical engineering design was carried out by the East Anglian Regional Health Authority in Cambridge, which has subsequently disappeared under reorganisation. The 'Best Buy' concept was quite foreign to us and we related it to the 'Bargain of the Week' that you might get at Tesco's or Asda; but in this case, buying a hospital. We were quite wrong; the design concept had been carefully considered and was, in fact, used for six hospitals in the south of England with four of the units being constructed in East Anglia at Bury St Edmunds, Kings Lynn, Great Yarmouth and Hinchingbrooke.

My role in the District Health Authority was to work with the Design Architects and Regional Health Authority to technically commission the hospital on completion and deal with any defects, of which there were a number. The main problem was the water tightness of the roof, which at one point had over 400 leaks. Nevertheless, with constant pressure on the Design Team and the Contractor, these defects were eradicated over a period of time.

Planning for the occupation and transfer of services from Yarmouth General Hospital occupied a great deal of time. Our main problem was to develop information which would allow staff to find their way around the hospital, as the building was some ten times larger than the existing General Hospital and appeared to be a maze of corridors and rooms. Faced with this problem, we issued the 'Blue Book', which became the Bible for people to find their way around the building. It was a simplified version of the architects' plans, with each room being uniquely numbered. The system worked extremely well, but nevertheless some people lost their way and were sometimes found two days later. In addition, equipment was often placed in the wrong room and sometimes in the wrong department.

The hospital had only been opened about six weeks and it was found that the car park facilities were inadequate for both staff and public. We were instructed to complete two car parks: one at the front of the site, known as Car Park B, and the other at the rear of the site, Car Park E. During the course of construction on Car Park B, and unknown to us, the main incoming electrical cable feeding the site had been left just below ground level. The JCB digger hit the main 11,000-volt cable, melted the front bucket and placed the hospital in total darkness. Fortunately, our brand new generators worked extremely well and six hours later the electrical supplies were reinstated.

Phase 2 of the hospital commenced construction in February 1982 and was completed in December 1984, at a cost of £4.5m, by Sindall Construction Limited. This development added nine additional wards, a Geriatric Day Hospital, Rehabilitation Department and Hydrotherapy Pool, together with additional car parks. As with all large developments, and after three years of occupation, we were able to identify shortfalls in accommodation. This was corrected under a Phase 2A contract, involving the introduction of a new Maternity Theatre within the Central Delivery Suite, with further modifications to other medical areas.

The enlarged hospital required more staff and the need for additional staff accommodation. The Phase 2 housing development was completed a year later to solve the problem, but unfortunately within two years we encountered major problems with the floor structures, due to a technical design fault. All houses had to be vacated and the ground-floor floor structures completely replaced. I am pleased to say the houses are still in use and have not caused any further problems.

Over the years, the hospital has seen further expansion in the development of additional car parks, provision of new Renal Services and the First

Phase of the New Outpatient and Treatment Centre, containing the Ophthalmic Day Case Theatre and Day Case Ward, sitting over the Dermatology Outpatient Development. This project won a prestigious Architectural award for the quality of workmanship and the design of the interior finishes, which is extremely unusual for a Health Service building.

As with all hospitals, due to their heavy usage and the passage of time, the facilities and the internal finishes are becoming outdated when compared with modern hospitals. James Paget Hospital is no exception, and the Foundation Trust is currently reviewing major upgrading works to all of the wards and support services. Hospitals are very much like hotels, and the patients (who are the Trust's clients) do expect improved services with the provision of dedicated en-suite facilities. NHS Guidelines now recommend that multi-placed wards should not exceed four beds, to allow improved dignity and privacy, but this also helps to minimise the risk of cross-infection among patients.

Having been involved with the hospital from its original construction, I believe it has stood the test of time compared with other hospitals and has provided excellent medical care throughout its 25-year life, mainly due to the team-work of all its dedicated staff, of which I am proud to be one.

I was asked if there had been any amusing incidents or disasters. Yes, there have been disasters and, at the time, perhaps I did not consider them to be amusing; but, looking back and reflecting on the events, it does bring a smile to my face. I can remember attending a meeting with the Design Architect prior to completing the original hospital as there were a number of problems and the architect was asked to attend the meeting at very short notice. I arrived at the meeting at 10 am with the remainder of the team, and everybody was looking for the architect. He arrived about 10 minutes later, covered in blood and tissue paper. We did not know whether to have a meeting or to send him to the Accident and Emergency Department for a blood transfusion. It turned out that he had attended our site from another meeting without his overnight bag and shaving equipment. Inadvertently, he had bought a Ladyshave by mistake and finished up with a heavily scarred face for several days.

The hospital has served the local community well over its 25-year life and I hope will continue to do so for the remainder of its design life."

~ 3 ~

Departments

Department of Surgery

Prior to the opening of the new District General Hospital at Gorleston in December 1981, General Surgery was based on hospitals in Great Yarmouth and Lowestoft. Mr. Hugh McDonald, who had trained at Guy's Hospital, London, had been appointed as the first full-time surgeon to the Yarmouth General Hospital at the start of the National Health Service in 1948. In fact, he had been the Resident Surgical Officer to the hospital from 1945 and was made up to Consulting Surgeon in 1948. Colin Craig, who also did his training in London, was appointed to the Lowestoft and North Suffolk Hospital in 1953. Between them, they provided surgical services along the coast from Winterton in the North to Southwold in the South, and inland to Acle, Beccles and Halesworth. They had some assistance from a few housemen, senior house surgeons and, later on, Mr. McDonald had an Associate Specialist. In addition, some GPs did a few sessions with Mr. Leedham Green doing a regular operating session at Lowestoft. Frequently, he would bring his patients in his car in the morning and drive them home after their operation in the evening.

In 1968, John Corson was appointed Consultant Surgeon with sessions in both Lowestoft and Great Yarmouth, and this increased the link between the two towns. With the prospect of the new hospital, it was decided to increase surgical services, and in 1979, Paul Aukland, who had been trained in Liverpool, was appointed to a new post as Consultant General Surgeon with an interest in Vascular Surgery. He was based at Lowestoft. A few months later, Hugh Sturzaker, who had been trained at Guy's and in the South-East Thames Region, was appointed as Consultant General Surgeon with an interest in Gastro-intestinal

Surgery. He replaced Mr. McDonald in Yarmouth and from that time Mr. Corson gave up his sessions in Lowestoft. Thus, we had Mr. Craig and Mr. Aukland in Lowestoft and Mr. Corson and Mr. Sturzaker in Great Yarmouth. Emergency work at night and weekends was shared, so that on alternate nights and weekends emergencies were sent to either Yarmouth or Lowestoft.

Colin Craig set up a monthly meeting where the four surgeons met over lunch at the Foxborough – a hostelry just north of Lowestoft – where we discussed surgical problems and the future of surgery. He retired in 1980 and for three months Mr. Pradeep Datta was appointed Locum Consultant. He went on to become Consultant Surgeon in Wick, North Scotland, where he established an internationally recognised course for young surgeons studying for the FRCS and subsequently MRCS examinations. For the last four years he has been Secretary of the Royal College of Surgeons of Edinburgh and in recent years has been a visiting examiner on two occasions for the Intercollegiate MRCS clinical examinations held at the James Paget. Julian Sansom, who had been trained at St. Thomas' Hospital in London and in Birmingham, took over Mr. Craig's position in Lowestoft and was appointed as a Consultant General Surgeon with an interest in Urology.

Over the next 18 months new surgical instruments were ordered and plans were drawn up as to how surgical services were to be provided. On Monday 21st December 1981 at 7 am, the Lowestoft and North Suffolk Casualty Department closed and the Accident and Emergency Department at the new District General Hospital opened to patients from the Waveney area. The Casualty Department at the Yarmouth General closed on Sunday 3rd January 1982 at 7 am. Patients in Lowestoft and Yarmouth Hospitals were gradually transferred to the new District General Hospital between Monday 21st December and 8th January. Outpatient clinics started at the new hospital on Monday 21st December and the last clinic at Yarmouth General was on 31st December.

Lowestoft patients were moved to Ward 2 and Yarmouth patients to Ward 3, so Mr. Corson and Mr. Sturzaker had most of their patients on Ward 3 and Mr. Aukland and Mr. Sansom had theirs on Ward 2. In addition, there was a Day and Emergency Unit.
The theory was that, during the day, patients were admitted here for Day Case Surgery and in the evening, when they had gone home, emergency

admissions were admitted to these beds. This meant that emergencies were in one area of the hospital and they did not disturb patients in the rest of the hospital. Unfortunately, it proved difficult to move the overnight admissions to other beds in the hospital, so many Day Case Surgical admissions had to be cancelled. As most of the emergencies were Medical, patients there frequently heard heated discussions between Physicians and Surgeons and eventually it was decided not to put emergencies in this unit.

Although Mr. Aukland, Mr. Sturzaker and Mr. Sansom had each been appointed with a special interest in surgery, they and Mr. Corson did all types of general surgery. This was great for teaching their Junior Staff and the medical students who came from Cambridge and other Medical Schools. However, there was a national feeling that there should be greater specialisation. As a result, over the years each devoted more time to their respective specialty and later appointees were more restricted in what they did.

The next surgeon to be appointed was John Studley, who had qualified at the Middlesex Hospital, London. He was appointed in 1990 with a special interest in upper gastro-intestinal surgery and to help Dr. Hishon with Endoscopic Retrograde Cholangio-Pancreatography (ERCPs). He was followed by Jerome Pereira in 1994, who had qualified in India and had worked around London and East Anglia as a Registrar. He was appointed with a special interest in Breast Surgery.

Hank Schneider, who had trained in London and the United States, was appointed in 2001 to help out with the Colorectal Surgery. Unfortunately, he decided he would rather live in the Home Counties and left in November 2005. In 2004, Vivek Chitre joined the team with an interest in Upper Gastro-intestinal Surgery. He had qualified in India and had been a Senior House Officer at the James Paget before joining the East Anglia Surgical Registrar Rotation.

In June 2005, Sarah Downey, who had been a Consultant Breast Surgeon in Bradford for over three years, joined the Department. The Trust was most fortunate, for at that time it was very difficult to find Breast Surgeons, and she had the added advantages of being keen to be on the emergency rota as well as being an enthusiastic teacher and examiner for the Royal College of Surgeons of England. In January 2006, Roshan Lal joined the team with special interests in Day Case Surgery and Laparoscopy. In addition, he took on some of the Colorectal Surgery. He had been trained in India and had been a Registrar at the James Paget in the past.

The Department was keen to develop Laparoscopic Colorectal Surgery and knew that Kevin Murray, who had trained in Ireland and had been a Surgical Registrar at the James Paget, was keen to return to the Hospital. He was spending a year in Australia learning Laparoscopic Colorectal Surgery, so it was decided to defer advertising Hugh Sturzaker's colorectal job. Kevin Murray was appointed and started in February 2006. He began to lay down the foundations of a good Laparoscopic Colorectal service but, unfortunately, for family reasons, he left in July 2006 for a post in Ireland. Mr. Achilles Tsiamis was appointed in March 2007 as Colorectal Surgeon, and he has extensive experience in Laparoscopic Colorectal surgery. He is due to start work in September 2007.

Vascular Surgery

This covers surgery on veins and arteries and the majority of elective surgery was done by Mr. Aukland. Mr. Sansom also did some elective arterial work. As far as the emergency work was concerned, this was done by all the original four surgeons at the new hospital and by Mr. Studley, Mr. Pereira and Mr. Schneider when they joined the staff. With Mr. Aukland's retirement in 1999, elective arterial work ceased. Matthew Armon was appointed to a joint post between Norfolk and Norwich and the James Paget Hospitals in 2002. His commitment to the latter was for only one operating list, one outpatient clinic and a ward round each week, and it was decided it was not feasible to carry out major arterial work. Emergency arterial work continued at the James Paget, but in late 2006, when only Mr. Studley and Mr. Pereira were able to deal with ruptured abdominal aortic aneurysms, it was decided that these would be transferred to Norwich. By this time there were five vascular surgeons in Norwich who ran an emergency rota dealing with all the vascular work in Norwich. The fifth vascular surgeon to be appointed in Norwich was Darren Morrow, who had been a senior house surgeon at the James Paget before joining the East Anglian Surgical Registrar Rotation, and he has sessions weekly at the James Paget. He was appointed in 2006.

Arterial surgery is required when the blood supply to part of the body is impaired. This is usually due to atherosclerosis, where fatty deposits narrow the artery. For Vascular Surgeons, the main vessels involved are those supplying the legs and the brain. Vascular units have Vascular Laboratories to assess the patient and the extent of the disease. In addition, imaging is required. All this is expensive and, with the drive for increased specialisation, it was decided nationally that vascular surgery should be centralised in hospitals which had a sufficiently large population to justify the expensive equipment and the number of vascular surgeons to provide the service.

For many years, Mr. Aukland relied on Dr. Tony Thomas, Consultant Radiologist at the Norfolk and Norwich – when he was appointed in the mid 1970s he had some sessions in Great Yarmouth – and subsequently other radiologists, to carry out angiograms in Norwich. This involves inserting a fine tube into an artery under a local anaesthetic and injecting a liquid which shows up on an X-ray. Up until the 1980s, most of the surgery involved either opening up the involved artery, clearing out the atherosclerosis and closing the incision with a patch of vein, or bypassing the narrowed segment with a length of vein or synthetic tube. This is still done, but increasingly narrowed segments of artery are being dilated by small balloons and the narrowed area is kept open by inserting a plastic or metal stent. This is usually done by Radiologists. It reduces the time spent in hospital and there is minimal recovery time. In 1994, Dr. Antonio Martinez was appointed to do this investigative and therapeutic work at the James Paget but, unfortunately, in 1997, he was headhunted by a University Hospital in Spain.

Ruptured abdominal aortas present as a major emergency. There is splitting of this large artery and without urgent surgery the patient dies. The operation involves replacing the artery with a synthetic graft. Many patients die before getting to theatre, and in those that reach the operating table the mortality is up to 50%. At least two audits of the results of this surgery at the James Paget by one vascular and four non-vascular surgeons showed that the results were as good as those from specialised vascular units.

In recent years, radiologists and vascular surgeons have been inserting stents through small incisions in the groins of patients who have abdominal aortic aneurysms, with increasing success. In addition, the newer, faster CT scans are able to produce excellent pictures of the arteries without having to resort to invasive arteriograms.

Thus, in the last 25years, the means of investigating and treating arterial disease has changed enormously. It has become less invasive, but the cost and need to specialise has meant centralisation into larger units and away from the average District General Hospital, such as the James Paget.

One of the consequences of poor blood supply to the legs which does not respond to reconstructive surgery is amputation. This is a disaster for the patient and his or her relatives. As a means of giving support to these people, an Amputees Club was set up in 1979 and met on a monthly basis in Great Yarmouth. The Club gave mutual support to its members, who also visited patients who were due to or who had just had an amputation. In the mid-1990s, fewer amputations were being done – possibly due to better surgery improving the blood supply to the leg and due to the decrease in cigarette smoking – and membership of the Amputees Club was declining. Decreasing membership was also happening with the local BLESMA – the British Limbless Ex-Servicemen Association – so the two organisations decided to amalgamate.

Varicose veins are common, but the number of operations performed on them is declining. Whether this is because they are less common than they were or the fact that GPs are discouraged from referring patients with varicose veins unless they cause symptoms is unknown. Certainly, referral purely for cosmetic reasons is not permitted by most primary healthcare trusts. When the James Paget opened, the waiting list for varicose veins was several years. Now it is no more than six months, and almost all operations are done as day cases.

Breast Treatment

Breast cancer is the most common cause of death from malignancy in women. This fact, and the fear of image change from the necessary surgery, makes it one of the most feared of diseases. Up until the late 1970s, mastectomy was the main treatment. Hugh Sturzaker and Walter Jackson, Consultant Radiotherapist and Oncologist, had started a fortnightly joint clinic at the Yarmouth General Hospital where they were able to discuss the management of patients before and after surgery. Many of these patients were able to have their tumour removed while retaining much of their breast; whereas, before then, a breast cancer was treated by removing the whole of the breast. This more conservative approach was achieved without any decrease in life expectancy and radiotherapy reduced the chance of the tumour recurring locally.

Apart from the physical scars of the treatment, there are the emotional ones; and to try and help with these, BRAS was founded in the early 1980s. This is the BeReAssuredScheme, which consists of a group of invited ladies who have had breast cancer who meet on a monthly basis and attend outpatient clinics and visit patients on the ward. Having been through the trauma of having had breast cancer, they are in a better position than anyone to appreciate how the patient and her family feel about the news and are able to sympathise and offer help.

In June 1993, Wendy Dwornik was appointed the first Breast Care Nurse Specialist. Her task was to work with the patient, surgeons, oncologists and others to improve the management of breast patients. The Health Authority did not have the money to fund this post and the Macmillan Fund agreed to pump prime the position for the first three years. In exchange, a fundraising committee was formed to raise money for the Macmillan Fund. Later, Jan McCarrick and Vanda Chaplin were appointed Breast Care Nurses. Wendy Dwornik left in 1998 and some months later Rachel Shearing joined the team.

Mammography (which involves taking special X-rays of the breasts) is essential in the diagnosis and successful management of breast disease. In 1980, Dr. Chris Brookings – a general practitioner in Gorleston – set up a private mammography service at the North Sea Medical Centre. After discussions with him, he agreed to provide mammography for some National Health Service patients at a slightly reduced rate. To meet the cost of this, money was raised by various functions organised by different groups throughout the District. One of the first people to be involved with this was Mrs. Jo Raven, who had had breast cancer and had seen the value of mammography. She was a dancing teacher and raised £2,000 from a musical show she put on at the Britannia Pier in Great Yarmouth. The money raised was split between the Hospital Surgical Instrument Fund and the Mammography Fund and brought much needed publicity for the latter fund. As a result of this, the ladies (and some men) of the District were the first people in East Anglia to have mammograms on the NHS, and so it was for many years. With increasing demand for mammograms, more and more money had to be raised each year and, eventually, after much pleading, the Health Authority agreed to partly fund this.

In the mid to late 1980s, the National Breast Screening Programme was established. This involved all ladies between the ages of 50 and 64 being offered mammography every three years. Unfortunately, the bid to have a Breast Screening Unit at the James Paget was turned down, but, after much hard work, The Big 'C' Trust agreed to fund some Breast Screening vans for the Norwich and Great Yarmouth areas, which would be set up in towns and villages. An arrangement was made with Ipswich to hire one of their vans to screen the ladies in the Waveney area. The films were read in Norwich and Ipswich and any abnormal ones were sent to Chris Brookings and Dr. Alleyn O'Malley, Consultant Radiologist, at the North Sea Medical Centre, where the patients were assessed. If there was an obvious lump, then the patient was referred to one of the surgeons at the James Paget. If the abnormality on the mammogram could not be felt, it needed to be localised with a needle prior to surgery. This was done at the North Sea Medical Centre and the patient was then transferred to the James Paget by taxi. This was not ideal and was another factor in support of the James Paget having its own Breast Care Unit.

Unfortunately, the Health Authority did not have the funds to finance a Breast Care Unit, so a public appeal was launched to raise the money in 1993. At the same time, a project team was established to set up the James Paget Breast Care Unit. David Hill, who was later to become the Director of Finance and subsequently the Chief Executive of the James Paget, was seconded from the East Norfolk Health Authority Finance Department to manage the project. In a surprisingly short time, the money was raised and a ground-floor dining room and some changing rooms adjacent to the Medical Imaging Department were converted into a Breast Care Unit and Outpatient Clinic. This was opened by Mrs Rene Burgess, the Chairlady of BRAS. Prior to this, Sue Jones had been appointed the Senior Radiographer of the Unit and Frances Holly Archer was appointed Consultant Radiologist with special responsibility for Mammography and Breast Screening. Although trained in this country, she had been running a large Breast Screening Unit in Australia for many years.

Jerome Pereira was appointed as a Consultant Surgeon with a special interest in Breast Surgery in 1994, and from that date it was decided that Breast Surgery should be done only by him and Hugh Sturzaker. This made it easier to standardise treatment, to hold weekly meetings with the radiologists, radiographers, histopathologists, oncologists and breast care nurses, and to have regular audit meetings to assess the results of management.

Jerome Pereira had trained in plastic surgery and was keen to offer breast reconstruction to patients who wished it. At that time, very few units offered this facility and, where it was done, the surgery tended to be carried out by plastic surgeons some time after the patient had a mastectomy. The advantage of a breast surgeon doing the reconstruction was that it could be done at the same time as the primary surgery, so saving two operations. He visited the Emory Clinic, Atlanta, in the United States and in 1997 he did his first reconstruction. For a number of years he was the only breast surgeon in East Anglia offering this service. From the outset, he audited his results and was able to encourage some other surgeons in East Anglia and elsewhere to join him. He then became instrumental in developing a National Audit involving Breast and Plastic Surgeons which has been funded nationally and he is the lead clinician for this project. Throughout this project he has been greatly helped by Margaret Brandish, who assisted with audit when the Breast Unit was first established.

There is very strict audit on the results of Breast Screening Units, and it is felt nationally that smaller units do not produce such good results as the larger ones. Fortunately, the stringent standards laid down by Frances Holly Archer and Brian Evans meant that the results from the James Paget were in the top three in the Eastern Region. Brian Evans had headed the Ipswich Breast Screening Unit and had been Regional Head of Quality Control and had given much useful advice and support in the setting-up of the James Paget Breast Care Unit. After retiring from Ipswich, he came to work at the James Paget from 2000 until 2006.

In the early years of Breast Screening, the abnormality on mammogram was localised with a needle and injecting some blue dye and the needle was removed. An operation was then required to remove this piece of tissue. The operation was later made easier by localising the abnormality with a hook on it which stayed in place during the surgery. As many of these abnormal areas were benign, it meant that many ladies were having unnecessary surgery. However, over the years better biopsying using a computer with fine needles and later larger needles which produced a core of tissue meant that rarely did benign lesions require an open operation and the operation for malignant lesions could be better planned.

To assess the degree of spread of a tumour, it is necessary to remove some of the lymph nodes in the armpit. This helps in deciding what further treatment should be recommended. Unfortunately, removal of many or all of these nodes can impair the drainage of fluid from the arm, so resulting in a swollen arm. However, recent work has shown that removal of the sentinel node – which is demonstrated by the injection of dye and /or radioactive material into the breast – can show whether the nodes are involved with tumour or not, so saving potential damage in those ladies whose lymph nodes are free of disease, as they do not require further surgery on their lymph nodes. At present, the James Paget Breast Unit is being assessed to see if it can offer this service to its patients.

Swollen arms can be helped by massage and elasticated sleeves and in 1997 Sandra Westrop was appointed as Lymphoedema Physiotherapist, and she has done much to improve the lives of those ladies who have this problem.

Patients who have had a breast, or part of one, removed can be helped by the orthotics department, and the hospital has been fortunate in having the services of Chris Tom for many years. She and her staff are able to give advice about brassieres, prostheses, swimwear, etc. In addition, some of the local stores in Yarmouth and Lowestoft have been most helpful in providing special facilities and garments for these ladies.

When Hugh Sturzaker retired, Breast Surgeons were in short supply and the majority wanted to do only breast surgery. The James Paget was, therefore, most fortunate in finding Sarah Downey, who was already a Consultant Breast Surgeon and who wanted to do emergency and laparoscopic work. Now she is being trained by Jerome Pereira to do reconstructive work and she heads the Breast Unit.

In the last 25 years, a specialised breast unit has developed which has the equipment to make earlier diagnosis and often without resorting to surgery. Its results in breast screening have put it among the top three units in the Eastern Region. It offers conservative surgery and, if a mastectomy or removal of a large part of the breast is required, it can offer immediate reconstruction. Jerome Pereira heads the National Audit on Breast Reconstruction. BRAS and the Breast Care Nurses help in giving compassionate care to the patients and relatives, and sometimes give support to the surgeons! The Unit has been active in breast cancer-related research projects and members of the team have presented a number of scientific papers at national and international meetings.

Upper Gastro-intestinal Surgery

This covers surgery of the oesophagus, stomach, duodenum and small bowel, the liver, gall bladder, pancreas and spleen. Over the last 25 years, there have been some significant changes in the incidence and the management of disease affecting these areas. Along with this has been increasing specialisation and edicts nationally that only units carrying out a certain number of procedures annually should be allowed to continue.

Thus, in the late 1980s, the James Paget Surgeons decided that patients requiring oesophagectomies (removal of the oesophagus) should have this undertaken at Norwich. With the Government directives, this now applies to patients with tumours in their stomachs. At present there is discussion about the management of cancer of the pancreas and whether this should be done in Cambridge, Ipswich or Norwich. However, it is likely that, in the future, this type of surgery will be concentrated in one centre only. National figures suggest that better results are achieved by surgeons doing more of these operations than by those who do fewer; but it will mean that patients will have to travel much longer distances to have their surgery.

John Studley replaced John Corson in November 1991 and was appointed with a special interest in Upper Gastro-intestinal Surgery and to help Stuart Hishon with the ERCPs (Endoscopic Retrograde Cholangio-Pancreatography). He had worked at the Hammersmith

Hospital in London and had a considerable experience in working on the pancreas, so the other surgeons decided that they would refer all future patients requiring pancreatic surgery to him.

In 1990, Hugh Sturzaker attended the first UK Conference and course on Laparoscopic Cholecystectomy at St. Mary's Hospital, London. On his return, he started setting up the facilities for carrying out the operation at the James Paget. Initially, this was with borrowed equipment with the firm's representative acting as assistant and offering advice. Eventually, the hospital bought its own equipment and John Studley and Paul Aukland made up the three surgeons offering this operation. The results were amazing as, with only four tiny scars, the pain post-operatively was much less and patients were able to leave hospital within one to two days, compared with four to five days after the more traditional open operation. In recent years many of these patients are going home the day of operation.

The surgeons had done an occasional diagnostic laparoscopy over the years, but adding a camera to the end of the telescope enabled the picture to be viewed by all in theatre and made it much easier to manipulate instruments inside the abdomen. The surgeons explored the repairing of inguinal hernias laparoscopically, but after a short time decided that it was expensive, could not be done under local anaesthetic and stopped the junior staff from learning an essential basic operation. Unfortunately, although eventually almost all gall bladders at the James Paget were removed laparoscopically, the surgeons did not extend the laparoscopic technique to other operations for a number of years. This development has moved forward over the last three years with the appointment of Vivek Chitre, Sarah Downey and, most recently, with Roshan Lal. Between them, operations performed laparoscopically in certain patients include groin hernia repairs, hiatus hernia repairs, splenectomies and appendicectomies.

One of the consequences of a tumour of the pancreas or stones which block the bile ducts is that bile is blocked from draining from the liver into the duodenum. As a result, the patient becomes jaundiced. In the 1970s, in the majority of places, this could be relieved only by an open operation. However, with the advent of the duodenoscope it was possible to either extract the stones from the common bile duct or, if this was not possible, a stent or tube could be inserted through the duodenoscope and through the stricture. This could be achieved without any scars or pain and by staying in hospital for usually less than one to two days. This was first done by Stuart Hishon, our first Gastroenterologist, soon after the new hospital was opened.

Until 2000, most of the endoscopy was done by the General Surgeons and the one Gastroenterologist. However, since that date the number of gastroenterologists has increased to four. Consequently, more and more endoscopic procedures are being done by them. Since the hospital opened, strictures of the oesophagus have been dilated with various instruments and balloons and, where there have been irremovable malignant strictures, stents of various sorts have been inserted to allow the patient to swallow. Matthew Williams has expertise with the Laser and uses it to core out channels in some patients who have malignant strictures of the oesophagus and rectum.

Some patients are unable to swallow after strokes or because they have some neuro-muscular incoordination. This can be overcome by the insertion of a PEG (Percutaneous Endoscopic Gastrostomy), which involves the insertion of a small tube into the stomach using a gastroscope and avoids the previous necessity of an open operation. This has been done for well over 10 years.

Not only have instruments and techniques changed, but so have diseases. Duodenal and gastric ulcers – once very common – are now less so. This is probably the result of different life styles and the introduction of new drugs and the realisation that these ulcers are associated with an organism known as helicobacter pylori. As a result, it is rare to operate on a patient with a duodenal ulcer unless it has bled or perforated. When the hospital opened, it was not uncommon to see patients on the operating list for a Gastrectomy, Vagotomy or Highly Selective Vagotomy. Open operations for duodenal ulcers are usually for the complications of perforation or for bleeding, which has failed to respond to various endoscopic measures, such as injection of adrenaline, heating or clipping the bleeding vessel. Such ulcers usually occur in elderly people who have been treated for arthritis or other painful conditions with non-steroidal anti-inflammatory drugs or who are on steroids. In short, these ulcers result from medical treatment.

While duodenal ulcers are much less common, pancreatitis is far more common and hardly a day goes by without at least one patient being admitted with this condition. It is usually associated with gall stones or excessive alcohol intake. Particularly in the elderly, it has a high morbidity and mortality rate, and many patients end up in the intensive care unit.

Cancer of the stomach occurs much more commonly in the upper stomach than it did and this makes surgical removal a much more difficult operation than for those tumours in the lower part. With operations for benign disease being so uncommon now, the upper gastro-intestinal surgeon has less experience of gastric surgery; consequently, it seems sensible to transfer surgery for malignant disease of the stomach to larger centres which have greater experience once Mr. Studley and Mr. Pereira have retired. In fact, Government directives may bring this about before then.

The majority of people with symptoms of reflux and hiatus hernia can be managed by losing weight and taking simple medication. However, there is a small number of patients who require surgery. In the past, this was done by open operation, with varying results. This operation can be done just as well with fewer problems and quicker recovery laparoscopically and Vivek Chitre has started to do these. Another operation to consider is laparoscopic surgery for obesity. Obesity is very much on the increase, causing diabetes, raised blood pressure, arthritis, etc; and, where all other measures have failed, such an operation can be a life-saver. However, the surgery is only one aspect of tackling this problem, and a team approach with dieticians, biochemists and specialist nurses is required.

One of the consequences of over-indulgence with alcohol is cirrhosis. This impairs the flow of blood through the liver, so causing varices, which are like varicose veins in the lower oesophagus and upper stomach which can bleed dramatically. Gastroscopy will demonstrate the cause of the bleeding and it can be controlled by injecting various compounds or applying clips to the bleeding vessels through the gastroscope. When the hospital first opened, such a cause for bleeding was uncommon, injection of the bleeding varices was rarely done and, if unsuccessful, a tube containing two balloons was passed through the patient's mouth and the balloons blown up in the lower oesophagus and upper stomach in the hope of stopping the bleeding.

This brief account shows how diseases, instruments and treatment have changed over the last 25 years. Many operations are now defunct or are rarely done; others are performed laparoscopically, leading to much more rapid recovery. These advances have been of great benefit to the patient and have dramatically shortened the time the patient spends in hospital, hence the need for fewer surgical beds.

Colorectal Surgery

Colorectal surgery involves surgery on the colon, rectum and anal canal. In the past, this surgery was undertaken by most general surgeons, but in recent years colorectal surgery has become a specialty in its own right and it is increasingly felt that operations on the rectum and particularly the lower part should be done only by such specialists. This has been the view at the James Paget over the last seven to eight years.

Colorectal cancer is the second most common cause of death from malignancy in the United Kingdom and much of a colorectal surgeon's time is spent managing this condition. Whereas the incidence of duodenal ulcer has decreased in recent years, there has been little change in the incidence of colorectal cancer over many decades. However, there have been advances in how it is detected, prevented, treated and how patients are managed.

The primary treatment of colorectal surgery is surgical and in most instances this involves cutting out the tumour and joining the bowel ends together. In the early 1980s, Mr. Bill Heald, who had trained at Guy's Hospital, London, and was Consultant Surgeon at Basingstoke, drew attention to the finer anatomical details around the rectum, which is the lower part of the large bowel. He emphasised the importance of the tissue planes here and the need for meticulous dissection. Using these techniques, he was able to show that the incidence of local recurrence of the tumour here was much reduced, as was the damage to the fine nerves in this region which could result in impaired sexual function. Initially, his results were not believed, but further work confirmed them and from the early 1990s surgeons at the James Paget have followed his teachings.

Soon after the introduction of Laparoscopic Cholecystectomy, some surgeons started operating on the colon and rectum by means of laparoscopy. Unfortunately, poor technique led to tumour growing in the small holes in the abdominal wall through which the instruments had been inserted. Although this was not common, it prompted the

Government to stop all laparoscopic procedures for colorectal cancer until the situation had been fully assessed in a number of medical centres in this country. This has now been done and throughout the country there is an increasing amount of colorectal surgery being done laparoscopically. Kevin Murray commenced this at the James Paget after his appointment in February 2006, but, unfortunately, he left within six months. Fortunately, Roshan Lal, who is an experienced laparoscopic surgeon, did some work with him while he was here and is continuing to do some laparoscopic resections. Fortunately, Achilles Tsiamis, the colorectal surgeon starting in September, has had extensive training in laparoscopic colorectal surgery.

The smaller abdominal wounds associated with laparoscopic surgery lead to less pain. Another method of improving the patient's stay in hospital is the enhanced postoperative recovery programme which has been introduced from Denmark. This involves the patient having an epidural anaesthetic (the nerves to the lower body are temporarily paralysed by an injection in the back), the restarting of oral fluids and food soon after surgery and early mobilisation. This, especially where it is combined with laparoscopic surgery, can lead to the patient leaving hospital days earlier than in the past and is now being evaluated at the James Paget Hospital.

Unfortunately, some patients ignore their symptoms for too long so that, by the time they present, the tumour has grown into surrounding tissues or spread to other organs, such as the liver. Up until about 1990, if a patient had a cancer of the bowel and they were sufficiently fit they were advised to have an operation to overcome their symptoms and to prevent a bowel obstruction. Rarely did they have ultrasound or CT scans of their liver because it was felt that even if they had liver tumours they would be better off getting rid of their bowel tumour and the symptoms it was causing or would do so if it were left. Unfortunately, at operation it was sometimes found that the primary tumour in the bowel was stuck to adjacent tissues and could not be removed and the patient would end up with a colostomy or ileostomy. These are openings of the bowel onto the abdominal surface which empty into a bag.

Improvements in the CT Scanning machines made them much more accurate, so their use before operation made it possible to plan operations better. Studies had also shown that rectal tumours would respond to radiotherapy and this response could be improved when combined with chemotherapy. An assessment of the need for this treatment could be made by simple examination, but it did mean that many patients were being subjected to such treatments unnecessarily. Fortunately, the increased accuracy of the new CT Scanners, and particularly the MR Scanners, has enabled the spread of the rectal tumours to be assessed with great accuracy, so that it is possible to decide before operation whether the tumour can be removed or whether the patient should have pre-operative radiotherapy with or without chemotherapy. Such treatment not only reduces the size of the tumour, but it can turn a tumour, which was previously inoperable, into one which can be removed.

Tumours which are low down in the rectum are technically difficult to operate on. Up until the 1940s and 1950s, most people with a rectal tumour would end up with a colostomy; but, as surgical techniques and instruments improved along with anaesthetic skills, surgeons were able to remove more of the rectum and still join the bowel together afterwards. However, there is a limit to this and a number of patients still end up with colostomies and ileostomies. Although this can be a life-saving operation for the patient, the physical and emotional handicap associated with this can be enormous. To help manage this, Gail Hunting was appointed Stoma Care Sister in 1981. She had been a Nursing Ward Sister in Lowestoft and was the first Stoma Care Sister in East Anglia. For further details about this, see the Stoma Care Service.

Medicine and surgery increasingly involves teamwork and since the 1990s a weekly gastroenterological meeting has been held. This involves surgeons, gastroenterologists, radiologists, colorectal nurse specialists, oncologists, histopathologists and the colorectal secretary/administrator. The first half of the meeting deals with upper gastro-intestinal cases and in the second half every new colorectal cancer patient is presented along with new results on ones previously presented. If the patient fits certain laid-down protocols, then there is minimum discussion; but if the situation is more complicated, a long, detailed debate might ensue. The findings and conclusions of the meeting are recorded and sent to the patient's GP and the patient is seen and informed of the management plan at the next available opportunity. Such meetings hopefully result in the best joint opinion being made for each patient and it is an educational experience for all involved. Palliative Care

Nurses are sometimes present, as are Junior Doctors and Medical Students.

Having had the bowel cancer removed, it is important to follow up the patient for signs of recurrent or new disease and a policy was worked out with colleagues at the Norfolk and Norwich which was felt to be effective and not too time-consuming. It was decided that the customary way of reviewing the patient in the clinic, asking them questions and examining them, was not particularly effective and reliable. If the tumour was going to present again, then it would do so near where it was originally or in the liver or lungs. Fortunately, the CT Scanner is very efficient at detecting such problems, so it was decided that these patients would have a CT Scan every six months and the results would be given to them by the Colorectal Nurses. The patients are also given a card of symptoms to be aware of and if they have any of these or any other worries they can telephone the colorectal nurses who will then decide whether the patient needs to be seen in a clinic. Patients who have had a rectal tumour removed are still assessed in the clinic.

The other follow-up is a colonoscopy. It is known that most colorectal cancers arise from polyps and if a patient has had such a Cancer he or she is more likely to have another as well as polyps. These can be detected by colonoscopy and in most instances the polyp can be removed completely thus preventing the development of a cancer. The procedure also checks whether there is any tumour growth where the bowel has been joined together. This is uncommon in the colon but is more so in the rectum hence the visits to outpatients for these patients.

This follow-up system saves Outpatient time, reduces the number of visits the patients need to come to the hospital and it enable them to have a quick access to the hospital should it be necessary. In addition, it should detect problems at an earlier stage and by removing polyps should prevent cancers developing.

Even better than first-class surgery, radiotherapy and chemotherapy is prevention and early detection of cancer. Bowel cancer is particularly common in places where people eat large amounts of red meat and is less so where people eat more roughage. So, reducing the intake of red meat and increasing the amount of vegetables and cereals in the diet can reduce the incidence of bowel cancer. Certain conditions do lead to a higher risk for a patient developing bowel cancer, such as long-standing ulcerative colitis (a chronic inflammation of the large bowel) affecting the whole colon and hereditary. Only a small number of bowel cancers are linked to hereditary, but should be considered where someone develops the disease under the age of 40 years old or where there are several members of the family with it. Similarly, patients with multiple polyps in their bowel are at risk. All these patients should be regularly screened by means of colonoscopy and this has been happening at the James Paget for many years.

Passing blood from the back passage is one of the symptoms of a colorectal tumour, although there are many other causes of this symptom. A patient reporting this problem to his/her GP is referred directly for a flexible sigmoidoscopy, where the cause of the bleeding can be determined or be further investigated. Such an arrangement means that a patient is referred directly for investigation without the delay of being seen in an outpatient clinic, and if a cancer is detected then there is a plan in place for its prompt investigation and treatment.

Many bowel tumours will produce minute amounts of blood which are not visible, and work in Nottingham by Professor Jack Hardcastle which started 20 years ago has shown that a screening programme testing people's stools for blood and following up the positive ones with a colonoscopy to examine the whole large bowel will detect bowel cancer at a much earlier stage than in those who do not have the screening and will save lives. In 2006, the Government started introducing a National Screening Programme for bowel cancer along these lines in which people over the age of 60 years will be invited to take part.

Inflammatory Bowel Disease is a group of conditions where there is inflammation of part of the intestine. In many instances the condition can be kept under reasonable control but occasionally surgery is necessary. In Ulcerative Colitis, surgery may be indicated when medical treatment has failed or the patient may present as an emergency, with the whole of the large bowel inflamed and distended. Failure to respond to medical management within two to three days is an urgent indication for surgery which involves removal of the whole colon and giving the patient an ileostomy. Until the early 1980s, the majority of patients had a permanent ileostomy and, as they tended to be in their teens or twenties, this was a horrendous handicap. However, in the late 1970s Sir Alan Parks of St. Mark's Hospital, London, devised an operation to fashion a new rectum for these patients out of their small bowel and stitch this onto their ano-rectal region. The initial results had some problems, but with modifications the success was much greater, so that in the late 1980s the operation was introduced at the James Paget Hospital. As a result, there is a large group of patients who have had their whole large bowel removed and are leading healthy lives without the need of an ileostomy. Nationally, about 15% of these patients do have problems with this operation and resort to a permanent ileostomy, and the James Paget figures are similar. The Colorectal Nurse Specialists have been a great help in managing these patients. For a time there was also a Pouch Group of patients who had this operation who met periodically and gave advice to patients who were considering this operation.

Piles, or haemorrhoids, which is their more technical term, are possessed by everyone, but they only come to the attention of the doctor when they bleed, become swollen or are painful. Many patients self-treat themselves with ointments and creams obtained from the pharmacist or via the internet, but it is most important that anyone over the age of 40 with rectal bleeding sees their GP, as the bleeding could be coming from higher up from a polyp, cancer or inflammatory condition. For this reason, such patients are referred to the hospital for a flexible sigmoidoscopy and if no cause is found other than enlarged haemorrhoids these can be treated there and then. Treatment has changed over the years. Injections have been used for many years and are still useful for the smaller ones. They have also been treated by freezing and applying infra-red, but probably the best, for the moderately enlarged ones, is the application of rubber bands. For the very large and prolapsing ones, surgical removal is the treatment of choice, although this is a painful procedure and requires admission to hospital. In the past, patients stayed in for up to a week, but recently this has been reduced to one to two days, and some go home the same day. A more recent procedure is the application of a staple gun to remove the haemorrhoids from inside the back passage. As a result, it does not cause the pain of a haemorrhoidectomy, but complications have been reported using this technique and it is still being evaluated. Fortunately, the majority of haemorrhoids are dealt with by injections and rubber bands and many fewer patients nowadays are being subjected to haemorrhoidectomy.

Many gastroenterological diseases are treated by both surgeons and gastroenterologists. It is, therefore, important that they should work closely together. To promote this, a Department of Gastroenterology was set up in the late 1990s, since when there have been regular meetings to decide policies and promote the work of the department. The gastroenterological patients in the surgical wards are now in the ward adjacent to the medical gastroenterological ward. This enables easier referrals between the two wards and hopefully there will be exchanges of nurses between the two wards to improve education in the specialty.

Stoma Care and Colorectal Nurse Specialists

A stoma is the opening of part of the bowel onto the abdominal surface and it drains into a bag. It may be temporary or permanent. The Great Yarmouth and Waveney Health District was the first to provide a stoma care service in East Anglia by the appointment of Gail Hunting as a Stoma Care Sister in 1981. She had been surgical ward sister in Lowestoft and Paul Aukland advised her to attend the Stoma Care Course at the North Tees General Hospital. Prior to her appointment, she had advised patients on her ward about stomas and a similar service was provided by Annabel Pritt, Surgical Ward Sister at Yarmouth General Hospital.

Gail was the ideal person for the post. She calls a spade a spade. She remembers the advice given to her at North Tees: "stoma patients do not always need a nurse, they firstly need a friend, preferably one that knows what she is doing". That is exactly what Gail was to so many patients. She took in people's animals so that they could go to their family at Christmas; she promised to look after the dog of an ex-patient should he die and she did, and she went swimming with a young mother, who had an ileostomy, and her three sons, to overcome her fear of getting into the pool wearing her stoma bag. Frequently, she looked after patients' plants while they were in hospital. One of these patients, William Spencer, left £300,000 to the hospital when he died 15 years later and this went towards the new Endoscopy Suite which bears his name.

As she was the only Stoma Care Sister in East Anglia for many years, her services were in demand throughout the Region and there was not one hospital that did not call upon her help and advice on more than one occasion. She organised study days for nurses, stoma nurses and patients and one memorable day the James Paget hosted a meeting to which Professor Bryan Brooke came. He had been the initiator of the Ileostomy Association of Great Britain and Ireland which was formed in Birmingham in 1956 and is now known as the Ileostomy and Internal Pouch Support Group.

She was a great supporter of the Ostomy Support Group which was founded around 1990. The protagonist for this was Bill Leeds and so popular is the group that attendance continues to be about a hundred at its quarterly meetings in the Burrage Centre. It is open to patients with colostomies or ileostomies and their families and it enables them to go out for a social evening without having to feel "different".

For many years she worked single-handed until the appointment of Yvonne Colmer, who was just as dedicated as Gail. Later, Sheila Howlett joined the team and she expanded the role of the stoma care nurse into a Colorectal Nurse Specialist. With training, this enabled these nurses to take on more responsibilities and help in the management of all diseases of the large bowel.

Gail did not like bureaucracy and management meetings, feeling that they kept her away from patients. For years she tried to obtain a secretary to help her with her work, but was unsuccessful. A computer was donated by a commercial organisation in 1992 to help keep track of her patients, but she never liked it, and eventually retired in 1997. In a typical Gail statement, she said at her retirement party on 23rd May 1997: "You cannot wipe a patient's bum with a computer."

Sheila Howlett took on the lead of the Department. It was decided that her role would be developed into a Colorectal Nurse Specialist but she would continue with her stoma care duties. This was contrary to developments in other hospitals but it was thought essential not to separate the stoma care service and this has proven to be a wise decision. After a year, Jane Tallett joined the Department and stayed for seven years working her way up to Colorectal Nurse Specialist, when she moved to Norwich. During this time, Sue Coote joined the team but unfortunately, within a year, she was diagnosed with cancer. In spite of needing chemotherapy she continued with her studies and work and was a great inspiration to the staff and her patients.

Sheila Howlett and her team developed the role of the Colorectal Nurse Specialist by holding nurse-led clinics for patients, producing a

Filofax-type system giving patients information about their disease and how it would be treated. Sheila helped to set up follow-up procedures for colorectal cancer patients and played a major part in the development of the Multi-Disciplinary Team meetings which are held weekly. She encouraged the educational development of her team and retired at the end of 2005, when her lead role was taken over by Mary Jordan.

This account shows that there have been many changes in the management of patients with colorectal disease since the James Paget Hospital opened. Patients with symptoms suggestive of malignancy are being fast-tracked to the hospital and having urgent investigations where they are indicated. The decisions about treatment are decided at a multidisciplinary team meeting, where all the investigations can be assessed by a group of surgeons, radiologists, histopathologists and oncologists. Surgical techniques have improved and are continuing to evolve, hospital stays are shorter and follow-up after treatment has been rationalised. The management of patients and their relatives has been greatly improved by the introduction of the Stoma Care Service and the development of the Colorectal Nurse Specialists. Screening has been introduced nationally to detect colorectal cancers earlier and people at risk are screened regularly at the James Paget in the Endoscopy Suite.

Urological Surgery

Urological surgery involves operations on the kidneys, ureters, bladder, prostate, urethra and testicles. These operations were done by the general surgeons until the appointment of Mr. Suresh in October 1995, when they gradually gave up most of this surgery, except for Mr. Sansom, who had been appointed with a special interest in Urology and had done about 50% of this surgery until 1995.

The commonest urological operation is on the prostate. This is a small gland beneath the bladder which normally is the size of a walnut. As men become older, this gland enlarges and narrows the upper part of the urethra, which passes urine from the bladder to the outside. In the early days of the hospital, many of these glands were removed through cuts in the lower abdomen; but, as instrumentation improved along with the experience of the surgeons, the majority of prostates were removed endoscopically. This involves inserting a telescope up the urethra and chipping away the prostate from inside. There is no abdominal wound to heal, blood loss is less, recovery is much quicker and the hospital stay is shorter: a week with an open operation and two to three days with a transurethral resection of the prostate, or even less. Diathermy – which is an electrical current – is usually used to cut out the prostate transurethrally, although a Laser can be used. In the last 10 years more and more men who have prostatic troubles are being treated with drugs which can improve urinary flow, so delaying or avoiding surgery.

Prior to Mr. Suresh's arrival, the surgeon looked directly into the telescope which was used for the operation. It was possible to attach an extension so that one other person could also see the operation. Mr. Suresh brought television into the theatre. A camera was attached to the end of the telescope and the picture on the TV screen could be seen by all in the theatre. Not only is this much easier for the operator, who no longer has to crouch between the patient's legs, but it is much better for teaching and adds greater interest for those in theatre.

Urinary stones are common and can cause severe pain when they cause a blockage in the ureters, which is the tube passing from the kidney to the bladder. Small stones will eventually pass, but larger ones can get stuck and cause a blockage. This can be relieved by passing a small tube – called a stent – up the ureters, which allows the urine to drain freely. The stone can be removed by passing flexible or rigid instruments (ureteroscopes) up the ureter and grasping the stone under direct vision. Alternatively, shock waves can be used to shatter the stone. Prior to the introduction of these instruments, stones in the lower ureter could sometimes be removed with a wire basket passed up the ureter and observing this on an X-ray. In most instances, up until the mid 1990s, stones stuck in the ureter were removed by an open operation, which required the patient being in hospital for up to a week.

Stones in the kidney can be managed either by shock waves or by percutaneous nephrolithotripsy (PCNL). This form of keyhole surgery involves inserting a guidewire through the skin and into the kidney under X-ray control in the operating theatre. The tract is then dilated and instruments passed down to extract the stone. These procedures have made open operations on the kidneys for stones a very rare event and the patient is usually able to return home the next day. Andrew

Simpson pioneered PCNL at the James Paget and Mr. Suresh took this over when Andrew Simpson left in 2005.

Cancer can occur in any of the urological organs and the modern CT Scans have enabled better assessment of the spread of the disease, which can be discussed in multidisciplinary meetings where decisions are made as to the best management for each patient. Where there are small tumours in the kidney, the kidney can be removed laparoscopically and Mr. Suresh has started performing laparoscopic nephrectomies for benign conditions. Most bladder tumours are dealt with endoscopically, using the same equipment and techniques as when a transurethral resection of the prostate is performed. Where the tumour is more advanced, it may need treatment with radiotherapy or removal of the whole of the bladder, in which case the ureters are joined to an isolated piece of small bowel which is brought onto the abdominal surface like an ileostomy. The urine then drains into a bag.

Where the bladder tumour has been removed by transurethral resection, the patient is brought back every few months to check for further growth. When the bladder has been clear on several occasions, it is unlikely that further resections will be needed, although check-ups are necessary. Mr. Sansom introduced the flexible cystoscope (a thin flexible telescope) in the early 1990s, which enabled these investigations to be done under local anaesthetic in the endoscopic suite. This had the advantage of saving patients' time, a general anaesthetic, theatre time and a hospital bed.

Cancer of the prostate is often a hormonally dependent tumour and in many instances it may respond very well for many years to female hormones. Where it is causing difficulty in passing urine, a transurethral resection of the prostate can be performed. In America for over 20 years there has been great enthusiasm for removing the whole prostate for malignant disease and this is increasingly performed in the United Kingdom in recent years. This operation is called a radical prostatectomy. It is a much bigger operation than other forms of prostatectomy, with potentially more complications, and Mr. Suresh introduced this operation in the late 1990s. Obviously, it is most important to make sure that the tumour is confined to the prostate before the operation and MR scans play a big part in this assessment.

Prostatic Specific Antigen (PSA) is a substance present in the blood in small amounts in all men. The amount increases where there is a cancer of the prostate, but also in some benign conditions; so it is essential that there is proof of a cancer before treatment commences. This is done by taking core biopsies of the prostate through the back passage using an ultrasound probe as a guide to which parts to biopsy. The level of PSA is used to monitor the effectiveness of treatment and progress of the disease.

Tumours of the penis are rare in this country and are treated either by radiotherapy or surgery or sometimes by both. There are different forms of tumour of the testis, but most occur in teenagers and young men. Treatment usually involves removal of the testicle and a single shot of chemotherapy, although longer courses of chemotherapy and radiotherapy are sometime required. Fortunately, the results of treatment are usually excellent.

Bleeding is one of the most frequent presentations of a urological tumour and Mr. Suresh introduced a Haematuria (blood in the urine) Clinic to minimise the delay of referral and to hasten the investigations. At this clinic, a short history is taken, a clinical examination is done, blood and urine tests are carried out and a flexible cystoscopy is performed. This involves passing a thin, flexible telescope up the urethra under a local anaesthetic. The pictures of the urethra, prostate and bladder are seen on a television screen and any abnormality seen can be biopsied. If no cause for the bleeding is found, an intravenous urogram is performed, which is an X-ray which shows up the kidneys and ureters. Thus, in a short space of time the cause of the haematuria can be determined and further investigations and treatment may be started.

To assess how well people pass urine, Mr. Sansom introduced urodynamic studies in the early 1990s, which have been overseen by the Urological Nurse Specialists. The first one was Christine Morgan, who also helped with incontinence problems in the District. Subsequent Urological Nurse Specialists have been invaluable in assessing erectile dysfunction, evaluation of lower urinary tract symptoms and management of urinary incontinence in men and women. In addition, they play a large role in dissemination of information and communication. They work closely with the Colorectal Nurse Specialists and are particularly helpful to patients who have ileal conduits after bladders have been removed.

Following Government directives, the major cancer work is being centralised, so radical prostatectomy and total cystectomy will be moved to Norwich. This is based on the fact that results tend to be better where a surgeon is performing a certain procedure more frequently. However, this seems unfair when Mr. Suresh's results are as good as, if not better than, those in some of the bigger centres. At least Mr. Suresh is going to be allowed to do some operating in Norwich to continue the work that he has developed at the James Paget, but it does mean that patients and their families will have to travel further for treatment.

Increasing specialisation and centralisation of services makes it increasingly difficult to attract Consultants to the smaller District Hospitals. This has been the case at the James Paget. Mr. Sethian, Associate Specialist in Urology, was appointed Locum Consultant after Andrew Simpson left and a few other locums were appointed. Fortunately, Mr. Suresh Gupta joined the staff as Consultant Urologist at the end of 2006.

In the last 25 years, Urology has become a much more specialised service, with the introduction of new techniques and investigations. Rapid access clinics have been established and Urological Nurse Specialists have been introduced who do much of the basic investigation and have played a large part in improving communication with the patients. Now, about 75% of urological operations are done as day procedures, but the centralisation of major cancer operations in Norwich has made it difficult to find new Consultants, and this threatens the future of the department.

Paediatric Surgery

Paediatric surgery involves surgery on babies and children. Complex paediatric surgery is restricted to children's hospitals and Paediatric Centres. However, such operations as circumcisions, operations for hernias, hydrocoeles and undescended testicles have always been done at the James Paget. These procedures are done as day cases. In the past, many circumcisions were done as it was thought to be the right thing to do. Now it is done only for tight foreskins, so the number done is much less than previously. Forty years ago operations for undescended testicles were done when the boys were reaching puberty, and often this was preceded by a trial of hormones. Thirty years ago most children had the operation performed when they were three to four years old, and this continued when the hospital first opened. However, in the 1980s work showed that results were better when the operation was performed in the first two years of life, so this policy was adopted at the James Paget.

Pyloric stenosis is a condition in which the outlet from the stomach is narrowed due to thickening of the muscle here. Babies usually present between the ages of 4 and 6 weeks old, and this requires a small operation to divide this muscle. This continues to be done at the James Paget and we are fortunate that a number of Consultant Anaesthetists are trained in Paediatric Anaesthesia.

Increasing specialisation in Paediatric surgery has decreed that all District Hospitals wishing to do Paediatric surgery should detail one surgeon to oversee or do all operations on children and preferably on designated lists. This came into force in the 1990s when Mr. Sansom took over this responsibility and gradually the other surgeons gave up this type of surgery, although with great reluctance, as one had been trained at Great Ormond Street Hospital for Children and another had worked at Liverpool Children's Hospital. Later, national criteria became tighter, requiring the named surgeon to be accredited in Paediatric surgery. Mr. Schneider had this qualification, so, when he arrived, he took over the responsibility of operating on children. This was taken over by Mr. Murray when Mr. Schneider left, and subsequently by Mr. Lal. He had done his Paediatric surgical training at the Postgraduate Institute of Medical Education and Research, Chandigarh in India, as well as in England.

ENT Surgery

ENT surgery involves surgery on the ear, nose and throat. When the hospital opened, there were two Consultant Surgeons, who also had sessions at the Norfolk and Norwich Hospital. Mr. Tony Couldry retired in 1991 and Mr. Khush Mangat in 1992. Mr. 'Prem' Premachandra joined the hospital in 1990 and Mr. Peter Prinsley in 1996. Mr. Junaid Hanif started in 2005.

With increasing specialisation and shorter working hours for junior doctors, it became increasingly difficult to run the department, but this was overcome by Mr. Premachandra arranging with Norfolk and Norwich Hospital to have a joint department for ENT. It resulted in him having sessions at the Norfolk and Norwich and, when Mr. Prinsley was appointed, he also had sessions in Norwich. In exchange, Norwich Consultants have held sessions at the James Paget. Norwich has also shared cover for emergencies during the week, but at weekends the ENT Department is closed at the James Paget and all emergencies are sent to Norwich if they cannot be dealt with in the Accident and Emergency Department.

Mr. Premachandra has a special interest in Head and Neck Malignancy and has extended his surgery to the thyroid and parotids. He has also continued the joint clinics with the radiotherapists which used to be held in the District before the hospital was built.

When the hospital opened, the waiting list for ENT operations was well over a thousand, with most waiting for over a year. Now, no patient waits longer than six months. Length of stay after operations has reduced dramatically, e.g. from five days to one day after removing tonsils. This operation is now done much less frequently than in the past. It is interesting to note that Mr. Allington, who was ENT Surgeon at the Yarmouth General for many years, used to perform a dozen tonsillectomies each Friday morning and the children were taken home by their parents in the afternoon. He admitted only those with red hair, as he felt they had an increased risk of bleeding.

The introduction of CT Scans to detect pathology in the sinuses has altered surgical management significantly. Mr. Prinsley has a special interest in ear surgery and, as ENT Regional Tutor, has played a big part in improving the training of young ENT Surgeons in the Region. In the early days, the Department had two Senior House Surgeons and one Registrar. It now has the equivalent of three Senior House Surgeons and two Specialist Registrars.

A major blow to the ENT Department was the loss of its ward without any real discussion. Not only did they lose their in-patient base in the hospital, but the specialised nursing expertise built up over many years was no longer centralised. Fortunately, the Tracheostomy Specialist Nursing Team remains and is responsible for over-seeing the management of patients with tracheotomies which may be temporary or permanent. This team was one of the first in the hospital to win a Government Charter Mark.

Eye Department

Based on an account by Peter Black

Prior to December 1981, the Ophthalmic Services in the Great Yarmouth and Waveney Health District had been supplied on three half-day clinics, each run by a different consultant, from the West Norwich Hospital. Originally, it was intended that the Eye Department at the then District General Hospital would be incorporated in phase 2 of the DGH in 1984. Political pressure, however, was such that this was moved forward and the Eye Department was incorporated into phase 1 of the District General Hospital and it opened its doors to in-patients on lst February 1982.

Peter Black was appointed at the end of July 1981 to take up his post as Consultant Ophthalmologist to the District General Hospital and to the East Anglian School for the Deaf and Partially Sighted, with effect from 1st November; but he spent the summer compiling equipment lists, etc., in order for the Eye Department to be fully operational as soon as phase 1 of the DGH was commissioned. He was joined by Dr. Geoffrey Hurst, a former Ormesby General Practitioner, who was a Clinical Assistant who had worked with the Ophthalmic Consultants from the Norfolk and Norwich Hospital. Two Senior House Officers were appointed for 1st February 1982. Sister Gill Parker, an existing Theatre Sister, was seconded for a fairly brief period to the West Norwich Hospital to acquire the necessary skills for ophthalmic surgery to be carried out and Sister Glynis Norman was appointed as Ward Sister to the Eye Ward and brought her considerable administrative and educational skills to bear on the many young nurses who were appointed to assist in the development of the eye services, both at ward and outpatient level. Many of these are still working today, having left to have families, and then returned. The Outpatients Clinic was under the control of Sister Sue Richards, who was the General Surgical Outpatient Sister.

The initial complement was 12 beds in two 6-bedded bays: 6 male and 6 female; with two side wards and one isolation bed in Ward 17, giving a total of 15 adult beds and 4 paediatric beds in the Children's Ward. The planned full complement of medical staff came about on 26th July 1982 with the appointment of Mr. Ali Amanat; a former colleague of Peter Black's when they worked as Registrars together at Addenbrooke's Hospital, Cambridge.

Over the years, new Consultants have been appointed and some have left. Mr. Tony Morgan was a long-term locum from September 1993 to March 1996. Mr. Nicholas Watson arrived in 1996 and is still here. Mr. Conal Hurley started in January 1999 but returned to Ireland in February 2001. Miss Kay Belfer started in April 2002 but left four years later and Mr. Tom Butler joined the Department in June 2005. In addition, Miss Bridget Mulholland has a joint appointment with the Norfolk and Norwich University Hospital and started in November 2004.

The Department investigates and treats all eye diseases and conditions, with the exception of those that are exceptionally rare and require the services of super-specialists. Up until the mid to late 90s, most ophthalmologists were general ophthalmologists and were able to manage most of the common medical and surgical conditions presenting to them. This included relatively uncommon conditions. With the advent of sub-specialisation, this has changed considerably and now all new Consultants on appointment have less general experience than before, but do have enhanced experience in one or two relatively narrow fields.

In the early days, other than orbital and rare paediatric conditions, the Consultants and the District General Hospital dealt with most problems that presented themselves to the Eye Department. These included retinal detachments, patients requiring corneal grafts as well as those requiring cataract surgery, and it should be noted that there was a considerable amount of trauma prior to the introduction of the seat-belt law in the 1980s.

Then, as now, the commonest surgical procedure carried out within the Ophthalmic Department was cataract surgery. In 1982, cataract surgery was carried out by the intra-capsular method. This involved removing the lens, including its capsular bag, almost always under general anaesthetic, and with a length of stay in hospital of 5–7 days, some of which was generated by the need to protect beds from the ravages of the physicians. It was common then for operating lists to have three cataract operations plus one eyelid procedure: that is, a total of four patients on a list; and nearly all patients were dealt with under general anaesthetic. At that time, it was unusual to insert intra-ocular lenses and there tended to be restrictions confining their use to the very elderly. There were considerable optical disadvantages to the sort of spectacle correction required following cataract surgery, and the threshold at which surgery was offered was quite high. In the ensuing years, increasing numbers of patients were offered intra-ocular lenses following cataract surgery, which were supported by the iris, a situation which occasionally meant that they fell out of place.

In 1984, there was a change in surgical technique to the extra-capsular extraction where the lens capsule was left behind, other than an opening in the front from which the lens nucleus and cortex had to be removed, and this was rapidly followed by much safer intra-ocular lens implantation, so-called posterior chamber intra-ocular lenses, which were inherently much more stable. From this time on, there was a slow move towards a day case service.

In 1991, Sister Jeanette Hipperson was appointed to lead the nursing and administrative development of the Day Case Cataract Service, at the same time as a significant change in cataract surgical technique occurred called phacoemulsification. This allowed the cataracts to be removed through a very small wound which only needed to be large enough to insert an intra-ocular lens. These wounds were considerably more stable than previously. Visual rehabilitation was much quicker and routinely cataract surgery was carried out as a day case under local anaesthetic; initially by injectable local anaesthetics around the eye. Jeanette Hipperson recruited three more experienced ophthalmic nurses to the Day Case Service, so there are now four nurses dedicated to this. Sister Annie George runs the team who operate the day unit on the days of surgery. Now, 98% of all cataract surgery is carried out on a day case basis.

Shortly after the move towards phacoemulsification – an inherently much safer form of cataract surgery – there was the development of the folding intra-ocular lens, so that by 1997 cataract surgery was carried out through incisions marginally larger than 3 mm, intra-ocular lenses were inserted folded in half and were allowed to unfold within the eye, where they were placed into the bag, creating a secure wound with visual rehabilitation which was unbelievably fast. At the same time, there was a change in anaesthetic technique, such that patients underwent their cataract surgery with the use of a few drops of local anaesthetic prior to the surgery and a little local anaesthetic within the eye during the surgery. This is now a walk-in-walk-out procedure that takes between 10 and 15 minutes and is regarded as successful in 95% of cases.

Now, ophthalmic surgery is predominantly day case surgery and usually has seven patients on a list, which is approximately double what it was when the hospital opened. There is a low morbidity, low complication rate and no need for beds. Ophthalmology has been the subject of many Government targets and this has led to a large expansion in the numbers of staff required to deliver the services in any modern eye department. In 2007, the Department has 4.5 Consultants, one Associate Specialist, 4 Staff Grade Ophthalmologists and 3 Senior House Officers.

In 1987, Alison Cliffe was appointed as a Senior Clinical Medical Officer and was subsequently converted to an Associate Specialist. Initially recruited as a General Ophthalmologist, she assumed increasing responsibilities for medical ophthalmology, in particular those patients with immunologically mediated disease and, more latterly, for the Diabetic Retinal Screening Services, which will be discussed later.

In the late 1980s and early 1990s, peripheral clinics were developed at Southwold, subsequently at Beccles and North Walsham, although the latter was finally given up as a consequence of the Norfolk and Norwich University Hospital opening up services at Cromer.

Throughout all the years, it has been possible to provide 24-hour cover for seven days a week at the James Paget University Hospital; however, that is going to change in 2009 with the advent of the European Working Time Directive. It will not be possible for Departments the size of the James Paget to provide this level of cover after that time and that will lead, almost inevitably, to some form of accommodation with the Norfolk & Norwich University Hospital, particularly at weekends.

Prior to the introduction of the seat-belt law, it was common for the ophthalmic team to be up all night repairing eye and facial lacerations. The introduction of the seat-belt law dramatically reduced the amount of serious trauma presenting to the Eye Department, and now lacerated eyes are relatively unusual, probably no more than 10 per year.

In 1987, David Wayne, Consultant Physician with a special interest in Diabetes, Madeline Borg, the Senior Medical Photographer, and Peter Black initiated a Diabetic Retinal Screening Service, based on a photographic service, held at the James Paget Hospital. The funds for this were raised from charity, notable of which was "PIGGY" (People in Gorleston and Great Yarmouth, a charity set up by Dr. Wayne and his wife). This service was never funded by the hospital. It developed to the point at which by the mid-90s it met all the criteria, other than those of audit, which would come to be imposed upon Primary Care Trusts in 2007.

This service was managed at lunchtime and provided a comprehensive retinal screening service for patients with diabetes mellitus other than those who were attending the eye clinic. It was fully integrated with the Ophthalmic Services and significant hiccups only occurred in 2006 when it became a requirement for a National Service Framework to be developed and the Screening Service was expanded to take on those of the Primary Care Trusts which had traditionally used Ipswich as their referral centre. This service now screens all diabetics from Winterton in the North to Hadleigh in the South. The development of the Diabetic Retinal Screening Service led to the only recorded drop in blind registrations in any part of Norfolk and Suffolk during the early 1990s. This was supported by public health statistics and was attributed solely to the success of the Retinal Screening Service.

The ophthalmic outpatients had always been a corridor and nothing has changed to this date. Originally intended to be four rooms only, as in all "Best Buy" hospitals, the accommodation was obsolete by the time the hospital opened its doors. Now this has expanded to the point at which it is necessary to use 8 or 9 consulting rooms at any one time and, although the number of rooms available for use has increased, the facilities have remained unchanged since the opening of the hospital in 1982, other than the acquisition of the odd room. The Eye Department is busy: upwards of 160 patients may be seen in any one day. The accommodation has been regarded as woefully inadequate for 20 years, but there is no sign of any future improvement.

In 1992, with the increasing rise of day case surgery, it became less necessary for ophthalmic beds to be available and all beds dedicated to the Eye Department were finally lost in about 2000. From then on, almost all surgery was carried out on Outpatient basis and beds are used as and when needed and often have to be planned for.

A dedicated ophthalmic theatre was opened in 2003, having been on-stream since 2002. It provides spacious, well-equipped and pleasant working conditions and is adjacent to a converted Ward 8, which is now a day case with a sitting-out area, consulting rooms and a large waiting area. This is a spectacular, and long overdue, increase in the facilities available to the Department.

It is hoped that the Ophthalmic Department at the James Paget University Hospital will retain its independence. There is, however, an issue about 24-hour, 7-day-a-week services, and these relate to the need to comply with the European Working Time Directive of 48 hours per week for all members of medical staff by 2009. It will just not be possible to maintain this level of service after that date and it is almost certain that an arrangement will be needed with the Norfolk and Norwich University Hospital for weekend on-call services, but this is still the subject of ongoing discussion and no agreements have yet been reached. It is probable that sooner or later there will be some interlocking and rationalisation of services with Norwich; this is inevitable with the current political climate and the way that Strategic Health Authorities are likely to plan services for the future.

An example of the increasing cost and specialisation is the management of Macular Degeneration. This will be an expensive business, with increasingly important intra-vitreal drugs coming on-line. Nevertheless, it will be something that the public will require of their Primary Care Trust, and bids are in for development of this service.

Since the opening of the hospital, a first-class Ophthalmic Department has been built up and with new equipment and techniques there has been a revolution in the ways in which eye patients are managed. Gone are the days when a cataract operation involved the patient needing a general anaesthetic and staying in hospital for five to seven days. Now the operation is done under local anaesthetic, the beds are replaced by comfortable armchairs and the patient returns home within a few hours. In addition, the results are far better. The Diabetic Retinal Screening Service was established well before there was any recognised National Screening Service and has been a shining example of what can be done by determination and charity money.

In 1982, just after Peter Black had been appointed Consultant Ophthalmic Surgeon, he was told by a senior member of the Regional Medical Officer's Department who had been at Medical School with him that the Ophthalmic Department at his new hospital was not expected to last longer than two years and he should start looking for another job!

Orthopaedic Department

Tony Ashford Hodges and David Burgess had been Consultant Orthopaedic Surgeons in the District for many years before the District General Hospital opened. Cold Orthopaedic Surgery was performed at the little hospital in Gorleston and emergencies were done at Yarmouth General and Lowestoft Hospitals. Ken Stewart had spent most of his professional life in Africa and came to the District in the early 1980s. George Heyse Moore replaced Tony Ashford Hodges in 1983 and Robert Jones took over from Ken Stewart in 1987. Raj Nadarajan replaced David Burgess in 1993 and he has a special interest in Paediatric Orthopaedic Surgery. Christopher Johnson Nurse and John Petri were appointed in 1994. John Petri's special interest is in Trauma Surgery. Mr. Venalainen worked here for one year between 2001 and 2002. Mr. Andrew Elliott started a long-term locum in 2003 and is now a Trust Surgeon. In 2005, Harsh Gupta was appointed, and Mr. Alban Bowers has been working as a locum since 2006. At present there are four Associate Specialists and two staff doctors in the Department.

The Department covers the whole range of elective Orthopaedic operations and deals with emergences which are usually the result of falls and road traffic accidents. Like all branches of medicine, it is becoming increasingly specialized, so occasionally some patients are referred to Norwich or to other centres.

Over the last 25 years, the main changes have been the shorter stays that patients spend in hospital after surgery and the application of the MRI Scanner to diagnosing knee, back and other problems. The arthroscope is used more frequently to examine the inside of joints as well as to perform operative manoeuvres such as the removal of menisci (cartilages) from the knee joint. This makes the procedure much less painful, the patient spends less time in hospital and returns to normal activities quicker.

The MRI Scanner gives excellent definition of the knee joint, helping to define damage to the ligaments, menisci and the bone. However, it is less reliable in patients older than 50 years of age, as age-related changes can obscure the picture. The MRI Scan is the investigation of choice to investigate the back, and any bone, disc or tumour pressing on the spinal cord or nerves is easily detected. Long gone are the days when myelograms were done which involved injecting contrast media though a needle in the back and into the fluid around the spinal cord.

In the 1990s, George Heyse Moore developed mini-discectomy, which was the management of prolapsed discs through small incisions in the back, and he invented instruments to do the surgery. He also worked with Dr. Willy Notcutt to provide a back service for people with back problems. Unfortunately, his early retirement through health reasons stopped these operations, but since 2006 Mr. Crawford and Mr. Lutchman, Orthopaedic Surgeons from the Norfolk and Norwich University Hospital, have been doing clinics and operating sessions at the James Paget for people requiring back surgery. This has been a most successful development, appreciated by all concerned.

When the hospital opened, total replacement of the knee joint was not performed very frequently, but, with the introduction of better prostheses, this operation is performed much more frequently than before and nearly as commonly as total hip replacements. Another development has been the unicompartmental knee operation, whereby the medial femoral condyle and the corresponding surface on the tibia (the inner part of the knee joint) are removed and replaced with artificial parts. This is a highly successful operation. Initially, patients stayed in for four to five days, but now stay for just one postoperative night, having had physiotherapy four hours after surgery.

Many of the patients having orthopaedic operations are elderly and this makes postoperative recovery prolonged and difficult. In order to prevent the blockage of the orthopaedic beds, it was decided to develop an orthopaedic rehabilitation ward at Lowestoft Hospital. This was opened in 1998 and was named the Gwen Baker Unit; but its functions were transferred back to the James Paget in 2006.

John Petri has been a key player in the development of orthopaedic surgery for trauma and it is unfortunate that his expertise will be lost when he moves to Switzerland in July. Over recent years he has developed dual-theatre operating whereby, while he is operating on one patient in one theatre, a second Anaesthetist is preparing the next patient in the adjoining theatre suite. This has enabled him to operate on many more patients on an operating list, but it is expensive in terms of theatres and staff. As a result, dual-Anaesthetist operating is being tried, whereby a second Anaesthetist prepares the next patient in the anaesthetic room of the same theatre while the operation on the preceding patient is being finished. This system seems to work well and does not tie up two theatres for one operating list.

Over the years many different models of hips and knees have been developed. They are not only expensive in themselves but all require different sets of instruments for them to be inserted. This makes it very expensive if each surgeon wants to use a different type of model and it can be confusing for the operating assistants. To get around these problems, the Surgeons are agreeing to restrict the number of joint models used.

Arthroscopy is used increasingly frequently to look inside and perform various operative procedures within joints. It results in less pain than an open procedure and leads to quicker recovery.

Robert Jones feels that the main advances are the result of better surgery and better rehabilitation. This has resulted in the stay after a total hip replacement reducing from 10–14 days to 7–10 days. Infection is always a problem after any surgery, but is particularly disastrous after joint surgery. He feels that this has not really increased over time.

Joint Review Nurses run clinics assessing the results of the operations, so freeing up the surgeons to do other activities. Although they are doing a good job recording the results, the computer software is failing to analyse and display the outcomes. This seems to be a problem affecting all aspects of orthopaedic surgery, leading to difficulty in audit and assessing the outcomes of their surgery. It is something which needs to be addressed.

In addition to John Petri leaving at the end of July 2007, three other Orthopaedic Surgeons will be leaving in the next two years, namely Christopher Johnson Nurse, Robert Jones and possibly Raj Nadarajan. This will be a great challenge for the existing staff and the new Consultants, but it does provide the opportunity to look at the Department as a whole and to plan for the future.

Day Case Surgery

Hospitals are dangerous and expensive places, so the shorter the time spent in them the better. In the 1980s, the James Paget had the highest proportion of patients having day case surgery in East Anglia. Since then, the number and types of operations which are done as day cases has increased. But to be successfully done the operations must have a low complication rate, the patient and his/her family must be well prepared and given good supplies of pain-relieving tablets and instructions what to do if there is a problem. There needs to be a point of reference at the hospital for this and the patient's GP needs to have been informed of what has been done. Advances in anaesthesia have meant that patients have fewer side effects and can leave hospital much earlier. In addition, the operation site is usually infiltrated with local anaesthetic and many operations are done completely under local anaesthesia or a nerve block.

When the Hospital was opened it had a Day and Emergency Ward, which was also known as Ward 22. The principle was that patients having day case surgery would occupy it during the day time and, in the evening, all emergency admissions would be admitted to it. The advantages of this were that all the emergencies were centralised into one area of the hospital and their admission would not disturb patients in the other wards. The only problem was that, in the morning, many emergency admissions – mainly medical patients – were still in the Day and Emergency Ward, as there no beds for them in other parts of the hospital. Consequently, many patients being admitted for day surgery could not be admitted. Eventually, it was decided that emergencies had to be admitted to the general wards. For much of this time the person in charge was Sister Murphy, who would stand no nonsense.

In order to try and improve the throughput of patients, it was decided to have some short-stay beds. This would enable patients who were not fit to go home after day surgery, for one reason or another, to stay in overnight. Also, it more or less guaranteed a bed to patients who needed to stay in for one to two nights, rather than subjecting them to the lottery of trying to obtain a bed on the general wards.

With the decision to move the Intensive Care Ward to Ward 22, there was the opportunity to build a dedicated Day Ward. It was officially opened on 21st October 2003 by Mr. Noel Johnson and was called the Oulton Unit. The nurses specifically asked that he should be the person to open the Unit because of his years of service to the hospital and his concern for the nurses' welfare.

The Oulton Unit has four bays and two side rooms catering for 31 patients at a time. To make sure that it would deal with only day cases, it was provided with only trolleys, but before long it was being used to take the overflow of medical and surgical emergencies (Déjà vu?). Now the Unit has 21 trolleys and 10 beds, which are for the admission of surgical emergencies which cannot be taken on the main wards. They are also used for patients who need to stay in overnight. As a result, there is sometimes no room for a day case. Every effort is made not to cancel an admission, but it may mean that the patient has to wait in an armchair until a trolley is available. These chairs are also used to assess ENT and Eye patients.

The unit is open from Monday morning until 1 pm Saturday. To accommodate these extended hours, the nurses have had to change their working schedules from 10 hours to seven and a half hours a shift. This has meant that, whereas a part-time nurse could do 20 hours' duty in two days, now she/he has to spread this over three days. The staffing consists of one charge nurse, two sisters, eighteen nurses, one health care assistant, two housekeepers, two ward clerks and two domestics. In spite of all these pressures, it is a happy unit and morale is good.

Charnwood Suite

The Charnwood Suite is a 9-bedded unit for private patients and can be used by members of staff if there is a vacant bed. One of the rooms is used for pre-operative assessments and postoperative checks. It was opened in May 1990 by Mr. Noel Johnson as a 6-bedded unit. It was intended that it would be a temporary place while a new building housing 26 beds to the north of the main hospital was planned and built. Sadly, in spite of a great deal of work being done on the project, it never came to fruition. It was enlarged to provide a total of nine beds in 1995. The first ward manager was Rosemary Smalley, who left to take charge of the Intensive Care Unit.

Up to 30 Consultants have patients in the Charnwood Suite from time to time. Mainly, they are Surgical Consultants and the revenue generated each year is in the region of £350,000. This is included in the Trust's budget and is enough to run a 34-bedded ward for six months.

The staff consists of three sisters, 12 staff nurses and one housekeeper. Some of them work part-time. They have the advantage of working in most pleasant surroundings and the work is very varied. Approximately 1,000 patients are treated here each year.

Central treatment Suite

Based on article from Tina Dyble

The functions of the Central Treatment Suite are to:

- Undertake minor surgery for both in-patients and outpatients.
- Give evidence-based practice to both in-patients and outpatients with regard to wound care.
- Teach students best practice in wound care.
- Give advice to patients, carers, medical and nursing staff concerning wound care, pressure ulceration and catheter insertion and aftercare.

Nurse-led clinics are undertaken within the Department for specialist treatment and Central Treatment Suite staff also work within the Dermatology Department several days a week.

The Central Treatment Suite has been headed by seven Sisters over the last 25 years. The first was Sister Jan Austin, who is now Nurse Consultant in Pain Relief. Maureen Reeves was next, and she later moved into procurement within the NHS. Sister Valentine then took over, to be followed by Sister Samantha Mann, who left CTS to head Urodynamics. Sister Yvonne Coleman then took over as head of CTS and then Sister Tracey Noakes. Sister Samantha Mann then returned for a second spell of managing the department until she left to undertake a research project and she now works locally as a Practice Nurse. Sister Tina Dyble took over as head of the Central Treatment Suite in 1998 and remains in this position.

Currently, there are seven members of the Central Treatment Suite team:

- Senior Sister, who has her B.Sc., is undertaking her M.Sc. in Tissue Viability.
- Three Senior Staff nurses: two are undertaking their B.Sc. and one is working towards her Diploma.
- Two Enrolled Nurses, one of whom is working towards her Diploma.
- One Auxiliary Nurse.

The number of staff working within the Central Treatment Suite over the years has increased slightly. The number of clients passing through the department has increased significantly. In 1994, around 800 patients passed through the Department a year. Now approximately 1,300 patients pass through the Department annually. This does not include the work undertaken within the Dermatology Department.

Various changes have been made to the Department over the past 25 years. The Central Treatment Suite started with five treatment rooms, a light therapy room, a sluice, a preparation room, a store cupboard and an office. The office was changed into a consultation room/reception for Pre-Assessment of patients being admitted for surgery and has now been converted into a further treatment room for our nurse-led clinics and outpatients treatments. The light therapy room has been dismantled and the equipment moved into the Dermatology Department. This room has been converted into an office for the Central Treatment Suite Sister. The store cupboard was altered to allow for storage and for use as an office for the Breast Care Nurses. Once they moved, the room was changed and made into a further waiting area and store cupboard, which is currently used to house dental equipment. An additional storage/changing area was made by dividing one of the treatment rooms. The preparation room now houses a small office area containing a desk and computer which is used by staff to undertake administration work.

The Central Treatment Suite has had many changes within its working practices over the past 25 years. Initially, the Central Treatment Suite was seen as a department where patients came to have dressings undertaken by the ward staff, who would accompany them to the Department. Endoscopy shared the department until they moved into their own space at the other end of Ward 22. The Pain Clinic used to be held here until it had its own area. Urodynamics was also undertaken within the Central Treatment Suite, until it moved into two rooms within the main outpatient department. The Breast Care Nurses had their office within the Central Treatment Suite for many years, until they appointed another member to their team and were then given a bigger office downstairs. Pre-assessment also had an office within the Central Treatment Suite for many years until their workload outgrew the room they used and they moved into their own department near the mortuary. Minor operations for outpatients were carried out within the Central Treatment Suite and PUVA treatment for Dermatology patients and all this has moved to the new Dermatology Department. Dental clinics are now carried out within the Department and minor operations on surgical patients continue, along with various procedures such as Lumbar Punctures and Paracentesis.

Today, Central Treatment Suite staff do all of the dressings within the Department, but ward staff no longer accompany their patients. Each week the Department undertakes a total of 18 outpatient clinics, which include minor operations clinics, nurse-led clinics, chest drain clinics, dental clinics and wound care clinics. The Central Treatment Suite staff also assist with an additional 10 clinics per week within the Dermatology Department and do most of the Supra Pubic Catheter changes within the Trust.

Nursing students are allocated a 2-week placement within the Department and Medical students visit the Department for various clinics and procedures. Teaching is undertaken via the in-house educational programme on wound care issues and catheterisation. In addition, the Central Treatment Suite runs a link nurse service four times a year to ensure Trust staff keep up to date with new developments, etc.

The Central Treatment Suite has proven to be very successful in giving patients the best evidence-based wound care treatments from staff who are specialists within the field of Tissue Viability. Patients are keen to attend the Central Treatment Suite, as they see this area as having the ability to address their problems. However, this success has also been its greatest failure, as ward staff have become deskilled at undertaking dressings. The Central Treatment Suite is not open at weekends and so treatment for patients at this time becomes limited, which leads to difficulties in ensuring treatment plans are successfully implemented. A solution to this problem would be to open at weekends, but this has always been refused due to financial limitations within the Trust.

There are major plans being implemented in relation to Tissue Viability within the Trust. Ward staff are to undertake the majority of the dressings on the ward and when the ward refurbishments which are planned have been completed each ward will have a treatment room in which to undertake their dressings. Central Treatment Suite staff will become a peripatetic team. They will see patients on the ward to give advice and guidance to both staff and patients. New nurse-led clinics are being developed for complex wounds so that GPs can directly refer their patients with problem wounds. The Department is currently undertaking a huge educational programme for all staff within the Trust to attend, so that they are able to start undertaking dressings.

The Central Treatment Suite is a remarkable Department. Originally it was to provide an area in which all ward dressings were to be done and minor operations could be performed. These functions still occur, but over the 25 years many other departments have started here, outgrown the facilities and now have even larger Departments, such as the Endoscopy Suite, The Dermatology Department, The Preadmission Clinic and the Pain Relief Clinic. Another remarkable fact is that, of the seven members of staff, Tina Dyble already has a degree and is working for her Masters and four of the other six members of staff are working for a degree or a diploma. This must be the most academic collection of nurses in the Trust.

Dermatology

Dermatology deals with skin diseases and disorders, some of which are malignant. Many general medical diseases manifest themselves with changes in the skin, so a good dermatologist needs to have a good knowledge of Medicine.

When the hospital opened, the Dermatology Service was provided by Dr. A. W. Mackenzie, Consultant Dermatologist at the Norfolk and Norwich, who did two sessions weekly in this Health District. He was assisted by Dr. David Stuart, a GP in Yarmouth, who had been a Hospital Practitioner since the early 1960s. Dr. Robert Graham was appointed as the District's first own Dermatologist in October 1987 and commenced work on 1st February 1988. Dr. Ingrid Salvary was appointed Associate Specialist in October 1995 and Consultant Dermatologist in December 1996. Dr. Elvy has been a Hospital Practitioner in the Department since 1975 and an Associate Specialist since 2005. Paul Aukland had done operating sessions for the Department since 2003. Dr. Sandy Anderson helps in the Lowestoft Clinic and Dr. Sue Lock in the Beccles Clinic. Dr. Ian Yates has been helping in the Department as a Hospital Practitioner since 2006 and Dr. Jams has been Staff Grade Doctor since 2004. In the past, Dr. Timms, Dr. Nagpal and Dr. Ahmed have been Hospital Practitioners.

In the last 20 years, the work of the Department has expanded enormously. The removal of most skin lesions, which used to be done by the General Surgeons, is now done by the Dermatologists, and a number of lesions are frozen. There is a well-laid-down plan dealing with skin malignancies and there have been big campaigns drawing attention to the dangers of sun exposure leading to skin malignancy. Over the years, there has been an exponential increase in demand for dermatological services, partly associated with an ageing population, but the number of in-patients has decreased.

In January 2003, the Department moved into its newly built dedicated dermatological building where outpatients are seen, operations are performed and teaching takes place. The dermatological training of the Medical Students at the University of East Anglia is shared equally between the Norfolk and Norwich University and the James Paget University Hospitals.

Karen Peat and Jill Rainsey were appointed Nurse Care Specialists in 2001. They have become Independent Nurse Prescribers, which enables them to run a number of Nurse-led Clinics and procedures such as Photodynamic Therapy, Cryotherapy, Patch Testing, Acne Clinics, Punch Biopsies, Leg Ulcer Management and Topical Therapies.

General Medicine

The first Consultant Physician to be appointed to the coast was Dr. Ronnie Gibbs, who was a General Practitioner in Lowestoft. He was appointed in 1956 as Assistant Physician to do four sessions weekly. Later, he was promoted to Consultant Physician and continued with his general practice until, some years later, he was given more sessions. In addition, some Norwich Consultant Physicians visited the coastal hospitals once or twice weekly. Dr. Wyllie Beattie and Dr. John Adams, Consultant Geriatricians at the Norfolk and Norwich Hospital, used to visit Northgate Hospital weekly to see the elderly patients. Unfortunately, the Geriatricians and Physicians were not on speaking terms with each other.

Dr. David Wayne started work as Consultant Physician in February 1974. A condition of his appointment was that, as the weekly visits to Northgate Hospital of Drs. Beattie and Adams would cease, he would have three months' training in Geriatrics, and he did this with Dr. John Agate in Ipswich.

Dr. Wayne did not like the isolated black holes into which the long-stay elderly were committed in Ipswich, nor in Northgate Hospital, nor the quality of Junior Staff who could be induced to serve in them. At Northgate, for instance, there was a senior house officer who had so settled in after five years in the job that he had built up a caravan-letting business in his spare time. His ward rounds were a cheerful walk-through before a cup or two of coffee.

Both Dr. Gibbs and Dr. Wayne thought it would be far better to integrate General Medicine and Geriatrics. John Agate and most of the Geriatric Establishment felt that integration would not work because, where it had been tried previously, the "Integrated Physician" soon tended to neglect the elderly in favour of the more pacey Acute General Medicine. Both Dr. Gibbs and Dr. Wayne enjoyed Geriatric Care and achieved a much better standard of junior staff to work the combined service, and they soon found grudging support for what happened – a better service for all patients. They achieved a better throughput of patients per allotted geriatric bed than anywhere else in East Anglia, except for Bury St. Edmunds.

Dr. Wayne had a particular interest in the management of Diabetes and over the years developed Endocrinology, which deals with disorders of such glands as the pancreas, thyroid, parathyroid, adrenal glands, etc. Over the next few years, other Consultant Physicians would be appointed with special interests such as heart, gastroenterology, respiratory and rheumatology, but each would have to devote a part of their time to looking after the elderly.

Wolf Grabau was appointed Consultant Physician and Cardiologist in 1978 and Stuart Hishon as Consultant Physician and Gastroenterologist in 1981. Both had a commitment to share the care of the elderly with Drs. Gibbs and Wayne, and when the new hospital opened these four Consultant Physicians were responsible for running all the services for the medical patients in the District. This was a big improvement from the 19 years that Dr. Gibbs had covered this responsibility with the help of some visiting Physicians and Geriatricians from Norwich and from the three years that Drs. Gibbs and Wayne had worked alone.

For many years the Physicians continued to look after medical and elderly patients at Northgate and Lowestoft Hospitals.

In 1983, David Ellis was appointed Consultant Physician and Respiratory Physician, taking over from Dr. Joseph Salmon, who had retired on 31st March 1983 as Chest Physician to the Lowestoft and Great Yarmouth Hospitals for nearly 30 years. In 1986, Peter Forster was appointed as Consultant Physician and Rheumatologist, replacing Dr. Gibbs, who had served as Physician for 30 years. Dr. Forster was the last of the Physicians to be appointed who was also required to have a responsibility for looking after the elderly. For nearly the next 10 years, the remaining Physicians continued unchanged and without additions. Each continued to develop their specialty as well as looking after the elderly, but there was increasing feeling that perhaps they should appoint a Geriatrician to help advance this field of medicine and, with this in mind, Dr. Ken Rhodes was appointed in 1994.

Whilst each specialty was becoming more specialised, all were still part of the Department of Medicine and covered rotas for the admission of medical emergencies, but it will be easier to trace the development of the Department by looking at each specialty in turn.

Diabetes and Endocrinology

Diabetes mellitus is a condition in which the body fails to produce sufficient insulin (a hormone produced by the pancreas) or does not respond to it, so causing the sugar level in the blood to rise, resulting in the patient passing increasing amounts of urine and feeling thirsty. If untreated, the patient may pass into a coma. The condition is associated with changes in the blood vessels, which may affect vision, the function of the kidneys, the blood pressure, the nerves and the blood vessels to the limbs, so resulting in poor blood supply and ulcers. Although the condition can present in children, when daily injections of insulin are required, in the majority of patients it presents in the middle-aged and the elderly and is often associated with obesity. Such patients may be controlled by simple dietary measures, although some need the addition of oral medication and some require insulin injections.

Clearly the consequences of diabetes may affect the whole body and Dr. Wayne set about providing supportive services, such as chiropody, for these patients, and in this he was greatly helped by the appointment of the Nurse Care Specialists Louise Stanton (she was based in the hospital and clinics) and Chris Allen, who was based in the community. He established an adolescent clinic with Dr. Tony Edelsten and a pregnancy and preconception diabetic service with Mr. Pozyczka. Patients with erectile dysfunction were referred to the urologists and referral standards were made with the Norwich Renal Physicians for managing diabetic patients who developed renal failure. Many of these patients did not require specialist hospital attention, so he educated and encouraged the General Practitioners to look after their patients and referring them to the hospital if there were problems or for special monitoring, such as retinal photography, which is done at least once a year on all diabetic patients to assess the blood vessels to see whether any treatment is required. This screening was set up with Peter Black, Ophthalmologist, and Madeleine Borg, Medical Photographer, with funding from PIGGY (People in Gorleston and Great Yarmouth, a charity set up by Dr. Wayne and his wife).

David Wayne claims never to have been an Endocrinologist nor a 'Diabetologist', for after House Jobs he trained in Cardiology, Respiratory Medicine, Neurology and Metabolic Medicine. Nevertheless, he was a first-rate General Physician and set up the basis of a good Department. If he had more advanced Endocrine and Diabetic problems, he referred the patients to Norwich, where he found the Endocrinologists always most understanding and helpful.

Nigel Huston succeeded David Wayne in September 1998 and has continued the development of the diabetic service. Feet continue to be a problem in diabetics, as these patients may have impaired circulation and this, coupled with poor sensation in some, may lead to ulcers. It is, therefore, essential that they have good foot care, access to good chiropodists and well-fitting shoes. Dr. Huston is keen to run joint clinics with a vascular surgeon, but so far this is still a dream. Dr. Jo Randall joined the Department in January 2007 and, apart from her general endocrinology work, she is running a joint antenatal diabetes clinic and joint adolescent diabetes clinic.

Geriatric Medicine

This involves the care of the elderly. They have the same diseases as younger people, but just more of them. In addition, the memory begins to fail, and catastrophically in some. For many years the Consultant Physicians decided against having a separate Geriatric Service as Consultant Geriatricians were in short supply and junior medical staff were not attracted to the specialty. In addition, Drs. Gibbs and Wayne enjoyed looking after the elderly and they felt they could provide a far better service with it integrated with General Medicine and its increasing specialties. Nevertheless, Dr. Ken Rhodes was appointed the first Consultant Geriatrician in 1994, but he left for a post in Bromley, Kent, three years later.

There was a Day Hospital for the Elderly at Northgate Hospital, which was opened on 30th February 1978. This took the pressure off the relatives at home and was a day out for the individuals, where they met socially with others, had a good meal and had the opportunity of being assessed and treated for various conditions. The unit was just as important, if not more so, for the individual who lived alone. This Day Hospital was the first of three planned for the Great Yarmouth and Waveney Health District and it was eventually closed just over 20 years later. The next one would be at the new District General Hospital and the third would be built in the southern part of the District. Because of overspending in the mid 1980s, the one at the James Paget was closed and was later turned into a Medical Outpatient Department.

On 1st April 1995, the Geriatric Rehabilitation Unit was opened. It was the inspiration of Drs. Ellis and Forster and was a significant advance in Geriatric Care, and was rather sumptuously done. It brought together the medical and nursing staff, the physiotherapists and occupational therapists and was adjacent to their departments. It also took on some surgical patients, but the surgeons felt that the patients had to be very fit before they could be transferred to the unit. Unfortunately, with the opening of the Stroke Unit and the closure of the GP Unit at Northgate in 2006, many of the staff transferred to the Stroke Unit and were replaced by some of the staff from Northgate. The Rehabilitation Unit is now overseen by GPs and its rehabilitation function has diminished.

Dr. Rhodes left in 1997 and Dr. Peter Harrison was appointed as Locum Geriatric Physician soon after. Fortunately, he was encouraged to stay and he has produced further improvements, especially the building of the Rehabilitation Unit and the development of the Stroke Unit, which opened in 2006. Here, all patients with a stroke are nursed on one ward (the old Ward 15), and there are protocols for the rapid investigation – which usually involves a CT Scan to assess the extent and type of stroke – and management of the patient. With this centralisation, there is the development of greater knowledge and skills from the many professionals who look after these patients, such as nurses, physiotherapists, occupational therapists, social workers, doctors, etc.

Gastroenterology

Gastroenterology involves the study and management of patients who have problems with their gastro-intestinal tract, liver, gall bladder, pancreas and spleen. Stuart Hishon was the first Gastroenterologist to be appointed to the Great Yarmouth and Waveney Health District and he started work in 1981. Until that time all the gastroscopies and colonoscopies were done by the four surgeons, and they continued to do this work. Dr. Hishon introduced Endoscopic Retrograde Cholangio-Pancreatography (ERCP), which uses a flexible telescope like a gastroscope through which a tube can be passed to inject substances to give X-ray pictures of the bile and pancreatic ducts. In addition, instruments can be passed through the endoscope to take biopsies, to cut the sphincter at the end of the common bile duct, to extract stones and to insert stents, which are plastic or metal tubes to allow the bile to drain past an obstruction. ERCP needed to be done in the X-ray Department, which meant that the patient, equipment and nurses had to travel downstairs from the Endoscopy Suite on the first floor. This was never an easy move and it was often difficult fitting in with X-ray schedules. It was not until 2005 that these procedures could be done in the Endoscopy Suite, when the unit had its own X-ray equipment.

There is always a demand for a new service and soon the waiting time for a Gastroenterological outpatient appointment was nine months. To help with this, Dr. Hishon introduced a Rapid Access Gastroscopy Service whereby GPs could refer patients directly for gastroscopy without the patient being seen in the Outpatients Department. The GP needed to fill in a pro-forma giving details about the patient and it was understood that this was purely a diagnostic service. If no cause was found for the patient's symptoms, it was up to the GP to investigate the patient further. The service proved so popular that soon there was a long waiting list for it. A study of the results showed that restricting the urgent referrals to patients who had difficulty in swallowing, a recent loss of appetite or upper abdominal pain in patients over the age of 40 years, the system was manageable and serious pathology was usually found and could be diagnosed early.

Most endoscopies at that time were done under some sedation and it was possible for some patients to be over-sedated. To check on this, Dr. Hishon introduced simple monitoring by having a device on the finger which measured the pulse rate and the level of oxygen in the blood.

Bleeding from the oesophagus, stomach or duodenum can be catastrophic and, although it can stop spontaneously, it may continue. It is therefore essential in the management of the patient to know from where the bleeding is coming. Thus, soon after the hospital opened, agreement was reached with all the physicians and surgeons that these patients should be gastroscoped within 24 hours of the start of the bleeding. This usually showed the cause of the bleeding and allowed decisions to be made as to whether the patient required surgery or could be treated conservatively. It was not until the mid 1990s, when Dr. Kang came, that much treatment was given down the gastroscope to try and stop the bleeding.

In 1982, Stuart suggested the formation of the East Anglian Gut Club for those interested in Gastroenterology and the first meeting was held in Norwich, at which the speaker was Sir Francis Avery Jones, the most famous Gastroenterologist of the time. The Club continues to meet twice yearly.

Unfortunately, in 1994 Stuart Hishon retired on health grounds. At that time there was a shortage of Gastroenterologists and a number of locums were appointed. Ultimately, in 1995, the hospital was fortunate in appointing Dr. Jin Kang, who had been Associate Professor of Medicine at the National University of Singapore. He had great technical skill and increased the number of endoscopic procedures which were done. He was also interested in research and produced a number of important papers while he was at the hospital. However, he was not keen on covering for general medicine and was keen to work in an academic department again. Eventually, he obtained a post at St. George's Hospital, London, in 1999.

Fortunately, by this time there were many more people looking for Consultant Gastroenterological posts and, in 1999, Dr. Crawford Jamieson and Dr. Ian Beales, who was to start six months later, were appointed on the same day.

By this time each medical specialty had its own ward and Gastroenterology had Ward 4, which was adjacent to Ward 3 and which had most of the Surgical Gastroenterological patients. Attempts had been made for many years to have medical and surgical gastroenterological patients in adjacent wards, but without success. Similarly, a Department of Gastroenterology was established to co-ordinate and promote the work of the physicians and surgeons in this field. This worked well and, from this, the new and expanded Endoscopic Unit was developed and opened on 8th July 2002. A Gastroenterological Registrar was also appointed.

With the development of the new Medical School at the University of East Anglia, Ian Beales applied for and was appointed Senior Lecturer and left the James Paget in 2001. Fortunately, he was replaced by Drs. Bernard Brett and Matthew Williams, and they were well in place when Crawford Jamieson moved to the Norfolk and Norwich University Hospital in 2004. There were some excellent applicants for his post and it was decided to appoint two: Dr. Anupama de Silva, who would help Dr. Brett with the ERCPs, among other activities, and Dr. Guy Vautier. This has resulted in an extremely strong Gastroenterological Department, although some of Dr. Brett's time has been taken up with being Director of the Emergency Division since 2005 and Dr. Vautier is to take over the running of the Emergency Assessment and Discharge Unit when another Gastroenterological Consultant is appointed later in 2007. He will continue his work on patients with Hepatitis C – a job which he has been developing over the last two years. Over recent years there have been many positive changes in Gastroenterology. There has been closer working with the Surgeons and Radiologists, more therapeutic procedures are being performed endoscopically and the throughput through the Endoscopic Unit has been improved. Further details of this work are given in the section on the Endoscopy Unit.

Endoscopy Unit

Endoscopy involves looking into structures by means of a telescope. This involves looking into the gullet, stomach, duodenum and large bowel with flexible telescopes, as well as into the urinary bladder and the trachea and bronchi, which are the passageways into the lungs.

Before the move to the new Hospital in Gorleston, Endoscopy mainly involved Gastroscopy, i.e. looking into the upper gastro-intestinal tract. At Yarmouth General Hospital it was done in a small room, which could hardly be called a theatre, next door to the main theatre. In Lowestoft, gastroscopy was done in the theatre.

With the move to the new hospital, a room in the Central Treatment Suite was taken over to house the endoscopy equipment and perform the endoscopy procedures. The endoscopists were the four general surgeons and Dr. Hishon. A group of nurses was trained to run the Endoscopy Suite and were led by Pat Wooden. Ian Walker, an operating theatre technician, oversaw the care of the instruments.

Flexible endoscopes are instruments which allow the inside of an organ, such as the stomach, to be viewed, biopsied and have other procedures performed through them. They have evolved and improved since they were invented in the 1960s. The early ones had a little light bulb at the end to produce the light, but the illumination was poor and the bulb frequently stopped working. This was replaced by having a powerful light bulb outside the endoscope and transmitting the light through fibreoptic bundles to the distal end of the instrument. Another fibreoptic bundle transmitted the picture through the endoscope, which was seen by the operator by putting his eye to the proximal end of the instrument. One other person could also see by looking through an attachment put over the eyepiece. Later, a TV camera could be attached to the eyepiece and the pictures seen by all in the Endoscopy Suite on a TV monitor. The next development was having a small chip at the end of the endoscope which picked up the picture and transferred it through the endoscope by means of wires to a box which analysed it electronically before displaying it on the TV monitor.

The lower end of the endoscope can be moved in different directions by means of wheels at the other end and channels can blow down air to distend the structure being looked at as well as removing the air. Water can be squirted down the instrument to clean the lower end of it and there are channels down which different types of instruments can be passed to perform such tasks as taking small pieces of tissue for analysis, removing polyps, squirting radio-opaque liquids into the bile and pancreatic duct so that X-ray pictures can be taken, or inserting tubes or stents to overcome an obstruction.

This single room in the Central Treatment Suite soon became too small and, in 1984, two rooms at the end of the Day and Emergency Ward were converted to give one large room – where the majority of gastroscopies and colonoscopies were performed – and a smaller one, where these procedures could also be done, as well as flexible cystoscopies, in which a very thin flexible instrument could be passed up the urethra to view the bladder. There were proper hanging cupboards for the instruments. Across the corridor was a changing room for the staff and facilities for sterilising the equipment. The hospital's WRVS paid for the refurbishment of the rooms from the profits made in their shop and trolleys which visited the wards.

The Endoscopy Suite came under the management of Ann Murphy, who ran the Day and Emergency Ward, and during this time Pat Wooden, Pat Nelson, Gabrielle Prettyman, Sylvia Craig and Gillian Hughes ran the Suite. As most of the procedures were done on outpatients, it was easy for the nurses to attend to the patients in the Day and Emergency Ward, which was adjacent to where the endoscopies were being performed. Christopher Smith was the technician, having previously worked in the main operating theatres. From 1996, Judith Dron took charge of the Unit.

With the increasing amount of work being done, it was necessary to have a full-time booking clerk, and Sandra Wadsworth, who had been doing a similar job in the X-ray Department, joined the team.

By the turn of the century, plans were being drawn up to move the Intensive Care Ward to the Day and Emergency Ward and the Endoscopy Suite was too small for the demands being made upon it. A new and much larger suite was created in Ward 16 on the ground floor and was opened by Lynn Faulds Wood on 19th September 2002. This new unit has three endoscopy rooms, two large bays where patients can be prepared and for them to recover from their procedures, a patient and relative waiting area, a room to discuss matters with patients and relatives and a large reception area. There is a large area for cleaning and sterilising the instruments, as well as a number of offices. There is a computer in each room for recording the findings of the procedure, which is linked to the hospital's main computer. The suite now has its own X-ray machine, which enables it to do the ERCPs here rather than having to transfer equipment, patients and staff to the X-ray Department. The Nd Yag Laser (purchased by Big 'C' in 1991), which was purchased for the main operating theatre block, is kept here and is used for destroying oesophageal tumours. There is also an Argon Plasma Coagulation Unit, three Diathermy Units and an Ultrasound machine.

Apart from doing all the gastroenterological endoscopic procedures here, many of which have already been described, such as oesophageal dilatation and stenting, Gastroscopy, ERCPs, PEGs, Flexible Sigmoidoscopy, Colonoscopy and Colonoscopic Polypectomies, the Urologists do flexible cystoscopies, trans-rectal biopsies of the prostate and the Chest Physicians do bronchoscopies.

Sister Judy Dron has been the Nurse Manager of the Endoscopy Suite since 1996 and, in 2003, was encouraged to attend a training course in flexible sigmoidoscopy. This has enabled her to widen her experience and now she has her own lists of flexible sigmoidoscopy. This involves passing a colonoscope up the lower bowel and taking biopsies of abnormal areas. In many patients it is done without sedation. It has become an increasingly common investigation for patients presenting with rectal bleeding or lower bowel symptoms and patients referred with these symptoms are usually booked directly onto a flexible sigmoidoscopy list.

Maintaining high standards and auditing results is most important and the Endoscopy Suite has participated in National Studies and conducted its own audits. Mr. Guruswamy has been particularly active in this regard and has shown that the completion rate of Colonoscopy by endoscopists is as good as any other unit in the country. Several members of the Department also teach endoscopy in the Region. Dr. Matt Williams is now the Consultant in overall charge of the Unit.

Cardiology

Cardiology is the study of various diseases which affect the heart, such as angina, heart attacks, heart failure, raised blood pressure, irregular heart rhythms and abnormalities of the heart valves.

Dr. Wolf Grabau was the first Cardiologist to be appointed to the Great Yarmouth and Waveney Health District in 1978. Prior to his appointment, Cardiology sessions were done by Dr. Bill Oliver, Cardiologist at the Norfolk and Norwich Hospital. Dr. Jesudason was appointed Consultant Cardiologist in 1997 and Dr. Al-Khafaji joined in 2004. His wife and family remained in Scotland, so it was not surprising that he resigned towards the end of 2006.

Historically, the cardiologist made a diagnosis by feeling the pulse, taking the blood pressure, looking at the veins in the neck, looking for fluids in the legs and listening to the heart and lungs with a stethoscope. Later, the electrocardiogram, which measured the electrical activity of the heart, gave more information. In the last 50 years, many more advanced investigations have been developed, along with many drugs and other treatments.

Among the investigations which have been introduced are the Echocardiogram, which is a non-invasive means of assessing the chambers and valves of the heart, and CT Scans give excellent definition of the heart. Coronary angiography is performed by passing a catheter through the femoral artery (the main artery to the leg) in the groin under local anaesthetic, up towards the heart, and inserting it into the arteries which supply the heart muscle. Contrast is injected into the coronary arteries and rapidly taken X-rays shows up the arteries and areas of narrowing or blockage. In many instances these narrowed areas can be dilated with a balloon passed along guide-wires inserted in the groin and, if it is thought that dilatation will not be enough, then plastic or metal stents can be inserted to maintain the blood-flow to the heart muscle. This procedure is done far more often than it used to be and has prevented many patients being subjected to coronary bypass surgery where, at an open operation, a piece of vein is used to bypass the blockage or blockages in the coronary arteries.

The heart is stimulated to beat by means of electrical impulses. Abnormalities can make the heart beat irregularly and inefficiently, and can be controlled by drugs. Sometimes, the heartbeat can become very slow, and, where this is the case, it can be stimulated to work properly by insertion of a pacemaker. This is done under local anaesthetic by inserting an electrical wire into a vein in the neck, which is passed down into the inside of the heart so that it stimulates the heart muscle. The other end of the wire is connected to the pacemaker, containing a battery, which is buried under the skin on the chest wall.

Heart valves may require surgery, either because the patient was born with an abnormal one or because of an abnormality due to the patient developing rheumatic fever years before. Fortunately, rheumatic fever is now rare, so the incidence of abnormal valves is much less common. Valves still fail due to degenerative disease and these may need reconstructive surgery or, more commonly, replacement by a freeze-dried pig valve or a metal one.

Occasionally, the heart may become so diseased and inefficient that it will no longer respond to drugs. In these cases, the only option is a heart transplant, and many local patients have benefited from this type of surgery at Papworth Hospital, near Cambridge.

Heart attacks are caused by impairment in the supply of blood and oxygen to the heart muscle. This is associated with diseased arteries allowing thrombosis to develop, so blocking the blood supply to the heart muscle. Giving drugs which will stop further thrombosis and break down the thrombus can restore the circulation and prevent further damage to the heart muscle. The sooner the drugs are given the better the results and GPs and Ambulance teams are encouraged to give them when a heart attack is suspected. This is now being done by dedicated nurses in the Accident and Emergency Department or on the Coronary Care Unit.

ECGs are good at diagnosing problems with the heart, but in the early stage of heart disease the ECG may appear normal and only show an abnormality when the heart's activity is increased. This is achieved by getting the patient to exercise on a treadmill and gradually increasing the speed and incline while continuing to monitor the ECG. This exercise ECG was introduced to the hospital in 1982.

Over the last six years, Jan Shreeve, Sharon Martin, Paula Baker and Julie Wash have been appointed as Cardiology Nurse Specialists and they have greatly assisted the running of the Department.

Coronary Care Unit

Patients with acute problems with their heart, such as a heart attack, need intensive monitoring and treatment. When the hospital was opened, some of these patients were nursed in the combined Intensive Care and Coronary Care Unit and in July 1996 an independent Coronary Care Unit was opened. This brought together in one area the equipment to monitor these ill patients and the nurses and doctors to manage them. There are 10 beds. Originally, this was on the first floor at the north-east corner of the hospital; but, with the reconfiguration of the wards, it has moved to Ward 2 and was officially opened by Dr. Grabau when he retired on 20th April 2007. Julie Wash was the Nurse Manager of the Unit from its opening until October 2005, when she became the Acute Coronary Syndrome Specialist Nurse and her job of Manager was taken over by Sarah McClintock. In the last six years, six cardiac specialist nurses have been appointed and they have greatly assisted in the running of the unit.

There are six whole-time equivalent (wte) Sisters, nine wte Staff Nurses and 2.6 wte Health Care Assistants running the Unit with three Consultants and three Cardiology Registrars.

The Unit treats one thousand patients annually. Some of these are patients with other medical conditions who cannot get onto ITU/HDU because it is full. Feedback from patients and relatives is extremely high, with many complimentary letters and only about one complaint a year.

Over the years, non-invasive ventilation has been introduced for heart failure patients and the introduction of a nurse-led thrombolysis programme has led to a reduction in the 'door to needle time', which is the time between the patients entering the hospital and receiving thrombolytic therapy.

Following a heart attack, patients are frequently depressed because they have been brought face to face with their own mortality. The future of their job may be under threat and their activities may be restricted. Most likely, they will be on regular medication and may be facing further investigation and possibly angioplasty or coronary artery bypass surgery. In the background is the fear of another heart attack. What is essential is that if they were smokers they must give up the habit and almost certainly there is a need for a change in eating habits. Many patients join the Hospital's Heartcare Group, which meets each month in the Burrage Centre for social activities, exercise and mutual activity. Gradually increasing exercise is important and this is usually arranged by the Physiotherapists for a number of weeks. After this, the GP can sign the patient up for ten weeks in a Gymnasium and some decide to continue their membership.

Although the number of people who smoke in this country is falling, a quarter of the population continues to do so and there is a worrying number of teenagers who start the habit. In addition, there is an epidemic in obesity due to poor eating habits and lack of exercise. All this predisposes to heart disease and perhaps the hospital and the Health

Service as a whole should be putting more effort and support into prevention than into expensive investigations, treatment and sick pay.

In the hospital's early years, the Department made rapid progress in developing non-invasive cardiology, but the rapid expansion of invasive techniques in the 1990s could not be undertaken in the average District General Hospital. Consequently, increasing numbers of patients are being referred to Norwich and Papworth for further investigation and treatment. This raises questions about the future of cardiology at the James Paget, particularly with Dr. Grabau's retirement. Perhaps the arrival of the new Chief Executive, who has been the Chief Executive of the National Heart Improvement Programme, will produce a solution.

Respiratory Unit

Based on an article by Dr. David Ellis

When the James Paget Hospital opened in 1982, there was an outpatient Chest Clinic run by Dr. Joseph Salmon, who had previously run the Chest Clinic and TB service in Lowestoft. The former Great Yarmouth service had been run by Dr. Ian Young, who retired in 1979. There was no in-patient service for Respiratory Medicine and the cases seen in the clinic were largely TB follow-ups and asthma. There was no service for lung cancer. A thoracic surgical service was provided by Mr. Findley Kerr. He visited once a month and had operating facilities at Kelling Hospital in North Norfolk and the Norfolk and Norwich Hospital.

Dr. Salmon retired on 31st March and Dr. David Ellis arrived in July 1983, and for the first time there were in-patient beds for chest patients, shared with four physician colleagues (Drs. Ronnie Gibbs, David Wayne, Wolf Grabau and Stuart Hishon). A bronchoscopy service and lung function testing service were both set up in 1983. There were four clinics per week, run by David Ellis; one was supported by Mohan, GP Clinical Assistant, and another by Stanley Cooper, Associate Specialist in Medicine. Mohan continued to work as a Clinical Assistant until 1995 and he provided a valued role in outpatient Respiratory Medicine providing links to Primary Care Services.

In 1983, the Chest Clinic was situated in the area which is now Ward 18. The clinic initially moved to the outpatient suite near the front of the hospital when the Chest Clinic was converted to Occupational Therapy, before it was later converted to a ward area. The Chest Clinic then moved to the Department of Medicine, which had formerly operated as a Geriatric Day Hospital.

In the 1980s, the in-patient service run by the Physicians was spread across Wards 4, 5, 15, 16 (now endoscopy) and 17. Patients could be admitted to any ward area, but it was intended that out-of-hours patients would be admitted through the Day and Emergency Ward (later the Day Surgery Unit and now ITU). There was no specialty ward-based service. At that time, each physician would be responsible for up 50 in-patients! Between 1985 and 1990, the Lung Cancer Service was further developed. David Ellis worked closely with Walter Jackson, Consultant Oncologist, running parallel clinics on a Friday morning.

David Ellis provided regular teaching in Respiratory Medicine for GPs, nurses and other Health Care professionals. The appointment of Sam Sawyer as the first Respiratory Nurse Specialist developed improved team working and provided better services and support for patients with chronic lung disease or lung cancer. She developed improved links with Primary Care and started an out-reach service visiting patients at home. She developed the backbone of the long-term domiciliary oxygen service which is still in use today.

The early 1990s were a time of consolidation rather than further development of the Service, but at the end of the 1990s there were more developments. Anna Blackburn was appointed as a Staff Doctor (part-time) in Respiratory Medicine in 1998; Dr. Tim Cotter was appointed as the second Consultant in Respiratory Medicine in 1999; Heather Matthews was appointed Senior Respiratory Nurse Specialist in 1999, when Sam Sawyer was appointed the first full-time Lung Cancer Nurse Specialist. The first Specialist Registrar in Respiratory Medicine was appointed in 1999 as part of the Eastern Deanery Specialist Registrar rotation in Respiratory Medicine. The Multi-disciplinary Team for lung cancer was one of the first cancer MDTs to be set up in Norfolk and Waveney and has been operating continuously on a weekly basis since 1998.

Dr. Abel de Kock was appointed as the third Consultant in Respiratory Medicine in December 2003 after a period of 18 months working as a locum. A second Specialist Registrar in Respiratory Medicine was appointed in 2004. In the last five years, services for patients with chronic obstructive pulmonary disease (COPD) have improved to take account of the increasing prevalence of the disease in the community. There is a specialist outpatient COPD service run jointly by Anna Blackburn and Heather Matthews. Following the move to ward-based care in 2003, we have developed non-invasive ventilation. This is provided either in the Accident and Emergency Department or the admissions ward or on the respiratory ward without the need for involving the Intensive Care service. In 2006, we started pulmonary rehabilitation, working with the Body Wellness Health Club in the Burrage Centre.

The specialist nursing service has expanded. Cathy Tooley and Carol Nicholls joined Heather Matthews as Respiratory Nurse Specialists in 2000. Gina Carter, Patient Pathway Coordinator for Lung Cancer, was appointed in 2001. Richard Furness took over from Sam Sawyer as the Lung Cancer Nurse Specialist in 2003.

The bronchoscopy service, initially a weekly day case service, expanded to a twice-weekly service in 1999. Bronchoscopy involves the passage of a thin fibreoptic telescope through the nose to inspect the major airways in the lungs. It is done under local anaesthetic and biopsies and specimens of sputum can be taken for culture and microscopy. In 2006, Abel de Kock started a medical thoracoscopy service which involves putting a telescope into the patient's chest to assess it and to take biopsies from the lung and chest wall for analysis. This is done under local anaesthetic and light sedation. Prior to this, patients needed to go to Norwich for the procedure, which was done under a general anaesthetic. David Ellis introduced advanced bronchoscopic biopsy techniques with the use of trans-bronchial needle aspiration biopsy of mediastinal lymph nodes in 2005.

The incidence of tuberculosis was already low when the James Paget Hospital opened its doors. The notification rate in the community was 6 cases per 100,000 population per year. The rate fell slowly to the lowest level in about 1985. Since then, the notification rate has been gradually increasing. In 2006, the notification rate was 8 per 100,000 per annum and it is likely to be higher in 2007.

The service treats about 130 new cases of lung cancer per year. The incidence rate in men has fallen gradually since 1982, due to their decreased rate of smoking, while the incidence rate in women has risen, so that the incidence in men and women is now roughly equal.

There has been a huge rise in the prevalence of Chronic Obstructive Pulmonary Disease (COPD) in the community, mainly because of the effects of tobacco smoking on the older population. Longer survival leads to an increase burden of disease. COPD is a chronic condition which typically produces 10–20 years of disability before death from respiratory failure. COPD exacerbations account for the majority of respiratory admissions to hospital, in contrast to the situation in 1982, when asthma was a more common cause of hospital admission.

Asthma used to be a common reason for hospital admission and now rarely requires admission. Management of asthma in Primary Care has improved vastly in 25 years. The Outpatient and In-patient Respiratory Medicine Services now deal almost exclusively with those patients who have severe or complex asthma not responding to conventional treatment.

Pneumonia remains a common infection, both in young adults and in the elderly. It is more likely in those people who are weak or who have a poor immune response, such as AIDS/HIV, and patients who have recurrent pneumonia need investigation to see if there is an underlying cause for the pneumonia.

Interstitial lung diseases, especially fibrosing alveolitis, are becoming more common, both because of the ageing population but also because of a real increase in prevalence, possibly related to occupational exposure to wood and metal dusts and possibly as a consequence of exposure to infections.

There is a much greater awareness of pulmonary embolism nowadays, partly because of the increased publicity about people developing deep-vein thrombosis and pulmonary emboli after long airplane flights and because it has become much easier to diagnose with modern CT pulmonary angiography. Hospital in-patients, both medical and surgical, are at increased risk of developing deep-vein thrombosis and pulmonary emboli and, to try to reduce the incidence, patients are risk stratified and receive appropriate prophylactic treatment. David Ellis was co-author of the first national guidance on pulmonary embolism in the UK, published by the British Thoracic Society in 1997.

Among the investigations performed in the Department are Chest X-rays, CT Scans, Respiratory Function Tests, Bronchoscopy, Thoracoscopy and removal of fluid from the chest, as well as various blood tests. A chest X-ray is the base-line investigation and sometimes a CT Scan is used for cross-sectional imaging. Prior to the advent of the CT Scan, the hospital used tomograms, which involved the patient lying on a table and the X-ray machine and the X-ray picture moving in opposite directions. This was done at different levels, which produced rather blurred pictures, but sometime gave some further information. Respiratory Function Tests are performed in the clinic or in the lung function laboratory. Measurements are made to assess airway function, lung capacity and gas exchange. Patients can perform simple tests at home using a hand-held device. Further information can be obtained by measuring gases in the blood, such as oxygen and carbon dioxide.

Fluid sometimes collects between the lungs and chest wall and this can be drawn off with a needle for analysis. The fluid can be cultured to see whether there are any specific organisms present and it will be examined under the microscope for the presence of abnormal cells or other structures. If more tissue is required from the pleura, which is the covering over the lungs and chest wall, it can be obtained by inserting a telescope into the chest and, after inspecting the area, taking some biopsies. This is known as thoracoscopy.

Sometimes it is necessary to biopsy an abnormal area in the lung which cannot be visualised on bronchoscopy or on thoracoscopy. This can be done in the X-ray Department.

The management of malignant disease has been speeded up in recent years. A patient who has had an abnormal chest X-ray is referred directly to a chest clinic, so avoiding the patient going back to the GP and then being referred.

Smoking of cigarettes, cigars and pipes is responsible for many respiratory diseases and they are the commonest cause of lung cancer. In 2001, the hospital appointed Vicki Snelgrove as Smoking Cessation Coordinator, to work in the hospital and community to educate people about the dangers of smoking and to help them to give it up. Smoking is contributory to so many other diseases, such as bladder cancer and vascular disease, which can cause hypertension, heart attacks, poor circulation to the legs and brain, etc., that it is surprising that this aspect of preventative medicine does not receive more attention and finance. Prevention is so much better than cure and, in the long run, is cheaper and prevents so much misery and unhappiness.

Rheumatology

Rheumatology involves the management of patients with diseases of the joints, connective tissue and bone. Peter Forster was appointed Consultant Physician with special interest in Rheumatology in 1986. He was the last of the five Consultant Physicians to be appointed who, in addition to their speciality, also had a responsibility for the elderly. He took over from Dr. Wenley, who was Consultant Rheumatologist at the Norfolk and Norwich Hospital and had served the Great Yarmouth and Waveney Health District for three sessions a week for many years. For most of his tenure, Dr. Forster has been a single-handed Consultant, but, in 2002, Dr. Tarnya Marshall, Consultant Rheumatologist at the Norfolk and Norwich University Hospital, joined him for one session weekly. In 2002, Peter Forster gave up his commitment to looking after general medical patients to devote all his time to Rheumatology and teaching medical students.

Rheumatology is mainly an outpatients specialty although, with acute flare ups, such as with rheumatoid arthritis, admissions are sometimes necessary. The establishment of a Paediatric Rheumatology Service with Dr. Richard Stocks has been a great success. In addition to clinics at the James Paget, he attends sessions at Northgate and Lowestoft Hospitals.

Investigations are various blood tests, X-rays and scans (CT, MRI and bone mineral density). Treatment is mainly in the form of drugs which reduce inflammation. Biologic agents for arthritis have improved the outlook for both adults and children with arthritis. A range of different medications is now available for the treatment and prevention of osteoporosis. Physiotherapy in various forms can be helpful, as well as the provision of supports for joints and specially made footwear. Surgery can be beneficial to repair tendons and replace joints.

There is a Rheumatology Support Nurse to help in the management of these patients. When Dr. Forster retires in 2007, he will be replaced by two new Consultants!

Stroke Unit

The Stroke Unit was developed in the middle of 2006 out of the old Ward 15, which previously had a general interest in managing patients with strokes. Prior to this, an in-patient therapy area had been developed in Ward 15, which allowed the physiotherapy staff to provide enhanced therapy for stroke patients at an earlier stage as they no longer needed to be fully fit to travel to the main gym. After some building work was carried out, there were 33 beds with 18 ring-fenced for acute strokes and 15 for rehabilitating stroke patients. The conversion and other facilities were financed by a donation of £500,000 from a patient in Beccles. Patients are admitted directly by their GPs or come via the Emergency Assessment and Diagnostic Unit and there are well-laid-down protocols for the management of the patients from early CT Scans of the brain – to assess the type of stroke and its extent – right through to the rehabilitation and discharge of the patient. The centralisation of services for patients with strokes has revolutionised their management and should greatly improve the outcome of this condition.

Neurology

Neurology involves the study of nerves and the brain. The service has always relied on visiting Neurologists from the Norfolk and Norwich and the longest serving has been John Pilling. Although he retired, he is back doing locum work. He was joined by David Dick in the early 1990s, and between them they do outpatient clinics and ward rounds. They also oversee Nerve Conduction Studies, which are performed in Norwich.

Investigations involve various blood tests, CT Scans, MR Scans, spinal taps – in which a needle is inserted into the back and into the fluid around the spinal cord and nerves – and occasionally biopsy of nerves. Any surgery on the brain is performed by the Neurosurgeons at Addenbrooke's Hospital, Cambridge.

Renal Medicine

Based on information from Senior Sister Belinda Burroughes

Renal Medicine involves diseases of the kidneys and this service has always been provided by visiting Renal Physicians from Norwich. The first was David Hamilton and he was followed by Callum Ross. The Renal Unit treats people whose kidneys are not working. This is done by using an artificial kidney in the form of haemodialysis, which filters out impurities and excess fluid from the blood in a similar way that a normal functioning kidney would do.

Dr Wayne started collecting money for a Renal Unit in the mid-1970s. In the early 1980s, it was decided that all the expertise for this should be concentrated in Cambridge and Norwich, but Dr Wayne hoped to provide CAPD (Continuous Ambulatory Peritoneal Dialysis). This process works via a Tenkhoff catheter passed through the abdominal cavity, using the peritoneum as a membrane to filter out the impurities. Fluid is passed into the abdominal cavity through the catheter and is left there for four or so hours, then drained out through the same catheter. This process is repeated four times a day.

Fortunately, the decision to concentrate renal dialysis in two centres was reversed and a Haemodialysis Unit was opened at the James Paget on 1st July 1991. A public appeal had raised £350,000, with £50,000 coming from the British Kidney Patients Association.

The Unit was built on the ground floor of an extension from the south side of the hospital and originally had six Haemodialysis machines. It was officially a satellite unit from the Jack Pryor Acute Renal Unit at the old Norfolk and Norwich Hospital, with Dr Hamilton, Consultant Nephrologist, attending the unit once weekly to review haemodialysis patients and attend to outpatients whose renal function was deteriorating.

Initially, 11 patients were transferred from the Old Jubilee Unit at the West Norwich Hospital along with two members of renal trained staff. Two other trained staff were employed from within the James Paget, as well as a part-time dietician. The ever-increasing need for haemodialysis soon became apparent and the Unit gradually took on more patients and recruited extra staff.

In 2001, with increasing numbers of patients having to travel to receive treatment in Norwich due to lack of space at the James Paget, the Unit expanded initially into the Parent-craft Room. This provided an extra six stations. A change of working practice was developed, due to recruitment problems and shortage of trained staff, in which more untrained staff were employed to work alongside the trained Nephrology Nurses.

In 2005, the Renal Unit underwent a further expansion and six new stations took over the Board Room, which was relocated to the old

Breydon Lecture Theatre. The official opening for this was performed by Rosie Winterton, Health Minister, on 20th February 2007.

Now, the Renal Unit dialyses 84 patients a week, most requiring dialysis three times weekly for between three and four hours a session. The Unit also proves popular with holidaymakers, providing dialysis for patients from all over the world. In addition, many of the Unit's patients have used other renal units throughout the world, so enabling them to have holidays abroad.

The unit is open from 7 am–9 pm and provides three sessions of dialysis a day: morning, afternoon and evening; thus dialysing approximately 50 patients a day. The patients' ages range from 18 to 90 years.

Access to the blood supply has taken on many forms over the years, with shunts (a length of tubing) between an artery and vein in the arm or sometimes leg. More recently, Permacaths are used as a temporary access until permanent access can be formed.

Nowadays, dialysis is provided mainly by use of an arterio-venous fistula, usually created in the patient's forearm by joining a vein to an artery. This creates a distended vein due to the increased flow of blood from the artery. Two fistula needles are then inserted into the fistula to gain access for dialysis. Many patients pass little or no urine, so are limited to the amount they can drink daily. Two dieticians now help in guiding the patients with the dietary restrictions which they also have to manage.

The Unit remains very much a nurse-led unit and, with the latest extension, a Nurse Practitioner was recruited who leads the unit clinically, liaising with wards when patients are in-patients, and also deals with patients before they commence dialysis. Now, two Consultants attend the Unit and Outpatients Department.

At present there are 26 members of staff employed by the Unit, which is overseen by Senior Sister Belinda Burroughes, who has worked in the Unit since it opened, coming over with the patients from Norwich 16 years ago.

Approximately 25 patients are awaiting a renal transplant, which will then free them from the confines of dialysis. Many of the patients who have received transplants still visit the Unit to inform the staff of their progress. Dialysis becomes a big part of the patient's life, with some patients attending for many years. Often, they become like members of a big family to the staff.

This is an expanding and first class service to the local community and, like so many developments, arose because local people raised money for the initial unit.

The Emergency Assessment and Discharge Unit

Based on an article by Dr. Bernard Brett

In the late 1990s and early 2000s, an increasing problem was the escalating number of emergency medical admissions. This resulted partly because of the increasing age of the population but also due to the fact that most GPs were not doing night and weekend calls for their surgeries. This duty had been handed over to agencies and the doctor on call would cover a large area and it was extremely unlikely that he or she would know the patient they were being called to see. This led to more patients being referred to hospital with little information about their medical history. These extra admissions overflowed into the surgical beds, hence stopping surgical admissions and playing havoc with operating lists.

A group of senior clinicians had reviewed the care of critically-ill patients within the Trust and had identified several possible ways to improve patient care. They presented their views to the Trust Board, advising the establishment of an Emergency Assessment and Discharge Unit. Initially, it was planned that it would take two or more years to bring in, but, because of the increasing crisis with the number of medical admissions, the programme was brought forward and the EADU was opened in February 2005; a year after the project had been approved by the Trust Board.

The project involved clearing the ground floor of the south-east corner of the hospital, finding alternative space for the displaced Medical Records Department, consultants and their secretaries and developing new ways of working in the proposed EADU. A new building was erected near the helicopter pad for the Medical Records Department. This Department took up most of the ground floor and subsequently it was decided to use the first floor for an expanded Training and

Education Centre. The Southside building was extended to house the displaced consultants and their secretaries and working parties were set up to look into how the EADU would function.

Prior to the opening of the EADU, the medical on-call team was often split and separated by a significant distance, with some members of the team seeing patients in the Accident and Emergency Department whilst others were seeing patients in the old Medical Admissions Unit on a different floor. Similarly, surgical patients were either admitted directly to the wards or were admitted via the Accident and Emergency Department, so the surgical team was often separated by a significant distance. Communication between the medical and surgical teams was hindered by the scattering of their personnel around the hospital. In addition, many patients had to wait a considerable amount of time before they underwent appropriate investigations and the Radiology Department was a significant distance from and on a different floor to the Medical Admissions Unit and the surgical wards. In addition to these and other important clinical issues, there was the Government target that all patients seen in the Accident and Emergency Department had to be admitted or discharged within four hours of entering the Department and the geographical separation of the Accident and Emergency Department, the Medical Admissions Unit and the surgical wards hampered the achievement of this target.

Following approval by the Trust Board, the EADU Project Group moved rapidly through a variety of work streams to design the geographical layout of the new unit and to develop new ways of working to ensure improved patient care. Despite the tight time-frame, the complexity of some of the work streams and the need to appoint new posts, the EADU was successfully opened on schedule. The first 6 to 8 weeks were rather hectic, as staff became familiar with the new working environment and new ways of working, but, when the project was reviewed approximately 12 months after opening, it was felt that things had gone remarkably smoothly.

The EADU has introduced many new ways of working which has enhanced the care of patients admitted as emergencies to the James Paget. Senior nurses are allocated to work as the nurse coordinator who overviews the care of all patients within the Unit and takes calls from GPs and nurse practitioners in the community for medical, surgical and gynaecological patients. The Unit is covered by clinical support practitioners (CSPs) and clinical support assistants (CSAs). The CSPs are highly skilled and trained senior nurses who can assess and treat critically-ill patients, advise and support ward nurses, assist with complex monitoring and, in addition, they can prescribe certain emergency medical therapies. They can undertake many tasks that used to be performed by doctors. The CSAs assist the medical and nursing staff with phlebotomy, intravenous cannulation, urinary catheter insertion and undertaking electrocardiograms. CSPs and CSAs also help cover the Unit and the hospital in the evenings and overnight. In addition, the Unit has also been helping to train one advanced nurse practitioner, who is being trained to an even higher standard in the assessment, diagnosis and treatment of emergency and critically-ill patients.

The working practices of medical staff have also changed considerably. The Medical Consultants now double-up, with two Consultants carrying out morning ward rounds between 8 am and 10 am and Consultant Physicians are available throughout the day until at least 6.30 pm. This increased presence of Consultant Physicians has allowed the earlier review and assessment of patients and has helped the Unit increase the number of patients discharged within the first 24 hours. It is also felt that this has led to an improvement in patient care, although this is less easy to demonstrate statistically. General surgical patients are also admitted via EADU. The presence of surgical and medical teams on the same Unit has facilitated early communication and case discussion, leading to improvements on the medical-surgical interface. In the recent Hospital at Night pilot, medical and surgical juniors worked together as part of a generic acute care team.

The geographical proximity, along with facilitation from the Matron and Ward Managers, has led to much closer working between the Accident and Emergency Department and EADU.

The Unit has successfully developed and introduced an in-house electronic white board which has greatly enhanced the tracking of patients within the unit. This system allows improved data collection, easier identification of patients waiting to be clerked or to be assessed by Consultants and the easier requesting of input from specialist nurses, physiotherapists and other professionals for each patient. The Unit was also one of the first areas in the hospital to introduce the PACS system for radiological investigations.

Already, the EADU has made a great impact, not only to patient care but to the smooth running of the hospital. The success of the Unit has relied upon the hard work of nursing staff, medical staff, occupational therapists, physiotherapists, specialist nurses, pharmacists and speech and language therapists. The commitment by both medical and surgical staff has been complemented by the hard work of locum acute physicians. Dr Guy Vautier, one of the Consultant Physicians and Gastroenterologists, will be switching over to the EADU as an Acute Physician from September 2007. He will be working alongside Matron Julia Hunt and, with his army training, experience and his personality, this should lead to a continued and enhanced development of the Unit.

Accident and Emergency Department

Accident and Emergency Departments have evolved from the 'Casualty' Departments which used to exist in most hospitals. Before the start of the NHS, the Casualty Department provided care for the 'casual' patient. This treatment was provided free of charge, but the GPs complained that it provided unfair competition for them who, at that time, charged for most of their services. As a result, an agreement was reached that patients would only be seen in these departments if they had a letter of referral from the GP, unless it was an emergency situation. However, the term 'casual attendee' was not defined and such patients continued to use the Casualty Department for primary health care even after the NHS was founded.

In 1962, the Platt Report was published and recommended that these departments should be renamed Accident and Emergency Departments and that their major function should be to care for victims of serious accidents and for medical and surgical emergencies. The report also identified the need to provide for appropriate staffing, equipment and that a named consultant should be identified to be in charge of the department. At that time, there were Casualty Departments at Lowestoft and Great Yarmouth General Hospitals. The latter was staffed by nurses and junior doctors, supported by the Casualty Consultants from Norwich: Mr. McNae and Mrs. Adams. In Lowestoft, Senior Medical cover was supplied from a rota of the hospital Consultants and local GPs, and Mr. Colin Craig, Consultant Surgeon, was the Lead Clinician.

In 1967, the first Casualty Consultant was appointed to the coast. He was Mr. Ahmed and he was based at Great Yarmouth General, but took over the running of the Lowestoft Department. With the opening of the new District General Hospital at Gorleston, the Accident and Emergency Department became operational at 7 am on Monday 21st December 1981 and the Lowestoft and North Suffolk Casualty Department closed. The Great Yarmouth General Casualty Department closed on Sunday 3rd January 1982.

Mr. Ahmed ran the Department single-handed until 1988, when Richard Franklin was appointed. Unfortunately, Mr. Ahmed had increasing problems with his eyesight and retired in 1994 and, after a few months, Miss Christine Taylor was appointed. She stayed for only a few years and Richard Franklin ran the Department by himself until 2003, when Victor Inyang and Duncan Peacock were appointed as Consultants to the Department on the same day.

A major redesign and refurbishment of the Department occurred in 2000. This had been discussed for some time and all the plans were drawn up with a view to going out to a Public Appeal for the money. Fortuitously, the Department of Health telephoned one morning to say that it was looking for schemes to support but needed bids in by lunchtime! As the hospital had done all the work on the scheme, the plans were sent to London and £800,000 was received from the Government's Modernisation Fund.

Computers were introduced into the Department in September 1992 and a customised Accident and Emergency system was implemented. This was improved by the introduction of the Hospital Information Support Services (HISS) in April 1994.

The Department was the first to set up a clean needle exchange for drug addicts and it set up a group of caring volunteers, led by a retired Accident and Emergency Nurse, who were always available to console relatives of patients who have either died or had very serious injuries. In some instances, these individuals have even given bed and breakfast accommodation to the distressed.

Pre-operative Assessment Clinic

Based on an account from Michelle Thompson

Pre-operative assessment was a service development initiated by Sister Tracey Noakes from the early beginnings of a service provided for day case patients in 1996. Subsequently, it was developed for the assessment of in-patients in General Surgery, Urology and Orthopaedics.

Its functions are to assess and identify patients who have co-morbidities, so that they can have the correct level of peri-operative care, so minimising post-operative complications and reducing the length of stay in hospital. The staff informs the patients of the peri-operative risks, the admission procedures and give details about the medication instructions, diabetic and anticoagulant control. They arrange blood tests, ECG and assess the need for thromboprophylaxis. Operations lead to a varying risk of developing thrombosis in the veins and the staff assess the risks and make arrangements for prophylaxis over the operation period, if it is indicated. The staff ensure that post-operative social arrangements are made well in advance and that the patients are psychologically prepared for their procedure.

In 1996, only day cases were assessed by the clinic. The following year, pre-clerking clinics for house surgeons and senior house surgeons in General Surgery, Urology and Orthopaedics were developed alongside nurse-led clinics. Oral surgery joined in 2003, and ENT and Ophthalmology in 2005. Gynaecology plans to be part of the service when the new outpatient facility is developed. After a pilot study in Orthopaedics by Dr. Nathalie Frayssinet, a Wellbeing questionnaire was introduced in General Surgery and Urology in 2005. It reached the semi-finals of the Healthcare Innovation Awards in 2007.

With their increasing workload and responsibilities, the number of staff has increased, from one Sister three days a week and a Staff Nurse five days a week in 1996, to two full-time Sisters, four Senior Staff Nurses (one of whom is part-time) and two part-time Clinic Receptionists. There are five anaesthetic sessions weekly to assess orthopaedic patients and to support the Pre-operative Assessment Nurses.

The accommodation moved from other fragmented offices in 1997 to the present suite in 2001, which provides five clinic rooms, an admissions office for six stations, waiting area and clinic reception. In 2002, the Surgical Admissions Department joined with the Pre-operative Assessment Clinic and they share the same accommodation.

Operating Theatres and Recovery

Based on a report from Sarah Morris (nee James)

The main operating theatres are in the centre of the hospital on the first floor and provide pre-, intra- and post-operative care to the surgical patient through a wide range of surgical specialties, which includes:

- Orthopaedics – Elective & Trauma.
- Ear, Nose and Throat Surgery.
- Maxillo-facial / Dental Surgery.
- General Surgery.
- Urology.
- Breast Surgery.
- Colorectal Surgery.
- Vascular Surgery.
- Gynaecology.
- Ophthalmology.
- Minor Accident and Emergency Procedures.
- Obstetrics.
- Pain Relief.

The first head of the Department was Mrs. Jackie Saunders, who had been Theatre Sister in Lowestoft. She was followed by Miss Debra Hendley for a couple of years before Kevin Barnes took over in 1990. Mrs. Sarah James was appointed in 1991 and continues in charge. This is a large Department and consists of 129 people (apart from the surgeons and anaesthetists). Some work part-time, giving 107.39 whole-time equivalents. The breakdown of the staff is as follows:

Position	*Number*	*Whole-time Equivalent*
Matron	1	1.0
Team Leaders		
Nurses	3	3.0
Technician	1	1.0
Deputy Team Leaders		
Nurses	5	4.57
Technicians	4	4.0
Senior ODPs		
Nurses	22	16.92
Technicians	11	10.06
Operating ODPs		
Nurses	35	27.77
Technicians	13	12.08
Support Workers	19	18.56
Recovery Porters	3	2.3
Support Manager	1	1.0
Theatre Receptionists	3	2.18
TSSU Assistants	4	2.95

ODP stands for Operating Department Practitioners.

Over the years the number of staff has increased as additional theatres have been developed and built. New ways of working and expanded roles due to the reduction in junior doctors' hours have also contributed to the increased staffing numbers, i.e. Advanced Scrub Practitioners (1st assistants), dual-operating lists, dual-anaesthetising lists.

The original Operating Department consisted of seven operating theatres. When Obstetrics moved to the James Paget from Northgate Hospital an additional theatre for obstetric cases, located in the Central Delivery Suite, was built. In 2006, it was found that upgrading of this theatre was going to be very expensive, so it has been closed and obstetric procedures are now carried out in the main theatre block.

In 1994, the original three storage areas located near the restrooms were converted into an eighth theatre, complete with anaesthetic room, scrub area, preparation area and dirty utility, which then undertook Gynaecology surgery. Storage for theatre instrumentation was re-provided by the Central Delivery Suite giving up one of their special delivery rooms which had been used for trial of forceps, suturing, etc. Since 2006, this is no longer the Gynaecological Theatre and gynaecological operations are done in several other theatres. This has resulted in the break-up of the Gynaecological Theatre Team.

The following year, the upgrade programme of theatres commenced and the paired Orthopaedic Theatres were the first theatres to become upgraded and have laminar air flow installed.

In 1999, an extension to the hospital on the north side was built. On the first floor, a ninth theatre was built to centralise the provision of Ophthalmic Surgery. This theatre has its own anaesthetic room, scrub area, preparation room, 2-bed recovery area and associated storage, rest room and changing facilities. This extension also provides a dedicated day surgery facility for ophthalmic patients and a new Day Surgery Unit / Short Stay Ward on the first floor. On the ground floor is the new Dermatology Department.

In 2001/02, the upgrade programme continued with theatres 3 & 4 being upgraded to laminar air flow.

Advances in surgical techniques have developed over the past 25 years, particularly the introduction of laparoscopic surgery. Although the actual operating time for the procedure in comparison to an open procedure is similar, there are many benefits to the patient, such as reduced post-operative pain, reduced lengths of stay and an earlier return to daily living activities.

Advances in Anaesthesia have seen the development of new drugs that result in fewer side effects to patients, thus allowing them to come round from surgery and resume normal activities much quicker. Other advances in pain management, with the introduction of nerve blocks and patient-controlled analgesia, have resulted in patients being more comfortable post-operatively.

Surgical procedures that previously had a length of stay of 5–7 days, e.g. open cholecystectomy and cataract surgery, can now be carried out as day surgery procedures. Lengths of stay have been significantly reduced through all surgical specialties due to advances in surgical and anaesthetic techniques.

The Recovery Unit originally had facilities for recovering eight patients at a time. Occasionally, lack of space could interrupt the operating until some patients could be moved out of recovery and onto the wards. For many years there was no recovery staff at night, which meant that the theatre staff had to recover a patient and another could not be sent for until the patient had been returned to the ward. This was very frustrating for all concerned and could mean that surgeons, anaesthetists and theatre staff were kept waiting unnecessarily. Over the years, better and more efficient monitoring of patients has been introduced and the recovery staff play an important part in giving effective pain relief at a most important time in the patient's recovery.

Funding for the developments and improvements in the service has been difficult to secure and has often resulted in a cost pressure to the Department budget. New service developments have to be supported through the Clinical and Management Action Review Group (CAMRAG) before approaching the Trust Investment Group (TIG) for funding. This is very frustrating for medical staff who just wish to provide the best possible care for their patients!

Sarah Morris remembers a number of memorable events and people who stand out, such as:

The surgeon's wife who used to telephone to enquire what time he was likely to be leaving the Operating Department so she knew when to prepare supper. Many times she would call back an hour later to be told a similar tale – "not much longer now!"

Elsa Figg, an enrolled nurse, is one of the most dedicated theatre nurses Sarah knows. She is still working on the bank following retirement and still delivering best practice standards of theatre nursing to the newly qualified and learners.

Sister Bailey – Gynaecology Theatre Sister – had been in charge of the theatre suite at the Yarmouth General Hospital. She gave the impression of being very formidable, but she had very high standards of theatre care and expected this from every member of her team. Privacy and dignity for this group of patients was paramount and only married male members of staff were permitted to be in theatre and they had to stay firmly up at the head end of the patient, well behind the patient screen!

Mr. Corson – one of the "old school" style of surgeons – ensured that his scrub nurses were never wasteful, as he would always attempt to get yet another stitch out of 3 cm of suture material. Sarah Morris is not so sure she could allow him to bring his hens' eggs and other produce into the theatre environment these days.

Betty Himpleman "Woman Friday" – long-serving domestic for theatres, who always went that extra mile to keep everyone in theatre happy. She feels that Mr. Paul Aukland would not have survived Fridays without Betty popping out to get his fish and chips for lunch each week.

Sarah Morris says: "In the Operating Department the working relationship between all staff (nursing and medical) is unique. Nowhere else in the organisation will you find such team work to ensure that we give the best possible outcome for our patients. We all rely and depend on each other to make it happen. There is a very special camaraderie and one that I have not experienced in other areas of the hospital."

As for the future, additional capacity will be required in the short to medium term to meet the national 18-week target. This may not be through the building of additional facilities, but may include exploring new ways of working, possibly using some of the European ideas relating to theatre session start and finish times.

Anaesthetic Department

"It is no exaggeration to assert that no discernible change from the 1930s was to be seen in any division of medicine ... in the north-east quadrant of East Anglia. Not one single department was adequately housed, staffed or organised to perform its appointed task, and in no division of medicine was this more clearly revealed than in the appalling shortcomings to be found in the coast's rudimentary Department of Anaesthesia." These were some of the reflections of Dr. Neville Hicks in the early 1980s, looking back to 1961, when he had been appointed Consultant Anaesthetist to the Coast with two sessions at the Norfolk and Norwich Hospital.

Until 1961, there was just one Consultant Anaesthetist at the Coast. Originally, he had been appointed as a General Practitioner in Lowestoft and would do some anaesthetic sessions. Within a short time, he had given up General Practice and had the title of Consultant Anaesthetist. He had assumed responsibility for the anaesthetic services in Great Yarmouth, but rarely worked there. Soon after Dr. Hicks arrived, two Senior Hospital Medical Officers who did some anaesthetic sessions were promoted to Consultant Anaesthetists. In addition, there were three General Practitioners who held three clinical assistant sessions each: two worked in Great Yarmouth and the third in Lowestoft. Dr. Hicks felt that none of his anaesthetic colleagues had had any real anaesthetic training and all had failed to update their knowledge. The senior Anaesthetist died in 1963 and was eventually replaced by a lady Consultant. Unfortunately, she did not fit in and resigned after a year.

In November 1963, Dr. Hicks took over complete administrative charge. There was no houseman or registrar and he realised that none would be attracted to the Coast without considerable improvement in working conditions. Whilst trying to improve these, he recruited local young doctors with anaesthetic experience into the clinical assistant ranks. He regarded this as a great and continuing success, but regretted the lack of support he received from the Regional Board. However, matters improved with the appointment of Dr. Jesser Hind a few years later. She had worked as a missionary in India and at one time was training to be a surgeon.

Although the situation was improving, it was not good and people might wonder why Dr. David Turner should apply for the post of Consultant Anaesthetist in 1969. He thought that the job had 'vast potential' and, of course, being a keen sailor, he appreciated the nearness of the Broads and the North Sea. No-one else applied for the job. There was a single Anaesthetic Department serving three surgical units at Lowestoft and North Suffolk Hospital, Great Yarmouth General Hospital and Gorleston Hospital, where the cold Orthopaedic operations were done. Obstetrics was housed at a new unit at Northgate Hospital; Electroconvulsive Therapy, which required an anaesthetic, was performed at St. Nicholas Hospital, Great Yarmouth, and there were domiciliary and flying squad services throughout the District.

At the time of Dr. Turner's appointment, there were three Consultant Anaesthetists: Dr. Hicks, Dr. Hind and Dr. Dowding; two Senior House Officers; and several GP Clinical Assistants. There was no secretary and no office. The service provided consisted of basic anaesthetic services and resuscitation and Dr. Hind provided some teaching. There was basic obstetric analgesia with little call for and nearly no provision for epidural services. There was no pain relief service and any patient requiring it was referred to Norwich. There was no post-operative recovery suite and no Intensive Care facilities. The General Surgical units in Lowestoft and Great Yarmouth were run as separate entities, with little contact between the two.

Dr. Turner accepted the post with the promise that full medical and surgical services would be developed and he would provide a Pain Relief Service. He took over the teaching in the Department, with Dr. Hind continuing to help. Shortly after his appointment, the Regional Hospital Board decided that all acute services would be moved to Norwich in the next few years. Fortunately, this did not happen.

Over the next few years, the Department expanded to three SHOs, one Registrar and Dr. Blackiston as Consultant. Dr. Kingsley Branch replaced Dr. Clyde Dowding. GP Anaesthetists continued, but they stopped giving cover at weekends. A Secretary was appointed and she shared an office with Mr. McDonald at Great Yarmouth General Hospital. Dr. Dowding was prominent in local medical politics and was Chairman of the Medical Staff, but he and Dr. Hicks, who was head of the Anaesthetic Department, rarely communicated with each other.

By the late 1970s, the Pain Relief Clinic had expanded to approximately one and a half sessions a week and recovery rooms were developed at Great Yarmouth General and Lowestoft and North Suffolk Hospitals where, after an anaesthetic, a person could be looked after and wake up before being returned to the ward. If the patients needed ventilating after an operation as well as intensive monitoring, then they would stay in the recovery room. This usually happened at night, after emergency operations on seriously ill patients, and, if the patient was not ready to return to the ward the next morning, that morning's operating list might be cancelled unless the patient could be transferred to the Intensive Care Ward at the Norfolk and Norwich Hospital.

Dr. Eirlys Davies, the wife of Graeme McLean, Consultant Obstetrician and Gynaecologist, was appointed at the end of 1980 with a brief to set up the Intensive Care Unit at the new Hospital. It was to have four beds and in the same area would be four beds for the Coronary Care Unit. In May 1981, Dr. Jenny Jenkins, who was married to Dr. Stuart Hishon, Consultant Gastroenterologist, started work as Consultant Anaesthetist. She has a special interest in Obstetric Anaesthesia and Analgesia and has done much to improve this aspect of the service.

The first patients were admitted to the new hospital on Monday 21st December 1981, following the closure of the Lowestoft and North Suffolk Hospital Casualty Department and the gradual transfer of patients from the Lowestoft and Great Yarmouth General Hospitals. Initially, only emergency operations took place at the new hospital.

In 1982, Dr. Willy Notcutt was appointed Consultant Anaesthetist with a special interest in pain relief, and he introduced patient-controlled analgesia (PCA). This is used particularly after operations and consists of a pump delivering small amounts of pain-relieving liquid into a patient's vein. This is controlled by the patient pressing a button when pain relief is required. It results in the patient receiving much more effective pain relief when it is needed. Overdosing is prevented by the fact that if the patient presses the button too often it makes him or her sleepy, so they are no longer able to push the button. The local community was very generous in raising money for these machines and at one time there were more of them at the James Paget than at any other hospital in the United Kingdom.

Towards the end of 1982, Dr. Hicks indicated that he was going to retire and Dr. David Turner took on the responsibility of running the Department. After discussions with his colleagues, he decided to develop sub-divisions of the Department with Consultants with special interests and responsibilities to these divisions. The divisions were: Intensive Therapy Unit, Obstetric Anaesthesia and Analgesia, Pain Relief – incorporating Continuing or Hospice Care – and Teaching. It was decided that the next Consultant appointed would take on the role of Education, and this was Dr. Richard Morgan. In addition, the Department employed a Locum Consultant for approximately eight months of the year.

There were still three Senior House Officers and one Registrar, and five General Practitioners were employed as Hospital Practitioners, plus one Clinical Assistant. An Associate Specialist post had been created and this was held by Dr. Jack Frost, who had been a GP and had joined the Anaesthetic Department at Great Yarmouth General Hospital a year or so before the move to the new hospital. He was not known for his speed, but he gave excellent anaesthetics. Unfortunately, he had to retire early because of increasing breathlessness due to chronic obstructive airways disease and his wife Bridget – a sister on the Intensive Therapy Ward – eventually gave up her work to look after him at home.

Dr. Bob Mann was appointed in 1983 and some of his time was devoted to pain relief, which he did with Dr. Turner and Dr. Notcutt.

Dr. Richard Morgan replaced Dr. Hicks and became heavily involved in running the Intensive Care Ward.

In 1990, Dr. Maggie Wright, who had done several long spells of Locum Consultant work in the Department, was appointed to a permanent position. She is the wife of Dr. Bob Mann and she was the third female Consultant in the Department who was married to another Consultant in the Hospital.

On 1st April 1993, the James Paget became a Trust and Directorates were established which would work through a Unit Management Team. The Anaesthetic Department became the Directorate of Critical Care Services and the first Director was Dr. Richard Morgan, with John Turner, Dr. David Turner's son, as the Service Manager. This Directorate incorporated the Main Operating Theatres.

In the early 1990s, the amount of work going through theatres was increasing and to meet the demand more Consultant Anaesthetists were taken on. They were Dr. Mike Hooper in 1991, Dr. Stefan Oosthuysen in 1994 and, in 1995, Dr. Thinus Mostert and Dr. Rangith Ganepola were appointed. In spite of Dr. Kingsley Branch retiring in 1997 – but coming back to do regular sessions – the number of Consultants in the Department was 12. Then Dr. Hooper returned to Australia as a Senior Lecturer with a strong interest in Pain Relief and Dr. Richard Morgan escaped to Blackpool to a job with a definite commitment to Intensive Care and Clinical Anaesthesia and away from Administration.

While he was here, Richard Morgan developed a critical care score. This depends upon recording simple observations such as pulse rate, blood pressure, temperature, respiratory rate and urinary output and adding up the points given to each value. The scoring can indicate deterioration in a patient's condition, so allowing corrective measures to be taken. The scoring system was eventually taken on throughout the Trust and its value has been reported at many meetings and in world literature.

Dr. Turner retired in 1996, to be replaced by Dr. Dean Millican, but came back to job-share with Dr. Branch for several more years. At that time, there were five SHOs, one Registrar and a Senior Registrar. All but two of the GP Anaesthetists had left and Dr. Raouf Kaldas was an Associate Specialist and Drs. Naeem Ahmad and Pushpa Thakur were Staff Doctors.

As far as Junior Staff in the Department were concerned, until the early 1970s and the establishment of the GP Training Scheme, nearly all the juniors had graduated in the Indian subcontinent. Gradually, the number of UK Graduates increased, either as career anaesthetists or as GPs with an interest in Anaesthesia. However, in the 1990s, with the development of the European Union, many of the posts began to be filled by continental graduates, particularly from Germany.

Intensive Care Unit

Based on an account by Dr. Maggie Wright

When the James Paget Hospital first opened, the Intensive Care Unit (ICU) and Coronary Care Unit (CCU) were combined within an 8-bedded area; 6 beds were open-plan and 2 were side rooms where patients could be isolated. Nursing staff covered both ICU and CCU; the anaesthetists managed the ICU patients and the physicians the cardiac patients. The first nurse in charge was Marina Gibson and many staff, who have gone on to various senior posts throughout the Trust, gained experience in ICU.

Initially, monitoring consisted of a basic heart monitor that could be extended to read invasive blood pressures. Anything else was an add-on and increased the amount and complexity of the equipment around the bed. This made access to the patient more difficult for staff but also for relatives wanting to hold a hand and talking quietly to the patient was tricky, especially given the levels of noise from the equipment and the alarms.

The open-plan design of the ward in many respects made nursing more flexible, but for those in the side rooms surrounded by equipment it could seem a very long shift. Then as now, all patients from babies to the very elderly were admitted if it was felt that they could benefit from the care provided. Age has never been a barrier to ICU admission and has ranged from a baby of a few days old to a 102-year-old lady.

Dr. David Turner was the first Anaesthetist to take the lead in ICU and he was followed by Dr. Eirlys Davies and then Dr. David Blundell. ICU very much had to fit in with the busy theatre work demands on Anaesthetists as the Consultants then covered both emergency theatre and ICU. Dr. Richard Morgan followed and was keen to advance ICU in line with the then national standards. A number of Anaesthetists were allocated day-time sessions and Dr. Maggie Wright was one of them. When Richard Morgan moved on to theatre and anaesthetic management, she took on the mantle of Director of Intensive Care and has remained so for the last 15 years.

The Physicians were not happy with the arrangement of beds, as every time there were more than four ICU patients the cardiac beds would be used. Similarly, an excess number of coronary patients could prevent an elective patient having an operation, as there would be no ICU bed for their planned admission. Although the Anaesthetists, Surgeons and Physicians had worked very harmoniously together, it was decided that cardiology would be better served by a separate CCU, so one was created in 1996 and much of the equipment and many staff moved to it.

The need for a 'High Dependency Unit' (HDU) to accommodate those patients, both medical and surgical, who were very sick and who required support for one or more failing organs, was identified. The Trust funded this expansion into the old CCU, so there was a combined 8-bedded ICU/ HDU in 1996. Initially, four and then five of the beds were funded for ICU patients and the other three for HDU. Needless to say, the beds were used very flexibly and sometimes there were eight or indeed more ICU patients. On those occasions there was an overspill into theatre recovery.

Advances in ICU brought even more sophisticated ventilators and much better monitoring and renal support machines. The nurses really had a very heavy physical workload both managing all the machines and lifting and turning the unconscious or very weak patients.

The Unit began to participate in national and regional audits and research projects which were trying to better identify standards of care and best treatment options. Dr. Ranjith Ganepola and then Dr. Thinus Mostert, both keen intensivists, joined the ICU and with Dr. Maggie Wright they decided that ICU had become so busy it was necessary to split away from the general anaesthetic rota to cover just ICU at night time and weekends. This enabled them to concentrate more on the sickest patients in the hospital. They wished to modernise the ICU and to be recognised as a teaching and training centre, which was achieved. Meanwhile, the nursing staff was becoming ever more expert in the management of their very dependent patients. Then came the arrival of the Hyperbaric Chamber, in conjunction with the North Sea Medical Centre, to treat patients who either had the 'bends' from deep-sea diving or carbon monoxide poisoning.

Rosemary Smalley had succeeded Steve Biddle as Clinical Manager / Sister in Charge of the ICU, with Steve Biddle retaining the lead clinical nurse role and it was Rosemary Smalley who organised the provision of care to the hyperbaric chamber.

Together, Rosemary Smalley and Dr. Wright led the campaign to provide a better environment for their patients and relatives, together with more ergonomically effective workstations. In addition, there were problems with the ventilation system of the Unit. They pleaded the case for an upgrade of the ICU ward and, in developing the business case, one of the options put forward was to move ICU to the then day case unit. Dr. Wright went to look at the day care ward and, when she saw the amount of daylight in that ward, she knew it was where their patients needed to be. There is plenty of research to show that critically ill patients do better if they are nursed in natural light. In addition, there were medical wards on one side, surgical wards on the other and the operating theatres were directly opposite. It was a hard fight, but they managed to convince the powers-that-be and it was selected as the next charitable appeal for the hospital. They were superbly supported by the Estates Department, with Arthur Harris and Brian Tate providing excellent plans; and the senior managers, led by David Hill, providing a first-class business case, which the Strategic Health Authority agreed to.

In order to accommodate the move, Daycare and Endoscopy had to relocate, so three separate departments benefited. Raising the money was hard work but great fun and everyone was overwhelmed by the generosity of the people of Great Yarmouth and Waveney and of the madcap things people would do to raise money. Dr. Wright says, "We had grand ideas and thanks to the local community we have been able to fulfill them. We have a fantastic, computerised ICU, with masses of natural light and essentially individual rooms which we knew would be necessary to enable us to try to fight the infections that are challenging all hospitals. We were very proud indeed when Her Royal Highness the Princess Royal came to open the Unit on 10th September 2003."

As far as statistics are concerned, 75–80% of patients admitted to the Intensive Care Unit leave it alive, and comparison with national standardised mortality rates show that the Unit's figures match the national average. Hospital-acquired infections, particularly MRSA and Clostridium difficile, have been a problem over recent years and are undoubtedly one of the factors why the length of stay in the Unit has increased in the last few years.

There are plans to expand further, but currently there is nowhere to expand to. There are seven ICU Consultant colleagues, and junior doctors from other specialties, as well as Anaesthesia, rotate through in order to gain experience in looking after the most critically ill patients. Dr. Wright says, "we have always remained a very happy Department and are extremely fortunate to have superb nursing staff, physiotherapists, dieticians, biochemists and radiographers as part of our team. In line with Department of Health recommendations, we are also fortunate to have a team of expert nurses – the Critical Care Outreach Team – led by Nurse Consultant Dr Kath Kite, facilitating the care of critically ill patients at ward level."

Maternity Services

Based on an article by Elayne Guest

The Maternity services in the Great Yarmouth and Waveney area have come a very long way over the last 40 years. Prior to 1968, when the brand new Maternity Unit opened on the Northgate Hospital site, there were 10 beds at the old Great Yarmouth General Hospital on Deneside and four beds at the Lowestoft and North Suffolk Hospital. Most women had their babies at home and only a few, who needed obstetric care, gave birth in the hospital.

The new Unit, which was headed by Miss Margaret Downes, Consultant Obstetrician and Gynaecologist, cost £328,000 to build. It incorporated a labour suite and its own obstetric theatre, an antenatal ward, a postnatal ward and nurseries. The new concept of some beds for General Practitioners and Midwives to bring in their own women for hospital delivery and early postnatal care was also included.

By the early 1970s, the Peel Report decided that it was safer for women to have their babies in hospital and more and more came for their delivery and three days' postnatal care. They were then transferred back to the care of the "District Midwife" and General Practitioner. Gradually, there was more monitoring and an increase in invasive procedures, with far fewer home confinements.

The first phase of the District General Hospital did not contain maternity nor paediatric beds, so the local Consultant Unit Maternity services stayed at Northgate Hospital until the end of 1984. The Central Delivery Suite and Special Care Baby Unit facilities had been included in the first phase, so they were misused initially as the children's ward. The second phase included the antenatal and postnatal ward facilities and the 10-bed isolation unit that is now the Charnwood Suite. In the original 'Best Buy' design, this was to be used for women or babies with postnatal infections to keep them separate from the so-called "clean ward areas". In fact, this area was never used for maternity patients and later it was decided to develop this as a temporary unit for private patients while a larger and permanent unit was developed. The permanent unit was never built.

During the planning and building of Phase 2 of the District General Hospital between 1982 and 1985, the Maternity services tried very hard to influence how the new facilities were to be built. For example, Midwives working in other 'Best Buy' hospitals stated that the bidets were not fit for their purpose. However, it was explained that it was impossible to make any alterations until after the building was completed. Later, it was possible to provide the Department's own obstetric theatre by converting one of the large delivery rooms into a fully equipped, if somewhat small, theatre, anaesthetic annexe and scrub room. Unfortunately, in late 2006, during refurbishment, it was decided that the air change plant required huge sums of money spending on it in order to bring it up to 2007 standards. It was decided that this was not feasible and since then all Caesarean sections and other obstetric operations are performed in the main theatre block, which is adjacent to the Obstetric Unit.

Although there was an excellent Obstetric Unit at Northgate Hospital, it was felt that the move of Maternity services to the District General Hospital was essential because, although only four miles as the crow flies, the travelling time via the Haven Bridge – which at that time was the only bridge linking Great Yarmouth to Gorleston – could be very prolonged, particularly during the Summer months when there were many visitors in the area. The Obstetricians and Gynaecologists spent much of their time at the District General Hospital and if they were needed urgently for an obstetric emergency it could be difficult for them to get to Northgate in time. Similarly, the Anaesthetists and Paediatricians were also less available for Northgate. The move of the Pathology services from Northgate into the second phase of the new hospital would have added to the difficulties if the Obstetric service had stayed in Northgate and for a long time it had been a long trek for people in Lowestoft and further south.

The move to the James Paget Hospital was planned with military precision. It was impossible to buy all new equipment, so a great deal had to be transferred. The antenatal clinic had to share accommodation with the Gynaecology outpatient department, so initially all the records and the administration for antenatal patients were based in one large room situated near the central delivery suite. The Paediatric Ward had also been built in Phase 2, so the children moved into their new accommodation on the north-west corner of the hospital, vacating the Central Delivery Suite and Special Care Baby Unit.

The Special Care Baby Unit was reinstated and suitably decorated for neonates requiring intensive and high-dependency care following birth. The nurseries were set out in such a way that babies moved from high dependency to lower dependency as their condition improved. The layout was poor, with the sluice and office having natural light and the nurseries having no windows, so relying on neon lighting. The premature babies must have felt like "hot house" plants as they were "fattened up" and "grown on". The Neonatal Unit was completely refurbished and had an official reopening on 12th July 2004. The nurseries now look out onto a courtyard and have natural light.

The Obstetric Ward areas are light and airy and there are several single rooms. In the early days, babies were gathered into the nurseries at night and mothers stayed in hospital for 3 to 5 days, or 8 days if they had had an operative delivery. Today, it is very different and many women go home a few hours after the birth and even those who have had a Caesarean section are home within 2–3 days.

Because of the shorter stay, there are fewer maternity beds and one part of the ward is used as a special unit dealing with sub-fertility – the Waveney Suite. Another 6-bed bay is used as an assessment area for women needing additional monitoring during pregnancy. This reduces the need for admission and women no longer come into hospital for 'rest' or treatment, as they prefer to travel in daily for monitoring and remain at home with their family.

One of the first tasks after the arrival of the Maternity services at the District General Hospital was to start planning a separate antenatal clinic. It was agreed to build this on the south side of the ward area, with easy access for staff and to avoid the long walk through the hospital for women, babies, fathers, flowers, balloons and bags, often with siblings in tow. The hospital also needed a renal unit, so this formed the ground floor with the antenatal clinic area and Ultrasonography Department on the first floor.

The ground floor link from the new unit to the original building was left as a large empty area and was used for storage. Later, when funds became available and the hospital sought Trust status, a traditional boardroom was created. The first Trust Chairman was heard on many occasions to say that it was not expensive – it was a void area. The panelling was all stained soft wood and it was only the décor and lighting that made it appear so splendid. He was afraid that the hospital would be accused of spending "public money" on such an ornate boardroom.

Over the years there have been other changes and developments in the way midwifery care is delivered. For instance, a large lagoon bath was installed in the Delivery Suite in the early nineties when "water birth" came into vogue. This room has recently been refurbished to make it more practical to actually carry out deliveries in the water.

A special room, "The Rosemary Room", has been created for parents who lose their baby at birth. Another room is set aside with mattresses on the floor, bean bags and large balls for women who choose to have an active birth.

As with most other aspects of modern life, fashions come and go, but currently the intention is to reduce intervention, operative deliveries and return towards the "normality model" for childbirth.

Prior to 1974, the hospital Maternity services were administered by the Norfolk and Norwich Hospital and the Community Services by Great Yarmouth Borough Council and East Suffolk County Council. After the formation of the Great Yarmouth & Waveney Health District in 1974, the three areas were run separately, with Miss G. Badger, Nursing Officer, in charge of the Maternity Unit at Northgate Hospital;

Miss G. Moore, Senior Nursing Officer, in charge of the Community Services in what had been Great Yarmouth Borough and Northern villages; and Mrs. Elayne Beeby (later to become better known as Elayne Guest, after she married the District Nursing Officer) as Nursing Officer in charge of Community Midwifery in the area from Lowestoft to Halesworth, Beccles, Bungay, etc. They were all responsible to the District Nursing Officer, Mr. Robert Guest, who was appointed in 1974 and was a member of the District Management Team.

In 1975, Miss Badger retired from running the Maternity Unit at Northgate Hospital and Mrs. Elayne Beeby, who headed the Community Midwifery in the south of the District, was invited to manage the Maternity Unit until a new appointment was made. The secondment continued and the community in the south of the District and the Maternity Unit remained under one manager. When Miss Moore retired from the Great Yarmouth area in 1978, that part of the community was incorporated and the Maternity services became an integrated unit. When the District General Hospital opened in 1981, Gynaecology and Paediatrics joined forces with Maternity and the Senior Nursing Officer – who by this time had become Mrs. Elayne Guest – became a Director of Nursing and Midwifery. When the Maternity services moved to the James Paget Hospital at the end of 1984, Mrs. Guest joined the Management Team for the whole hospital.

Outpatients Department

Based on information from Penny Cox and Jill King

The first outpatients were seen at the District General Hospital on Monday 21st December 1981. Sister Sue Richards was in charge of all the clinics, which included General Surgery, Medicine, Gynaecology, Orthopaedics, Dental, ENT and Ophthalmology. The staff rotated around all the clinics and most of them were held in the main Outpatient Department in the front of the hospital. In the early 1990s, the Geriatric Day Hospital was converted into the Medical Outpatients Suite and, later still, the Broadland Suite was built to accommodate Oncology and some surgical clinics. More recently, the Department of Dermatology has had its own Department built, where it sees its own outpatients.

In November 2006, Teresa Norton and Penny Cox were appointed Nurse Managers for the whole of Outpatient services and Wendy Mitchell became the Service Manager in overall charge.

Jill King remembers that, for many years, metal sigmoidoscopes were used for examining the lower bowel, after which they were put in a bucket of water before being sent away for sterilisation. Nowadays, they have been replaced by plastic ones which are disposable and are not so cold.

Genito Urinary Medicine Department – The Bure Clinic

Based on account by Sister Chris Souter

The Bure Clinic provides comprehensive screening and treatment for people with sexually transmissible infections, including people with HIV and AIDS.Originally, there were Genito-Urinary Clinics in Great Yarmouth and Lowestoft, but in the late 1970s they were combined into the Bure Clinic, a purpose-built clinic on the Northgate Hospital site. This was not convenient for people in the Lowestoft area, but matters improved following the Monks Report (Department of Health, 1988) which recommended that a Department of Genito-Urinary Medicine should be sited within a District General Hospital. The Bure Clinic moved from its old site at Estcourt Hospital to its present site on 28th October 1991. Previously, this area was the site of the staff changing rooms and showers. Many staff may remember using this facility, where uniforms were laundered at the hospital and nurses could pick up a new paper hat.

The Clinic was purpose-built, complying with the recommendations of the Monks Report and was overseen by Dr. Sulaiman, Consultant at the time of planning. The Clinic was officially opened on 3rd December 1991 by Dr Nichol Thin, a specialist from St. Thomas' Hospital, London, who was an advisor on Genito-Urinary Medicine to the Department of Health and had links with the World Health Organisation. By this time, Dr Balakumar had become Consultant in charge of the Unit. Sister Sue Harrington headed the Department with Shirlene Phillips as Health Advisor. The team consisted of:

- 1 Registered Nurse.
- 2 Senior Enrolled Nurses.
- 2 Bank Enrolled Nurses.
- 3 Medical Secretaries working part-time.

In addition, there were five Clinical Assistants who were local GPs with an interest in Genito-Urinary Medicine, but in recent years they no longer work in the Unit.

In 1995, Dr Balakumar died unexpectedly, leaving a wife and two daughters. He was a quiet, kind and thoughtful person and in his memory staff and patients subscribed to a magnificent, colourful painting which hangs just within the entrance to the hospital. At the opening of the Unit, he said, "Medical and nursing training teaches practitioners to deal with the whole person, not simply the symptoms and treatment of the disease. There is no specialty where this is more important than Genito-Urinary Medicine." The post remained vacant for nearly a year with a Locum Consultant covering until Dr. T. C. Harry filled the post in 1996.

In the last ten years the team has expanded and now consists of:

- 1 Consultant.
- 1 Staff Grade Doctor.
- 1 Hospital Practitioner.
- 2 Clinical Psychologists.
- 2 Sisters.
- 2 Health Advisors.
- 4 Nurses.
- 1 Bank Nurse.
- 2 Health Care Assistants.
- 3 Medical Secretaries.

Three of the original team from Estcourt Hospital still remain in the Department.

The Clinic participates in the training of medical students and F2 doctor placements. Dr. Salvary, Consultant Dermatologist, does one Genital Dermatosis Clinic each month.

Over the years, the Clinic has seen an upward trend in all Sexually Transmitted Diseases (STDs), with an increasing number of new cases of syphilis being a worrying development recently. New diagnoses of HIV have increased rapidly over the last few years, but deaths due to AIDS have become a rare occurrence due to the very effective treatment now available in this country. This does mean, however, that GU Medicine now has a large cohort of long-term clients needing regular medical assessment.

The Bure Clinic website was developed and came on-line with assistance from Great Yarmouth Rotary Club on 5th July 1998. The website provides information on clinic services, local epidemiological statistics and options to discuss problems with the Consultant.

The Clinic received a visit in May 2005 by the Strategic Health Commission. The visiting team made various recommendations:

- Improvement in services to allow access to appointments within 48 hours.
- Nurse-led Clinics.
- The introduction of Health Care Assistants.

All of these recommendations have been met without any additional funding from the Department of Health.

The Clinic continues to see steady rises in all sexually transmitted diseases.

Oncology Services

Based on an account by Dr. Joe Ostrowski

Prior to the opening of the new District General Hospital, Oncology services were provided by Dr. Walter Jackson at Yarmouth General Hospital and Dr. Joe Ostrowski at the Lowestoft and North Suffolk Hospital. They were Consultant Radiotherapists at the Norfolk and Norwich Hospital and each provided for the coast two clinics each month and visited patients on the wards. All treatment, which in those days was mainly radiotherapy, was done in Norwich.

With the move to the new District General Hospital, the clinics increased to two weekly. Dr. Ostrowski came on Wednesday and Dr.

Jackson on Friday, usually on his motorbike with the patients' notes in containers behind him. Walter Jackson and Hugh Sturzaker had established a joint clinic at the Yarmouth General Hospital in 1979 and this continued on the new site. Initially, it was mainly for breast patients, but those with other malignancies were also seen. They met each Friday morning to discuss various problems and would visit patients on the wards at 'lunchtime' before the afternoon operating list. Once a month there was a mammoth 'Joint Clinic' at which up to, and sometimes more than, one hundred patients were seen. Each would see patients separately and where there was need for discussion about management they saw the patient together. Seeing such a large number of patients was far from ideal, but they felt that it was better to do this than not to provide a joint service. In addition, it educated them and was the basis for developing the Breast Care Service. With the appointment of Mr. Jerome Pereira in 1994 and the change in rotas, he took over the Joint Clinic from Hugh Sturzaker and built up an equally good relationship with Walter Jackson.

Central to the efficient running of the Clinic was Sheila Blamire, who was Dr. Jackson's secretary. She would sit in a room with her typewriter; take down dictation from both Clinicians and type up the letters for them to be ready for signing at the end of the Clinic. In addition, she would type up the dictated clinical notes at the same time, always with a smile on her face.

Soon after the hospital opened, the first Oncology Nurse, Stephanie Grimes, was appointed and outpatient chemotherapy was initiated in clinics for certain disease groups. Patients having more toxic and complicated chemotherapy required admission to Norwich. By 1985/86, a dedicated clinic for giving chemotherapy was established and a year or two later certain cytotoxic drugs were being prepared in a dedicated unit in the pharmacy.

In 1995, Dr. Jackson retired and was replaced by Dr. Craig Martin as Clinical Oncologist (the name change from Radiotherapist was a result of an increasing amount of a radiotherapist's time being taken up with chemotherapy). In addition to taking over Dr. Jackson's Breast Clinic, he saw patients with lung and head and neck tumours, which were his special interest.

Dr. Bulman was appointed a little later in 1995 with a special interest in breast and colorectal cancer. He started the programme of giving radiotherapy to certain patients with rectal cancers. With his increasing commitments in Norwich, he gave up his sessions at the James Paget in 2003 and Dr. Daniel Epurescu, who had been appointed Medical Oncologist (a Physician who treats patients with chemotherapy but who has not had radiotherapy training) to the Norfolk and Norwich University Hospital, took over the sessions. He increased the amount of chemotherapy being given but, unfortunately, as he did not have the radiotherapy training, it meant that patients being considered for this treatment had to make another appointment to see a Clinical Oncologist in Norwich.

In 2002, Dr. Adrian Harnett was appointed to the Norfolk and Norwich University and James Paget Hospitals. One of his special interests is breast cancer, so Jerome Pereira and Hugh Sturzaker arranged to see their newly diagnosed patients as well as any others who needed joint discussions at the same time that Adrian Harnett had his clinic. Also attending were the Breast Care Nurse Specialists and the BRAS ladies who have had breast cancer, so are particularly helpful at meeting patients (and their partners) who have been newly diagnosed with the condition.

Radiotherapy involves the use of complex and expensive machines and most people in this Health District receive it in Norwich. With the opening of the new Radiotherapy Department at the new Norfolk and Norwich University Hospital in 2002, there were not only new machines for giving treatment but also new machines and computers for planning the treatment. In addition, several new Consultant Oncologists were appointed around this time, along with Professor Ann Barrett. As a result, waiting times for Radiotherapy were drastically reduced. For the few years before this, the delay in patients receiving their radiotherapy was becoming rather alarming, due to a combination of an increased number of patients requiring treatment, a shortage of therapy radiographers and one of the radiotherapy machines not working. In view of the imminent move to the new hospital in Norwich, it was decided that it was not justifiable to replace it. Because of these delays, a number of patients seen at the James Paget were referred to Ipswich for radiotherapy.

In 2002/2003, a Clinical Assistant was established to look after outpatients attending for chemotherapy in the Sandra Chapman

Centre. Unfortunately, patients requiring in-patient chemotherapy still need to go to Norwich for it, but hopefully, with the appointment of a dedicated Consultant Medical Oncologist based at the James Paget, these patients will be treated here. Unfortunately, although this post was approved in 2006, it has yet to be advertised and it will also require the provision of trained oncology nurses.

In 1996, the Calman Hine cancer reforms were introduced, with each Oncologist limiting the number of diseases they would treat. This is akin to the increased specialisation which was happening throughout the Health Service. In addition, Multi-disciplinary Teams (MDTs) were advocated to manage patients with gynaecological tumours, cancer of the breast, lung, bowel, etc. Such teams consist of surgeons, oncologists, radiologists, histopathologists and specialised nurses and most meet weekly, usually at lunchtimes, as there is no other time in busy schedules when these groups of people could get together.

At the MDT meetings, each new patient with a malignancy is discussed and the management is planned. In many instances the management is fairly standard and not too much discussion is required. However, more complex problems are discussed at length. With the transfer of the Histopathology service to Norwich in July 2005, it became increasingly difficult for histopathologists to attend these meetings, so communication had to resort to teleconferencing. This saves a great deal of travelling time, but it has meant the loss of the close contact which used to exist among Clinicians and Histopathologists.

In the area covered by the Norfolk and Norwich and the James Paget University Hospitals, a third of patients with cancer are seen at the latter. The number of new patients seen has doubled since the hospital opened. This is the result of a combination of an ageing population (the incidence of malignancy increases with age), more cancers being diagnosed due to screening and better investigations, more treatments being available and the decision to treat certain conditions which in the past were not treated.

In the last 25 years, there have been many advances in Oncology. Means of detection have increased and improved with screening for cervical, breast and now bowel cancer detecting many cancers at an earlier stage, which can make the results of treatment better. CT and MR Scanners, along with Ultrasound, have enabled the spread of the disease to be much more accurately assessed and treatments have become more advanced and refined, allowing many more cancers to be treated and cured than was the case 25 years ago. Along with this there are more Oncologists and sessions available at the James Paget, with better accommodation. Before the hospital opened, there was the equivalent of one session weekly. Now there are eight sessions a week. Stream-lining methods of referral has meant that patients are seen sooner and Multi-disciplinary Meetings have helped in the joint management of patients. In addition, Nurse Care Specialists have helped in the development of the various services and patients are given more time and explanations about their condition.

Oncology Chemotherapy Team

The Oncology Chemotherapy Team is based in the Sandra Chapman Unit and works alongside the Haematology Team. It treats approximately 100 patients per week, mainly with chemotherapy, but also giving supportive therapy to cancer patients. Treatment times vary from 20 minutes to 5 hours and chemotherapy is given only on an outpatient basis. All oncology patients attending the Centre are under the care of an Oncologist based at the Norfolk and Norwich Hospital.

Treatments requiring the patient to be admitted necessitate the patient being sent to the Norfolk and Norwich University Hospital, as there is no on-call Senior Oncologist service at the James Paget. However, all oncology patients now have out of hours access to Ward 17 in the event of infection or pyrexia.

The Oncology Chemotherapy Team is managed by a part-time Senior Sister and Deputy Charge Nurse. Lesley Cutting recently retired as Oncology Nurse Specialist and there are also four Staff Nurses and one Healthcare Assistant working within this area.

Sandra Chapman Centre

Sandra Chapman was Deaconess of the Corton and Hopton Parishes. Whilst she was a patient on Ward 17 in 1987, she suggested to Dr. Mitchell and Dr. Ostrowski that some form of day room was needed to improve the comfort of patients and relatives as the accommodation for day patients on Ward 17 was overcrowded. This idea was developed into a plan to build a day treatment centre as an extension to Ward 17. It provides a base for giving outpatient chemotherapy and for the general needs of patients with malignant disease.

Sandra Chapman was a prominent figure in the initial fundraising for the Centre, which raised over £500,000. Sadly, she did not live to see the project realised. At a ceremony in May 1992, the Bishop of Norwich officially opened the Sandra Chapman Centre.

In June 2001, an extension providing a further five treatment rooms, counselling and office space was opened by Dr. Terry Mitchell, Consultant Haematologist. This project had once again been entirely funded through the support of charitable donations to the Sandra Chapman Centre Fund.

Because of the increasing numbers of people having chemotherapy, the Centre underwent further refurbishment to make another seven treatment stations in January 2007.

Pathology Department

Based on an account by Dr. John Ball

Dr. John Ball was appointed sole Consultant Pathologist to the Health District in 1972 and a newly constructed laboratory in the grounds of the Northgate Hospital, Great Yarmouth, was opened the following year. At his appointment, he was assured that a new hospital for the area was forthcoming. Until the opening of this new laboratory, all Pathology was carried out at the Norfolk and Norwich Hospital. Only out-of-hours Haematology and Biochemistry were performed at the Yarmouth General and Lowestoft Hospitals. The new laboratory was established to serve all the coastal hospitals, from Cromer to Southwold and inland from North Walsham to Beccles and Bungay.The new laboratory provided services in Histopathology, Haematology, Biochemistry and Microbiology and Dr. Ball's Canadian training ensured that he had received experience in each of these subjects. The technical staff consisted of one Laboratory Chief and one Senior heading each department. Very few new laboratories were being built in 1972, so there was something of a surfeit of newly qualified technicians. This enabled the Laboratory to choose excellent people. Mr.

Bill Butt was eventually appointed to manage the Laboratory, but only after he was prised out of the Royal Air force with the help of the local Member of Parliament, who raised questions in the House of Commons as to why this man could not be released to serve in a needy area of the country. Not everyone was delighted to use the shiny, new and efficient laboratory. Dr. Ball and Mr. Butt were forced to cross swords with both medical and public people in the eventually successful attempt to close local small, and sometimes dangerously inefficient, laboratories. At that time, there were few Consultant medical staff in the area. Mr. Hugh McDonald had been General Surgeon at the Great Yarmouth General Hospital since 1945 and he also performed Coroner's Post Mortem Examinations for the area. He had done this for many years and it was with some reluctance that he agreed to the Coroner's request that he should leave these Post Mortem examinations to the new Pathologist. In 1974, Dr. David Harrison was appointed as second Pathologist and he shared Histopathology with Dr. Ball.

In 1981, Dr. Terry Mitchell was appointed Consultant Haematologist and his wife, Dr. Anne Gerkin, was appointed Consultant Microbiologist. The work that had originally been done by Dr. Ball alone was now being shared with three others, who confined themselves to their chosen specialty. Dr. Ball continued with the Clinical Biochemistry until the arrival of Dr. Steve Absalom in 1992. From then on, each specialty developed and expanded and Dr. Ball remained in overall charge until he retired in 1993.

It is a measure of the pride and dedication which the laboratory staff had in their work that when the "big move" from Northgate to the James Paget came in 1985, every item and piece of equipment was moved by the staff themselves. Nothing was entrusted to anyone else.

Dr. Ball feels that if he made any contribution to the James Paget Hospital it was based on his conviction that "central to a good hospital are good doctors and central to good doctoring is a good laboratory."

Clinical Biochemistry

From information given by Barrie Dean

Clinical Biochemistry provides a comprehensive service for the hospital and general practitioners for routine biochemistry, hormones, tumour markers, therapeutic drugs, drugs of abuse screening, specific proteins and electrophoresis, HBA1c for monitoring diabetics, screening tests in immunology and maintenance and support of hospital blood gas analysers.

The laboratory and offices are on the first floor at the back of the hospital and transferred from the laboratory at Northgate Hospital when the hospital opened in December 1981. It is amazing that of the 11 qualified staff that moved into the hospital then, seven remain, and there is still the same number of qualified staff (10.98 whole-time equivalents now) as in 1981. The worry is that there is a 15% vacancy rate in qualified staff with a failure to recruit from the last four rounds of advertising. In addition, more than half of the staff is over 50 years of age.

Apart from Barrie Dean as Head Biochemical Scientist, there are two Senior Basic Medical Scientists, 7.98 wte Basic Medical Scientists and 3.6 wte Medical Laboratory Assistants. Dr. Steve Absalom is the Consultant Chemical Pathologist. He was appointed in 1993 and worked hard to obtain accreditation from the CPA (Clinical Pathology Accreditation (UK) Ltd.) which has been maintained, whereas many other hospital laboratories have failed in this respect.

In spite of only minimal increase in staff numbers (this has been at Medical Laboratory Assistant level from 2 to 3.6 wte), there has been a staggering increase in workload from 180,000 tests in 1982 to over two and half million annually now. Much of this is due to the greater reliance on more sophisticated machinery which still has to be supervised and checked by the laboratory staff. The repertoire of tests has expanded considerably to approximately four hundred different tests and a greater percentage of tests are performed on-site, with less than 0.6% referred to other hospitals.

There has been little change in laboratory space over the years, except for a decrease to accommodate the increasing number of histopathologists who have now moved to Norwich. Benching has been removed to accommodate larger analysers and to provide a cold room for storage of reagents and archived specimens.

Barrie Dean considers the success of his Department is that it provides a service within budget despite relentless increases in workload and other demands placed upon it. He does not like the inadequate and insensitive funding and suggests that people should pay for what they

(Wellcome Library, London)

James Paget

as a young man,

at time of retirement,

and in old age.

Unveiling of the bust of Sir James Paget by his Great Grandson Sir Julian Paget in 1995.

Original Consultants at District General Hospital

Anaesthetists

Dr Neville Hicks

Dr David Tunner

Dr Kingsley Branch

Dr Jenny Jenkins

Dr Eirlys Davies

General Surgeons

Mr Paul Aukland

Mr Hugh Sturzaker

Mr Julian Sansom

Mr John Corson
General Surgeon

Mr Tony Ashford Hodges
Orthopaedic Surgeon

Mr David Burgess
Orthopaedic Surgeon

Gynaecologists

Mr John Breeze

Mr William Costley

Mr Graeme Mc Lean

Original Consultants at District General Hospital

Physicians and others

Dr Ronnie Gibbs

Dr David Wayne

Dr Wolf Grabau

Dr Stuart Hishon

Dr Eric Back
Paediatrician

Dr Tony Edelsten
Paediatrician

Dr Alleyn O'Malley
Radiologist

Mr Ejaz Ahmed
A&E Consultant

Mr Khush Mangat
ENT Surgeon

Dr John Ball
Pathologist

Dr Terry Mitchell
Haematologist

Dr David Harrison
Histopathologist

Dr Anne Gerken
Microbiologist

Dr Ifor Williams
Radiologist

Mr Tony Couldrey
ENT Surgeon

Selection of Consultants who have been appointed since the hospital opened

Shalal Sadullah
Haematologist

Peter Greenwood
Gynaecologist &
Obstetrician

Dr Vinod Kumar
Radiologist

Dr Willy Notcutt
Anaesthetist

Peter Black
Ophthalmologist

Jerome Pereira
General Surgeon

Dr David Ellis
Physician

Dr Maggie Wright
Anaesthetist

Robert Jones
Orthopaedic Surgeon

Bernard Brett
Physician

Mr Andrew Pozyczka
Gynaecologist &
Obstetrician

John Studley
General Surgeon

Dr Robert Mann
Anaesthetist

Dr Michael Webber

Mr John Petri

Miss Jane Preston
Gynaecologist &
Obstetrician

Noel Johnson

General Manager and Chief Executives

Mr Andrew Butcher
General Manager

Mike Pollard

David Hill

Adrian Pennington

Medical Directors

Dr David Ellis

Mr Graeme McLean

Wendy Slaney
Medical Director &
Acting Chief
Executive

Chairmen

Garry Muter

John Wells

John Hemming

Senior Nursing Officers

Sally Cockrell

Vanessa Wood

Christine Smith

Nick Coveney

Directors of Finance

David Hill

Stephanie Davis

Julie Cave

Some of the original staff still working at the Trust in 2007

Christine Thompson

Madeleine Borg

Pat Mullen

Christine Eagle

Dr Stanley Cooper

Elayne Guest

request. Service level agreements operated in the early days of fund-holding GP practices, but attempts to roll out the system to all users, including the hospital, were thwarted. As Bill Butt, the Pathology Laboratory Manager at Northgate and James Paget for over 20 years, said on Anglia Television in the early 1990s, "It is like Sainsbury's without tills". A financial brake on requesting investigations would certainly lead to more sensible requests and should save money. There might be questions about the cost of introducing such a system, but similar schemes are already in operation in private hospitals and apply to private patients who are treated at the James Paget.

One worry for the future is the Government's increasing privatisation of the National Health Service, and there is the threat of this being applied to Pathology and particularly to Clinical Biochemistry. Unfortunately, many previous private initiatives introduced in the last few years have increased the costs to the Health Service.

A great regret of the laboratory staff is the sense of isolation. Few users visit the laboratory and the members of staff rarely get out and about the hospital. This lack of personal contact is sad, as the aim of having a staff social club and building the Burrage Centre was to encourage the integration and mingling of staff. Are members of staff invited to medical meetings when topics of a biochemical nature are being discussed and if not why not? Occasional sessions in the laboratory for Junior and perhaps not so Junior Medical staff would perhaps be mutually beneficial.

Haematology

Dr. Terry Mitchell was the first Consultant Haematologist and, until he was appointed in 1981, all the Haematology was supervised by John Ball. Jane Braithwaite was appointed as second Consultant in August 1990, after having worked in the Department for two years as a part-time Senior Registrar. Dr. Talal Jeha was appointed as Consultant Haematologist in 1996. Jane Braithwaite left in December 1996, to be replaced by Dr. Helena Daly. The next few months were very unhappy for everyone working in the Department. There was an investigation into the running of the Department, Helena Daly left and Terry Mitchell retired early to continue his work on chronic fatigue disorder. A recently retired Consultant from the Norfolk and Norwich Hospital did a prolonged locum attachment until Dr. Shalal Sadullah was appointed in 2000. Dr. Jeha left in 2003 and Dr. Sadullah worked as sole Haematologist until Dr. Jane Braithwaite returned in December 2003. They were joined by Dr. Cesar Gomez in 2006. At last, following the turmoil and unhappiness in the latter part of the 1990s, the Haematology Department has had a period of calm, expansion and innovation since Dr. Sadullah took over as clinical lead of the Department. A combined Lymphoma Clinic has been established with the oncologists, nurse-led anticoagulant clinics have started with radical changes to the management of anticoagulant services using a computer decision software system (APEX) and there is now an optimistic air in the Department. In addition to the three Consultants, there are three staff grades, two Clinical Nurse Specialists and 2.4 whole-time equivalent Anticoagulant Nurse Specialists.

The Nurse-led Anticoagulation Service started in 2000 by taking over the Anticoagulant clinics on two mornings a week, which previously had been run by Dr. Stanley Cooper. Since then, the service has expanded to cover in-patients at the James Paget, Lowestoft, Patrick Stead, All Hallows, Southwold, Northgate and a few other cottage hospitals. All local GP surgeries and some in Norwich buy into the service and there is a walk-in clinic Monday to Friday in Pathology between 8 and 10 am. Although for some patients the anticoagulant dosage is calculated by hand, for the majority this is done by computer and is based on the result of a blood test. Over 3,500 patients in the area are on anticoagulants.

The Service is run by three part-time Anticoagulant Nurse Specialists, who also run a Deep-vein Thrombosis (DVT) Service, which assesses whether a patient has a DVT or not.

Diagnostic Imaging Department

Based on advice from Dr. Vinod Kumar

Diagnostic Imaging is the more modern name for the X-ray Department. In the past it was only the X-ray machine which could produce images of the organs in the body. It was able to do this due to the fact that different tissues allowed the passage of variable amounts of X-rays through the body. This produces a picture and further information can be obtained by passing radio-opaque liquids into the stomach and large bowel or by injecting other substances into the arteries, veins or around the spinal cord. Later, ultrasound started to be used, mainly in Obstetrics and Gynaecology initially, and this works by detecting the image produced by high-frequency sound waves. Hownsfield showed that by sending X-rays from different angles and analysing the results in a computer it was possible to obtain very detailed pictures of the body. This was the basis of the CT Scan and, more recently, the development of Magnetic Resonance subjects the electrons in the body to a large magnetic field and analyses their movement when the magnet is turned off.

When the hospital opened, there were two Consultant Radiologists, Dr. Ifor Williams and Dr. Alleyn O'Malley, who provided the radiological services at Great Yarmouth and Lowestoft. Dr. Vinod Kumar joined the staff in October 1982 and Ifor Williams retired in 1984, to be replaced by Dr. Philip Lawrence. Dr. Michael Webber commenced the next year and, although he retired several years ago, he continues to work in the Department two days a week. Similarly, Dr. O'Malley retired in the early 2000s, but for many years did locum work in the Department. Dr. Antonio Martinez arrived in 1994 to progress the interventional radiology but, unfortunately, he was head-hunted by a Spanish University Hospital and left in 1997.

Dr. Holly Archer was appointed in 1994 to head the Breast Imaging Unit, which was about to open, as well as to do General Radiology. Dr. Eryl Thomas came in 1996. Dr. Hamid (1999 to 2002) and Dr. Almari (2000 to 2002) stayed for only a few years, and, in 2006, Dr. Amit Suri and Dr. Kashif Ashraf joined the staff. In addition, there have been several Consultants who have done a number of locums of varying lengths of time and notable among these have been Dr. Bruce Smith and Dr. Alfred Kruger, who now has a permanent position in the Department.

The first Superintendent Radiographer was Brian Baker, who continued to do locums for many years after he retired. He was followed by Colin West and subsequently by Kol Kishon. For the last few years, Kol Kishon has also been the Head of Department. A great deal of the Radiology is done by Radiographers and in recent years several have been trained to do such procedures as Barium Enemas, Ultrasound Examinations and Intravenous Urograms and to report upon them.

This has enabled the Department to increase its workload without lowering its standards. The efficient working of the Department also depends on the office staff, secretaries and voluntary workers.

In the past, all films had to be sorted, filed and moved between clinics, wards, theatres and various medical meetings. Fortunately, this is mainly in the past, since the introduction of the Picture Archiving Communication System (PACS), which enables the Department to go 'film-less'. Now the image of any patient can be brought up onto a computer screen anywhere in the hospital. Gone are the days of lost films, of searching through folders containing multiple films and of carrying a weighty bundle of films around the hospital. The images can also be sent to places outside the hospital.

The Imaging Department is in the centre of the hospital on the ground floor and when it opened it had six radiographic rooms and one for ultrasound. In 1984, it was decided to purchase a CT Scanner, diverting the funds allocated to install a Nuclear Medicine Department and raising the remaining money by a Public Appeal. It was thought that this would take about three years, but in six months the money had been raised. This produced a problem, as the Health Authority did not have the money to run it and to take on the extra staff. Fortunately, the Appeal was so successful that extra money from this was used to run the scanner for the first two years. At that time in East Anglia, only Cambridge and Ipswich had a CT Scanner and, shortly afterwards, Norwich was given one by the Department of Health. Before then, if a CT Scan was needed, patients had to travel to Cambridge or Ipswich.

The CT Scanner lasted much longer than was expected and was eventually replaced by the latest model in 1997 and, at the same time, an MR machine was installed into a joint suite as an extension to the Department. Fortunately, the money from the original appeal had increased to one million pounds by further donations and wise investment, so only another £500,000 needed to be raised by a further appeal for these two scanners.

The centre of an MR machine is a vast magnet in which the patient lies, and it cost £40,000 alone for the crane which was needed to hoist it over the hospital buildings into a courtyard before it could be installed. This was accomplished without incident one Saturday morning, with a number of spectators on the roof – including John Wells, Chairman of the Trust – each wearing a hard hat.

In 2005, a new multi-slice CT Scanner was installed into a new suite a short distance away from the main Department and the CT and MR Scanners in the joint suite were replaced by the latest models. Thus, in 20 years, the original scanner has been replaced twice and we have an additional one, giving us two. Also, the MR Scanner has been replaced after 10 years. Fortunately, these last three scanners were provided by the Department of Health.

These machines have revolutionised the investigation and management of many patients. They give accurate pictures of the size and position of tumours and whether the tumour has spread. This enables better decisions to be made about the management of patients. Before the scanner was on-site, it was sometimes necessary to perform urgent burr holes on patients who had had severe head injuries and who were deteriorating. Fortunately, a few benefited and survived. With the introduction of the scanner, it was possible to obtain an accurate assessment of the injury and the pictures could be sent down a telephone line to the Neurosurgical Unit at Addenbrooke's Hospital, where a neurosurgeon would decide whether the patient needed transferring there or could be managed at the James Paget. This was a great relief to all concerned and saved unnecessary operations and journeys.

Over the years, the Department has upgraded its Ultrasound machines. In the past the fuzzy pictures could only be interpreted by the person doing the scanning, but now the pictures are far more distinct.

Over the years, the importance of osteoporosis has been increasingly recognised. It is responsible for many fractures, severe back pain and shortness of stature. In recent years, assessment of bone density was done on the CT Scan, but lack of time with only one machine available meant that this was not done very often and the waiting list was up to 18 months. A DEXA Scanner, which measures bone mineral density, was obtained, but, unfortunately, there was no space in the Department for it. Fortunately, space was found for it on the Northgate Hospital site. This has proved most valuable and now the waiting time is a matter of a few weeks.

Over the years, several Radiologists have provided an interventional radiological service. This involves such procedures as putting needles into blocked kidneys to allow urine to drain or into the liver to drain bile, which has become blocked by stones or tumour. The latter procedure is rarely required now, due to the increased ability to pass stents into the bile ducts at endoscopic retrograde cholangio-pancreatography (ERCP). Stuart Hishon, the Hospital's first Gastroenterologist, started this procedure in the Department with Dr. Vinod Kumar. The procedure continued in the Department for many years, until the Endoscopy Suite had its own X-ray facilities.

Other interventional procedures involve taking biopsies of tissues or suspected tumours in the abdomen or chest, and occasionally the limbs, under ultrasound or CT control. An angiographic service was being developed in the mid-1990s by Dr. Martinez, but this stopped when he left, so patients had to go to Norwich for these procedures. Now, the more advanced CT Scanners can produce equally good pictures of the arteries without invasion and these can be done at the James Paget.

Since 2006, Specialist Registrars in Radiology from the Norfolk and Norwich Academy have been having sessions in the Department. This has brought a new dimension to education. Similarly, the Department has been taking an active part in the education of Medical students, which seems to be appreciated by both teachers and students.

Among many amusing incidents was the time when one of the nurses handed Dr. Webber's glasses to a patient at the end of the procedure. The patient went home happily wearing Dr. Webber's glasses, only to be telephoned later when the mistake was realised. Apparently, he was disappointed at having to return the glasses. Another example occurred while fundraising for the CT Scanner at a local primary school. Dr. Lawrence, who is not particularly tall and is rather pale, was with Dr. Kumar, who comes from India and is nearly six feet tall. Both wore identical T-shirts with the appeal logo emblazoned on the front. Some of the children were noticed to be whispering in the corridor. Eventually, one of them picked up the courage and walked up to the doctors and asked in a very innocent voice, "Excuse me! Are you two twins?"

In the last 25 years, the Imaging Department has seen many changes. The Consultant staff has expanded from two to six, with several other sessions being done by locums. The quality of the pictures produced has improved immensely and now no films are needed as the images are transferred directly to computers, enabling them to be viewed on screens throughout the hospital. The biggest innovation is the CT

Scanner, which produces amazing pictures, helping greatly in diagnosis and management. It is perhaps unfortunate that the Department was built in the middle of the hospital, for this has made it difficult to expand to house its new scanners and the Breast Imaging Department; but this has been achieved and by being in the centre of the hospital the Department's facilities are easily accessible.

Breast Imaging Department

Based on an article by Susan Jones

Susan Jones was appointed Head of Breast Imaging/Superintendent Radiographer on 11th August 1993, with the task of setting up this new department and service, which opened on 1st April 1994. The unit was funded entirely from the proceeds of a public appeal, to which the local population responded extremely generously. The official opening ceremony was performed on 9th May 1994 by Mrs. Renee Burgess, Chairlady of BRAS, a long-standing patient and friend of Mr. Sturzaker, and a prominent supporter of the appeal fund.

The Department was set up primarily to provide a diagnostic breast imaging service to the population of the old Great Yarmouth and Waveney Health Authority. Prior to 1994, a limited mammography service was available from the North Sea Medical Centre, a private clinic, paid for by donations to an endowment fund. The National Health Service Breast Screening Programme for women aged 50 to 64, which was launched nationally in 1989, had been provided by the Norfolk and Norwich Hospital for the Norfolk women and Ipswich Hospital for those living in Suffolk. The new Breast Care Unit, as it was called then, was destined to take over provision of this service in its entirety during 1994. For four years, the unit had to rely on the loan of a mobile unit from Norwich and Ipswich in turn, to take the screening service to the community.

When it opened, the unit in the hospital had one mammography room, one ultrasound room and one film processor. There were two Radiographers, including the Superintendent, two part-time Receptionists and a Secretary. Dr. Holly Archer and Dr. Alleyn O'Malley were the Consultant Radiologists. Over the years the work has increased and now the present staff levels are:

Present staff levels	*People*	*wte*
Consultant Radiologists	2	0.9
Head of Breast Imaging/Superintendent Radiographer	1	1
Specialist Practitioner/Deputy Superintendent	1	1
Advanced Practitioner	1	0.6
Radiographers	7	4.4
Assistant Practitioners	2	1.8
Imaging Assistants	2	1
Office Manager	1	0.8
Admin Assistants	2	1.4
Secretary	2	0.8

Once available, the service experienced a rapid increase in demand. By the late 1990s, there was a national shortage of both breast radiologists and radiographers, so the Unit embraced the Government's New Ways of Working policy and embarked on the training of Radiographers to support the Radiologists' role. Two Radiographers, Eileen Clark and Moira Simmons, have successfully completed postgraduate modules to become Advanced Practice Accredited Breast Screening Film Readers, and Eileen Clark went on to achieve, with distinction, her postgraduate diploma. She is now a Specialist Practitioner and undertakes film reading, clinical and breast ultrasound examinations, needle biopsies and pre-operative wire localisations.

Imaging Assistants were appointed to support the Radiographers by processing and collating films, loading and unloading roller viewers, preparing clinics, entering results and chaperoning patients. This allowed the Radiographers to concentrate on the vital role of actually taking mammograms.

The Government decided to extend the breast screening programme and, in 2001, the Unit commenced the first stage by implementing two-view mammography at every screening episode. By the end of 2004, the age extension had been completed, with all women up to the age of 70 receiving a screening invitation routinely. In effect, this was a 38% increase in workload and, in order to cope with the numbers, it was decided to appoint and train Assistant Practitioners to undertake a large part of the routine screening mammography.

The Assistant Practitioners received their clinical training from working alongside the Radiographers in the Unit and had their standards assessed by one of the national mammography trainers. The academic component was a newly devised and validated Higher Certificate of Education distance learning course from Anglia Ruskin University. The two trainees from this Unit were in the first cohort of students and successfully qualified in September 2006.

In just over 10 years, the number of symptomatic mammograms taken has increased by more than three times and the number of ladies who have had breast screening has more than doubled. The actual figures for 1994/1995 show the Unit did 1,357 symptomatic mammography and ultrasound examinations and screened 4,719 women. In 2005/2006 it did 4,178 symptomatic mammography and ultrasound examinations and screened 9,021 women.

By the end of 1997, it was apparent that the Department could no longer cope with the workload. Plans were drawn up to extend the Unit and a second mammography room and additional film processor came into use in 1998. The Hospital staff coffee lounge disappeared at the same time to make way for another film reading room (where the weekly Multi-disciplinary Team meetings were held) and the development of the Broadland Suite to accommodate breast, oncology and some surgical outpatient clinics. Around this time, the Breast Care Unit became known as Breast Imaging in order to distinguish it from the Outpatient facility and to lessen confusion for patients who frequently turned up at the wrong place.

The Big 'C' charity has been very generous to the department. In 1997/98, it funded the purchase of a brand new, fully equipped mobile breast screening unit which gave complete control over the screening programme schedule for the first time since April 1994. The mobile unit goes to central Great Yarmouth, Halesworth, Beccles and two sites in north and central Lowestoft to take the screening programme out to the population. In 2000, the Big 'C' funded the purchase of a small field digital stereo-tactic unit to attach to one of our existing machines. This allowed for much more effective and faster needle biopsies for the diagnosis of breast disease.

A third roller viewer and a replacement ultrasound machine were provided by New Opportunities funding in 2000.

Over the years, a strong team has been forged with Breast Imaging working closely with breast surgeons, pathologists, oncologists and breast care nurses. The unit was highly commended at the last inspection by the Regional Quality Assurance Team in 2005. Improvements to patient service and increased cancer detection rates were attributed to the hard work and dedication of staff. However, equipment and accommodation are now the limiting factors to any further service improvement.

2007/2008 will hopefully see considerable change in Breast Imaging. The mammography and ultrasound machines are old technology and have reached the end of their serviceable life. The way forward now is to install PACS and full field digital mammography equipment that embraces the latest in diagnostic technology.

In addition to running the Department, Sue Jones is the Regional Quality Assurance Radiographer for the Eastern Region, which involves her visiting, examining and reporting on other hospitals. This position is an honour for her and the Unit and helps to keep her informed of advances in other places.

The Breast Imaging Department has been a great success story. Having been the first hospital in East Anglia to provide mammography for National Health Service patients through using the mammography unit at the North Sea Medical Centre and paying for the mammograms for many years by money raised from the public, the hospital was very disappointed not to have been appointed a screening centre. A compromise was reached whereby Norwich and Ipswich screened the local population and sent the abnormal films to the North Sea Medical Centre, where the patients were examined and, if a biopsy was required, this was done at the James Paget. A Public Appeal enabled a Breast Imaging Unit to be built at the James Paget and in recent years its results have been equal to the top two hospitals in the whole of the Eastern Region. This has justified the decision for the hospital to have its own unit, but it will keep it only if the high standards and dedication of the staff are maintained.

The Nick McIver Hyperbaric Unit

Based on information supplied by Dr. Pieter Bothma and Bob Mann

Oxygen is essential for life and makes up 21% of ordinary air. Hyperbaric Oxygen Therapy involves breathing in oxygen at a pressure greater than normal atmospheric pressure while in a specially designed pressure chamber. It is used for treating decompression illness (known as 'the bends', which occurs when divers come to the surface from a deep dive too quickly, so causing bubbles of nitrogen to be released into the blood stream and tissues), carbon monoxide poisoning, gas gangrene and necrotising fasciitis, radiation necrosis, compromised skin flaps and severe burns.

The early offshore and diving medical work in Great Yarmouth started in August 1965, when Dr. Michael Evans, a GP from Central Surgery in Gorleston, was called to a drilling ship after a driller had been felled by a falling pipe.

The first diving medical involvement arose in 1966, when Dr. Robin Cox, a fellow GP from Central Surgery, was called to a diving accident in the West Sole Field. Subsequently, The North Sea Medical Centre (NSMC) was established in 1974 by the five GPs at the Central Surgery.

Until 1987, the Hyperbaric Chamber (a twin-lock, Seagull 60? unit), which now exists within the James Paget University Hospital, was owned and run by Bernie Stockton for the company Maritime Offshore Projects (MOP) and then his own company, Seaweld Diving Services. Seaweld operated from a shed by the river on Southtown Road. Bernie Stockton sold his business and the Chamber was bought by Stena Offshore, who ran it on the Harfrey's Industrial Estate from 1988 until they moved out of Great Yarmouth in 1996.

In 1987, when Dr. Thomas Pace joined the Medical team, Dr. Nick McIver was the lead diving medical figure for the unit and had gained an international reputation for his expertise. At that time, Central Surgery received only a small and inadequate retainer for all the hyperbaric work it carried out and a new contract was negotiated by Dr. Pace and Dr. David Watson with the Regional Public Health Consultant.

When Stena Offshore pulled out of Great Yarmouth, another company endeavoured to take over the Chamber and the running of it; but Dr. Pace saw an opportunity for the North Sea Medical Centre to take it over. One of his partners at Central Surgery, Andy Colvin, was also undertaking training in Occupational Medicine under Dr. Pace's direction through the North Sea Medical Centre and it was decided to involve him in the deal, and the Chamber was ultimately purchased for a 'peppercorn' price from Stena Offshore. Mike Pollard was the James Paget Hospital Chief Executive at the time and David Hill the Director of

Finance. They both agreed that the service could be moved into the James Paget Hospital and provided the real estate and installation costs. Since that date, the Chamber has been jointly run by the North Sea Medical Centre and the James Paget Hospital.

The Hyperbaric facility at Great Yarmouth was a founder member of the British Isles Group of Hyperbaric Therapists, formed in 1990 to promote the understanding and safe practice of Hyperbaric Medicine, and to provide a forum for discussion of Hyperbaric Therapy Practice in the British Isles. In 1993, the group was renamed the British Hyperbaric Association (BHA) and the Medical Team at Great Yarmouth were actively involved in drawing up the constitution of the BHA. The Unit achieved the status of a Category 1 BHA facility and, working in close co-operation with the Trust, saw a varied caseload of mainly emergency referrals, including ITU cases, from all over the east of England. Carbon monoxide poisoning, anaerobic infections and threatened plastic surgery wound flaps are regularly treated, in addition to the usual number of divers with decompression sickness. All other conditions recognised by the European Underwater and Baro-Medical Society are catered for.

Dr. Nick McIver became the Chamber Director and Dr. Andy Colvin his Deputy. Phil Smith of NSMC was appointed Manager of the Unit. When Dr. McIver retired in 2000, Dr. Pace appointed Dr. Colvin as Director and became Deputy Director himself. Dr. Colvin left the practice in August 2002, at which time Dr. Pace assumed the Directorship. Dr. Bob Mann, with the assistance of Dr. Thinus Mostert and Matron Smalley, did a mammoth task to set the standards for the Category 1 facility.

In 2005, the North Sea Medical Centre and its assets, which included the Hyperbaric Chamber, were sold to Abermed Ltd., an Aberdeen-based company specialising in Occupational Health Medicine. In 2006, discussions between the James Paget University Hospital and Abermed Ltd. over the long-term development of the service culminated in the Chamber and service being purchased by London Hyperbaric and Wound Healing Centres Ltd.

As from 1st February 2007, the Hyperbaric Service at the James Paget is being re-provided by London Hyperbaric and Wound Healing Centres Ltd. in the framework of a Private Public Partnership with James Paget University Hospitals NHS Trust. Dr. Pieter Bothma, currently head of the Department of Anaesthetics within the Trust, is currently the Medical Director of the Unit and Phil Sayers is the Managing Director. The medical cover is given by several hyperbaric-trained Anaesthetists, Accident and Emergency Consultants, and some of the original Occupational Health Specialists. The diversity of expertise allows the whole spectrum of hyperbaric medicine to be practised and that includes caring for critically ill patients. The new state of the art chamber that has been ordered will make this easier and safer.

Pain Relief Service

Based on article by Dr. William Notcutt

The first Pain Relief Clinic was set up in the early 1970s by David Turner, Consultant Anaesthetist. These were the early days of Pain Relief Clinics worldwide, which grew out of the recognition that there were many patients who had chronic pain for which modern medicine did not have cures. He managed to obtain space at the Gorleston Hospital, where the Orthopaedic Department was based, and did one and a half sessions weekly. With the opening of the District General Hospital, he transferred his clinics there and these were held in the Central Treatment Suite.

Pain treatment at that time revolved mainly around the use of injections into painful areas. Sometimes, injections were used to destroy nerves, especially for pain from cancer. In 1982, William Notcutt joined the Department and the Clinic was expanded. In 1983, Bob Mann was appointed Consultant Anaesthetist and joined the team as the third Pain Consultant. The three Consultants were then able to support the emerging Palliative Care Team in pain and symptom control.

By 1986, it was becoming realised that pain management in acute situations such as post-operative pain was not being very well managed. A new technique had emerged, Patient-controlled Analgesia (PCA), whereby the patient used a pump to give morphine intravenously. This enabled the patients to control their pain after operations and give themselves as much or as little as they needed.

The technique was new in the United Kingdom and James Paget Hospital was one of the first hospitals to embark on it. By 1990, the hospital had treated over 1,000 patients with this technique and had developed the methods for using this technique on ordinary wards. As the team's experience grew, it was approached by many other hospitals, including a large number of London teaching hospitals, to find out how to introduce this technique in their hospitals. In 1990, Consultant Anaesthetists Willy Notcutt and Richard Morgan published an article on the introduction of PCA to a District General Hospital, based on the results of the first 1,000 patients. Since then, PCA has been an established part of the management of pain after surgery and the experience of Willy Notcutt and his team have contributed much to what is current practice and also to the design of the pumps used.

By 1990, it was being suggested that every hospital should have an acute pain team. Jan Austin, who had been Sister in Charge of the Central Treatment Suite, joined the Pain Team to develop the specialist nursing role in Pain Management. Now she is Consultant Nurse in Pain Management. As time went by, it was realised that the concept of an acute pain team separate from chronic pain services was impractical and probably fundamentally wrong. Therefore, at the James Paget these two elements of pain management have always been run together. Most acute pain is on the wards, and most chronic pain is seen in the clinics. However, there is significant overlap and the Pain Team has been invited to many national meetings to present its views on this matter.

In the mid 1990s, Dr. Notcutt and his team started to embark on clinical research and undertook several multi-centre studies on new analgesics (painkillers). This has resulted in many international presentations and publications.

In 1995, the foundation of the Back Pain Service was established, based on the three elements of pain, Orthopaedics and Specialist Physiotherapy. With Mr. George Heyes Moore, Dr. Notcutt and his team undertook a major evaluation of this in 1997/1998 and were able to show there were major difficulties in the delivery of primary and secondary care in patients with back pain. At this time, George Heyes Moore was doing mini-discectomies (operating on prolapsed discs through small incisions in the back) and had appointed a specialist Spinal Physiotherapist to advise patients and the Trust on back management. Unfortunately, Mr. Heyes Moore had to retire on grounds of ill-health in 2000. From then onwards, the Back Pain Service was revised, bringing it under the management of the Pain Service and out of Orthopaedics. This enabled a close integration of pain management, occupational therapy and psycho-social support alongside the core element of specialist physiotherapy in the management of spinal problems. The final element that was necessary was the involvement of a Consultant in spinal surgery, doing clinics and operating at the James Paget University Hospital. This was achieved in 2006 with clinics and surgery being done by Messrs. Crawford and Lutchman, from the Norfolk and Norwich University Hospital.

Throughout the 1990s, Dr. Notcutt developed an interest in the use of synthetic derivatives of cannabis to try and help people with intractable pain. Cannabis has been used since the dawn of history for the relief of symptoms and evidence started to emerge of the presence of a cannabis system within the body similar to that associated with morphine. Most people have heard of endorphins (the body's own morphine); now it is recognised that there are endo-cannabinoids (the body's own cannabis).

In 2000, new extracts of cannabis were made available and the James Paget led the way in clinical research, and this continues. Primarily, patients with multiple sclerosis have been studied, but the work is expanding outwards to try and find out what the place of these therapeutic agents is in the management of pain and other symptoms.

At the end of the 1980s, the Pain Clinic left the Central Treatment Suite and moved to the clinic room on the corridor to Wards 4 and 5. At the time, this provided more flexibility and enabled the team to increase its service. However, as time went by, the facilities became increasingly cramped. Furthermore, the environment was unsatisfactory for patients. There was increasing concern that people with severe back pain and other unpleasant conditions were sitting on poor quality chairs in a dimly-lit corridor with traffic constantly going past in all directions. For many years attempts were made to find alternative accommodation, but there was none.

In 2004, the old Intensive Care Unit, next to the Operating Theatre Recovery Ward, became vacant and agreement was quickly obtained that this could become the Pain Clinic, but there were no funds for it. However, shortly after this agreement was reached, the Team was surprised to receive over half a million pounds from two benefactors –

Miss Phyllis Crews and Mrs. Grace Evans – within a matter of two or three weeks. Over the succeeding six months, the old Intensive Care Unit was converted and in June 2005 the new clinic opened. The new Unit provides three general consulting rooms, two Consultant offices, offices for the Specialist Nurses and the Administrative Team, plus a research office. Most importantly, there is a pleasant waiting area for the patients, customised to their needs as far as is possible.

More or less overnight, not only had the working conditions improved dramatically, but patients found the experience of coming to the clinics so much more pleasant.

This increase in accommodation allowed for the expansion not only of the clinical staff but also of the secretariat. Furthermore, it allowed other professionals such as Physiotherapists and Occupational Therapists to work alongside the team. Even staff from the Disability Employment Agency now come and see clients in the clinic facility.

The next goal is to use the new clinic in the evening and possibly at weekends for private complementary therapy such as acupuncture, aromatherapy, etc.

At the end of 2006, the Government brought out a Paper on musculoskeletal services focusing on chronic problems. In reviewing this, the James Paget Team finds that it is well "ahead of the game" and there is no doubt that, in the future, management of chronic pain is going to become increasingly important as the population ages.

Palliative Care

Based on articles by Dr. William Notcutt, Kathy Nobes and Gerda Gibbs

In 1983, Dr. Willy Notcutt approached the District Health Authority over the absence of any Palliative Care Service. At that time, this was a relatively new concept, and most people considered that Palliative Care meant building a hospice. The District Health Authority asked him to come back with a plan for the future, but stipulated that it must not cost very much!

He spent the next two years meeting with a variety of people both locally and nationally. Two important themes emerged. Firstly, hospices had focused on patients with cancer. However, Palliative Care was about people with life-limiting disease from all causes. Therefore, any service that was developed should incorporate this principle. Secondly, there was a perception that to do Palliative Care one had to take the patient to the hospice, but it was clearly impossible to build an institution to accommodate the needs of everybody who was dying. The elongated shape of the District meant that many people would be a long way from it. Therefore, the alternative approach of taking the "hospice to the patient" became the guiding principle.

There were two important elements to the second principle. Firstly, there was the need for clinicians who had been trained in this field. Secondly, there was the need to disseminate their knowledge out to every nurse, doctor, physiotherapist, manager, etc., who came into contact with dying patients. Continuous education would be the essential element of this.

With this approach, all other principles of "hospice care" have been embraced by the service, and comprise:

- A focus on quality of life, which includes good symptom control.
- A whole-person approach, taking into account the person's past life experience and current situation.
- Care which encompasses both the person with the life-threatening illness and those that matter to that person.
- Respect for patient autonomy and choice.
- An emphasis on open and sensitive communication which extends to patients, informal carers and professional colleagues.

In 1985, the first Palliative Care Nursing Sister (Macmillan Nurse), Diane Bryan, was appointed. The funding for this was initially from Macmillan Cancer Relief. She was succeeded the next year by Chris White and Kathy Nobes, as it was realised that such a service was impossible for one individual.

From those early days, the clinical service was primarily to support those with complex palliative care needs, over and above the needs that can be met by most hospital and community nurses and doctors. Patients would still need high levels of support from these 'frontline' generalist services. It was clear that patients needed a range of services, from primary and secondary care, health and social services, independent and voluntary agencies. To improve palliative care provision, collaboration and co-operation of all partners involved in palliative care was essential, and the Palliative Care Working Party was formed, continuing until 2006.

Over the next five years, the service slowly developed, focusing both on clinical care and on education. Both these elements were well received within the district and the nurses were rapidly accepted in all health areas (general practice, the community, outpatient clinics and in the hospital wards). There were no "no-go" areas. Naturally, many clinicians needed to realise the benefits of the Palliative Care support that could be brought to their dying patients. The skills of the nurses in the team quickly brought a widespread acceptance.

In 1990, the team was expanded when Sister Gerda Gibbs joined Andrea Baxter-Pownall and Kathy Nobes. The Palliative Care Team was located next to the Pain Clinic, in the centre of the hospital. It was always felt that this was an ideal location as it demonstrated the importance of Palliative Care in clinical medicine. So often, Palliative Care Teams are relegated to some distant room in the hospital – or worse, to an outlying hospital – and can find it very difficult to come into the mainstream.

The medical support for the Palliative Care Team has come principally from the Pain Relief Consultants, who principally have provided expert knowledge on the use of drugs and other techniques to provide symptom control. The main development in the 1980s was the growth of the use of morphine and other pain-relieving techniques. There had been a huge reluctance to use morphine, seeing it partly as a drug addiction but also as being potentially dangerous. Changing attitudes to this and improving skills at managing pain were an important early priority. Sadly though, this has never been taken up by the medical schools, and the team has been faced with new junior doctors every six months who have little or no knowledge of how to manage pain and other symptoms for the dying (nor in other areas of medicine).

During the 1990s, a rolling programme of palliative care education was established. Through links with Suffolk College and the University of East Anglia, team members contributed to the planning and delivery of palliative care education modules. In 1992, Gerda Gibbs developed a Palliative Care Link group to "promote the highest standards of palliative care in all healthcare settings". This was followed by 'Widening Horizons', the first 'in-house' palliative care course for trained nurses, social workers and allied health professionals, in 1993, and, from 1996, monthly courses for healthcare assistants (formerly nursing auxiliary and support workers) commenced, and continue today. *Ad hoc* training events were frequently held in community settings, in response to specific requests, strengthening the local network of palliative care services.

In 1996, reviews of palliative care needs of local people, by Amanda Jones and Vanessa Woods, for Norfolk Health Authority, and by Robert Jones for Suffolk Health Authority, identified a shortfall of palliative care resources within Great Yarmouth and Waveney, compared to all neighbouring services, and additional posts were deemed a priority. With Health Authority funding and further support from Macmillan Cancer Relief (now Macmillan Cancer Support), six new posts were created between 1998 and 2000:

- Trust Specialists in Palliative Care (now Associate Specialists), 2 x 0.5 wte posts: Dr. Jenny Mallion and Dr. John Shutes, with the latter replaced by Dr. Bernadette Auger in 2002.
- Lymphoedema Specialist Physiotherapist: Sandra Westrop.
- Specialist Occupational Therapist: Alison Wall (later Bev Chilson).
- Macmillan Nurse Specialist / Team Leader: Kathy Nobes.
- Macmillan Nurse post: Julia Hunt and Liz Crowe.
- Head of Palliative Care Education: Gerda Gibbs.

Vacated Macmillan Nurse posts were later taken up by Jane Beales, Michelle Crump and Sharon Fish.

Both Health Authority Reviews and a further Palliative Care Health Needs Assessment by Dr. Phil Berry (2001) endorsed the local philosophy of 'hospice to the patient' care, and of empowering all local staff to give good palliative care, by the comprehensive palliative care education programme. The co-ordination of care, made possible by a single specialist palliative care service, with team members working across hospital and community settings, was also deemed responsive to the changing needs of patients. Sadly, most patients will be admitted to hospital at least once in their last year of life, and often, such patients have multiple admissions in that final year.

With the addition of these new colleagues, the multi-disciplinary specialist Palliative Care Team extended its influence. In recent years, student therapists and medical students have regularly work-shadowed members of the team, and a small number has had secondment to the service, so increasing their awareness of palliative care.

From 2002, Dr. Patrick Blossfeldt became the Lead Consultant for Palliative Care, although still on a voluntary basis, with no designated time for these duties until 2003.

In 2002, Dr. Patrick Blossfeldt and Kathy Nobes led the development of a business plan for Lottery funding to expand the Palliative Care services available locally. In collaboration with representatives from Great Yarmouth and Waveney Primary Care Trusts, Norfolk and Suffolk Social Care Services, Macmillan Cancer Support, Waveney Hospice Care, and Norfolk and Waveney Cancer Network, a Hospice at Home service was planned. The award of Lottery funding led to the addition of:

- 0.5 wte Lead Consultant for Palliative Care: Dr. Patrick Blossfeldt.
- Hospice at Home Service:
  - Care Coordinator: Jan Foster, replaced by Di Futter in 2006.
  - 4.6 wte Hospice at Home Carers.
- Specialist Social Worker: Babs Williams.
- 2 wte Macmillan Nurses: Denise Berrisford and Jeramy Philpott.

With these new colleagues, it became possible to offer rapid-response visits, hold a rapid-access clinic, provide additional support to those families who are disadvantaged and to give high quality, 'hospice at home' care over some of the acute and changing episodes within the patients' last year of life. Together, these initiatives help to prevent unnecessary admission to hospital, support rapid discharge home from hospital, and enable patients to spend more of their final year of life at home, in accordance with their wishes.

Also at this time, the service was given excellent accommodation for the expanding team within the offices formerly used by the Intensive Care Unit. All team members work from this central base, allowing easy access to all other members of the multi-disciplinary team, for networking, advice and multi-disciplinary discussion regarding the more complex aspects of care. Easy access to hospital records, diagnostic services and reports, and the wide range of specialists available within secondary care facilitates rapid, high level, one-stop assessments of many patients who present with complications, recurrence of their illness, or the many palliative care emergencies.

Equally, the hospital is reasonably central to the Great Yarmouth and Waveney locality, enabling staff members to radiate out to their caseload locations when visiting patients in their own homes, which forms the greater part of the service, with over 75% of the total caseload within the community at any time.

More recently, Department of Health documents were published confirming the role of Specialist Services. Most influential was the NICE Guidance (NICE, 2004) which underpins the team's commitment to implement the Gold Standard Framework and the Liverpool Care Pathway in both the community and hospital settings. Macmillan Cancer Support generously funded two posts for three years – a full-time and a part-time Macmillan Nurse post – leading to the appointment of Mandy Whitehouse and Jo Fuller, to assist with the implementation of these pathways.

When caring for patients who are near the end of their lives, these two pathways anticipate and plan for patients' needs, whenever possible, rather than later reacting to crises. The enthusiasm and willingness of generalist colleagues, when introducing these concepts, is most encouraging. Health carers, working in hospital and community settings, demonstrate great commitment and passion to improve the care of those who have a life-threatening illness.

Non-clinical staff play a vital role in the provision of good palliative care, and from the outset of the Specialist Palliative Care Team, the contribution of the secretarial staff has been exceptional. The secretaries' good interpersonal skills enable them to rapidly establish a rapport when patients and their relatives contact this service, and to give an initial level of support until a clinician is available.

Professor Mike Richard's view is that: "The way an organisation looks after the dying reflects the quality of care throughout that organisation."

Although it is not possible with current staff levels to provide a 24-hour advice line, as recommended by NICE Guidance, the service has commenced a Saturday advice line and will extend this service further when there is sufficient staff to do so.

Very recently, Nicky Downs and Steve Newman have come into post. They job-share, and are developing plans to establish a Bereavement Counselling Service. This new service will embrace the additional opportunity and value afforded by skilled volunteers, some of whom have a wealth of experience and qualifications, and have generously offered to provide counselling or support to those who are bereaved.

Of increasing importance are the many ethical issues that relate to the end of life. Ensuring the autonomy of patients, giving them choice regarding the place and priorities of their individual care, using Advance Care Planning, Advance Directives and Lasting Power of Attorney to facilitate care in accordance with the patient's wishes – these are all increasingly important, and are only possible when staff have the necessary knowledge and skills to secure informed consent.

Finally, on our easterly horizon, is the vision and plan of a new Palliative Care Centre, funded by the Trust Public Appeal, which will make it possible to meet, assess and support patients and their families in privacy, and in a comfortable environment, where they can have the support of skilled volunteers around one-stop, in-depth assessments by expert clinicians.

The dignity, courage and humour of those approaching the end of their life makes it a privilege to be involved in the delivery of palliative care, and drives the motivation to continually improve the services we can offer.

Infection Control

Joanna Kingston was the first District Clinical Nurse Specialist in Infection Control and she ran the Department with Dr. Anne Gerken, Clinical Microbiologist, for a number of years. Linda Hawtin succeeded Joanna Kingston and her Department has increased in size as infections have become more serious and more common. This has been associated with the increasing resistance of bacteria to antibiotics as a consequence of their use being much more widespread, not only in hospitals, but in the community. In addition, the population is older, the elderly are less resistant to infection and increasingly invasive measures are being used to monitor patients. In the 1990s, efforts were made to prevent Methicillin Resistant Staphylococcus Aureus (MRSA) entering the hospital by swabbing patients prior to elective admissions to detect those harbouring the bacterium. This was expensive in time and money and did not work. Attempts were made to isolate infected patients in side rooms, but often there were not enough rooms. In the last few years, there have been major campaigns to try and reduce the incidence of infection in the hospital and an index of its effectiveness is the fact that the annual number of patients having MRSA in their bloodstream has reduced from 50 to 27 in the last two years. For many decades, Clostridium difficile has been known to cause membranous colitis, resulting in diarrhoea and abdominal pains. Clostridium difficile is a bacterium which is found in the intestines of many people and causes them no problems. However, if the person is in a weakened state, or has had some antibiotics, which kill off the normal bacteria in the intestines, then the Clostridium can multiply and make the patient ill. This used to occur infrequently but, in the last 10 years, has become much more frequent. At the beginning of 2007, it was noted that affected patients were far more ill than usual: some needed emergency surgery to remove their diseased colon and some died. Prior to this, it was exceptional for such patients to require this type of surgery and further investigations showed that a particular strain of the bacterium was responsible. New measures of cleaning, using steam and bleach, were started and extra cleaners were employed. Infected patients were nursed in a ward separate from other patients and staff; patients and visitors were reminded of the importance of hygienic measures. Some wards reduced the number of beds in a bay from six to four. On Friday 30th March, a Press Conference was called to explain that there was an outbreak of a virulent strain of Clostridium difficile which had been associated with the deaths of 17 patients in the preceding three months. This resulted in banner headlines in the national press and coverage on the radio and television implying that such outbreaks are associated with dirty hospitals. This was very upsetting to all concerned, as the James Paget has an excellent record of cleanliness. Later, it turned out that many other hospitals had similar, and even worse, problems. Fortunately, the various measures which had been started proved effective and the outbreak was rapidly brought under control. A national expert on this condition visited the hospital and was so impressed by the measures which had been adopted that he was going to recommend them to other hospitals. A brochure on how the outbreak was tackled is being prepared and will be circulated by the Department of Health. This outbreak has been tragic for the patients and the relatives affected; it gave the hospital adverse publicity and has cost the Trust nearly one million pounds to bring in measures to deal with it. However, it has brought in new measures to combat infection, it has shown the importance of isolating infected patients and it has demonstrated the importance of good teamwork in tackling a problem. Nick Coveney, Director of Nursing and Patient Care, Wendy Slaney, Medical Director and Acting Chief Executive for much of the time, Dr. Ngozi Elumogo, Consultant Microbiologist and Director of Infection Prevention and Control, and Linda Hawtin, Senior Infection Control Nurse Specialist, and her team are to be congratulated on the way they tackled this outbreak.

Department of Nutrition and Dietetics

Based on an account from Eileen Duckworth

The Department provides a dietetic service to the hospital and the community of Great Yarmouth and Waveney Primary Health Care Trust. Diane Holt was Head of Department from 1984 until 1999, followed by Patrick Friel from 1999 to 2000. Eileen Duckworth has been Head of Department since April 2002.

The aims of the Department are to provide:

- Specific nutrition counselling on dietetic needs to patients and carers on an in-patient and outpatient basis.
- Open access to general practitioners for referrals and advice.
- Dietetic training for other healthcare professionals and catering staff.
- Advice to hospital catering departments on menu planning for patients and staff to ensure appropriate meal provision.
- A nutritional advisory and information service.
- Advice and support to local and national groups, for example Coeliac UK and Diabetes UK.

The number of staff in the Department has increased significantly over the last 25 years, but particularly over the last six years. This is a reflection of national changes and the increased awareness of the importance of the part nutrition plays in health and disease. There are nine Dietitians but, as some work part-time, there are only 7.9 whole-time equivalents. There is one Community Nutritionist, two Dietetic Assistants and one Secretary.

Among the changes which have happened over the years is the introduction and development of the role of the Dietetic Assistant. National studies and campaigns have raised the awareness of malnutrition in hospitals and brought attention to hospital catering and the patient experience of eating in hospital. Now, on admission, all patients receive nutritional screening to identify those at risk of malnutrition.

Dietitians play a major role in trying to assess the part of allergy in certain patients and in helping in the management of patients who have poor nutrition, either due to inadequate intake, disease or the result of surgery. In these circumstances, they give advice for those patients receiving nutrition enterally (via the gut) or parenterally (via major veins).

After major surgery, some patients are unable to eat and drink for some time. If, for some reason, the gastro-intestinal tract cannot be used, then liquids and nutrition can be given through tubes placed into large veins in the neck. There can be complications with this technique and the ideal method is to give the nutrition through fine tubes placed through the patient's nose into the stomach or upper small bowel. This is more effective than intravenous nutrition, is cheaper and has fewer complications.

All-in-one nutrition liquids were developed for man's trip to the moon on 21st July 1969. Very soon afterwards, they were being used in hospitals. Initially, the liquids were gravity fed to patients, but, by the 1970s, feeding pumps were being used, which more accurately control the speed of the fluid into the gut. These fluids are also used for the long-term nutrition of patients who are unable to swallow, e.g. after strokes, head injuries or in patients with cerebral palsy. The fluid is delivered into the patient's stomach by means of a Percutaneous Endoscopic Gastrostomy (PEG), which is inserted under local anaesthetic using a gastroscope. The Dietitians work closely with the Clinicians in the management of these patients and in Norfolk and North Suffolk there are 200 adults and children living at home and in care homes requiring PEG feeding. Before the early 1980s, when PEGs were introduced, the only means of introducing a feeding tube directly into the stomach and not through the nose (which in the long-term situation is unpleasant and can lead to complications) was by means of an open operation and this was rarely done for someone who had recently suffered a stroke.

Since January 2004, the dietetic students have spent their clinical placements at the James Paget and the Department is playing its part in the training of medical students. Closer links have developed with the Norfolk and Norwich University Hospital over the last five years, which has enabled the two hospitals to share resources and benefit from holding joint study days. The Annual Nutrition Days organised by the Department have been well attended and are a great success.

In the last 25 years, the Department of Nutrition and Dietetics has expanded its staff and its role. It highlights those patients who have poor nutrition and helps in their management. It makes sure that patients, staff and visitors in the hospital have food of good nutritional value and it gives advice to patients who are overweight. It helps in the education of dietetic and medical students and is aware that it needs to focus more on primary care where there is an epidemic in obesity and people still suffer from malnutrition.

Pharmacy

Based on information from David Todd

The Pharmacy is responsible for the delivery of drugs and other substances to patients in the wards and outpatients. It also makes up solutions for intravenous feeding and prepares drugs for oncology patients.

The Pharmacy is in the centre of the hospital towards the front and is one of only a few Departments which has not moved since the hospital opened. However, there have been some changes, such as new Dispensary benching and shelving in the mid-1990s, refitting of the Clean Room in 2002 and halving the size of the waiting area and refurbishing it to allow the Cancer Information Office to take over part of it.

Malcolm Brown was in charge of the Department when the Hospital opened and his successor was David Todd in 1995. There are 10 Pharmacists, 19 Pharmacy Technicians, 15 Assistant Technical Officers, 4 Secretarial and Clerical Staff, 2 Pre-Registration Pharmacists and 3 Pharmacy Technician Students. Some work part-time, so the number of whole-time equivalents is 43 compared with 33 in 1996/1997 and 22 in 1982.

The Department had the hospital's first stores computer in the early 1980s and this was followed by a Dispensing computer and a computer for Total Parenteral Nutrition. In 1985, it started chemotherapy reconstitution and its Pharmacy Computer System was upgraded in 1995/ 1996. An Oncology/ Haematology Pharmacist was appointed in 2002 and an Antibiotic Pharmacist started in 2007.

Over the years, there has been a move from supply to the managed use of medicines. Ward pharmacists check prescribing and advise patients about their drugs before they are discharged. There has also been the development of a strong training element.

For the future, David Todd sees more Clinical input and integration across primary and secondary care.

Department of Orthotics

Based on information from Mrs. Chris Tom

Orthotics involves the assessment and provision of appropriate orthoses for in-patients and outpatients. These include wigs, shoes, spinal supports, trusses, calipers and breast prostheses. The Department has one Manager, three Clerical and two contracted staff. The first Manager at the hospital was Miss Phyllis Middleditch, who had held a similar post at the old Great Yarmouth General Hospital. She retired in February 1987 and was replaced by Mrs. Jackie Munnings. She left in August 1991 and her place was taken by Mr. Alan Burgess from June 1987 to August 1989. Mrs. Chris Tom has been in charge since August 1991.

In 1992, there was a very small extension made to the Department, giving space for a larger clinic plus the provision of an examination couch instead of two small areas.

In the past, a number of different manufacturers would come to the Department every day, but this has been restricted to having only one company each day. This enables the Department to provide a much better service and continuity.

Among its successes has been the setting-up of an open clinic for ladies who have had mastectomies or who have other breast-related problems after surgery. It has also established a hairdressing clinic for patients requiring wigs, which are an increasing problem with the wider use of chemotherapy. The Department has co-ordinated – with the paediatric and neurology multi-disciplinary team – the setting-up of Botox clinics for children with cerebral palsy. The injection of Botox paralyses muscles for several weeks and has dramatically helped the muscle spasms in these patients. The Department also deals with babies with congenital dislocated hips and those with club feet.

The James Paget was the first hospital in the country to trial and develop Lycra gloves for cerebral palsy and the first glove ever manufactured for this condition was for a James Paget patient. The gloves help to reduce muscle tone and increase the patient's proprioception, i.e. the awareness of the positions of the fingers. The James Paget and Norfolk and Norwich University Hospitals are now working together on trials for the use of Lycra leggings and Lycra is being used for patients who have had strokes.

From a small Department, the staff is helping and providing many patients with a large range of orthotics and has participated in groundbreaking work in the application of Botox and Lycra garments. Each year, over 5,000 patients are seen in the Department.

Audiology Department

Based on an account by Jenette Powell

Prior to the opening of the James Paget Hospital, Audiology and Hearing Services were supplied by the Norfolk and Norwich Hospital, twice a week to the Great Yarmouth General Hospital and once a week to Lowestoft Hospital. The clinics were often undertaken in far from ideal conditions, so it was a great joy to open the Audiology Clinic on the day the hospital first held Outpatient Clinics – 4th January 1982 – and to have dedicated consulting rooms and sound-proofed Audiology rooms.

The Department was managed from the Norfolk and Norwich by the Head of Department, John Drake. He, along with Audiologists Moray Macnab, John Cook and Maureen Chapman, would alternate on a daily basis to cover clinics, along with the student Audiologist, Jenette Powell, who was the only permanent member of the Audiology staff based at the District General Hospital. The Department was also fortunate to have its own secretary, Pam Stott. As time went on, Janet Lawrence, from the Audiology Centre in Norwich, provided Hearing Therapy services two days a week.

The new Audiology Department consisted of two separate clinical areas at either end of the orthodontic corridor; one of which was the Hearing Aid Department and the other was the ENT and Audiology Department, where the Audiologists provided diagnostic support to the ENT Consultants at the time, Mr. A. D. Couldry and Mr. K. S. Mangat and their teams. The Audiologists also provided a comprehensive rehabilitation service which included hearing-aid fitting and maintenance. Open hearing-aid repair clinics were offered three times a week and often in those days patients would treat the sessions as a social event, going back to the waiting area to continue their conversations, which could sometimes be disheartening for the Audiologists as the queue did not appear to shorten!

One of the biggest difficulties in the early years was that the Audiology Department did not have its own budget for the provision of hearing aids. Hearing aids were brought over from the Norfolk and Norwich as required. However, as money was often tight there and they had a larger cohort of patients, invariably the District General Hospital did not get the number or type of aid they required. This made for interesting repair clinics when there could be in the region of 20 patients waiting to be seen and only a half a dozen hearing aids in the cupboard. It also made the Audiologists more inventive, as they had to solve patients' problems without necessarily changing their hearing aid.

After several years, the decision was made by Geoff Briggs, Hospital Administrator, to separate financially from the Norfolk and Norwich. This enabled the Department to set its own budget and for the first time become self sufficient. Not long after this, the Department broke away managerially as well and Jenette Powell became Head of the Department. The Department continued to grow. Moray Macnab had joined on a permanent basis and, subsequently, Robert Shepheard and John Middleton joined the Team, with Carol Lowe as Secretary. An extra hearing therapy session was provided one day a week by Clare Gatenby.

Janet Lawrence retired and was replaced for the other two days by Michael Horwood.

The Department went from strength to strength and in 1993 purchased Auditory Brainstem Response equipment and upgraded its vestibular testing equipment, so that the Audiologists could undertake advanced audiometry and balance testing, previously undertaken at the Audiology Centre in Norwich. In 1997, the Trust purchased Otoacoustic Emissions Equipment so that the Audiology team could provide neonatal hearing screening targeted to "At Risk" babies (mainly on the Special Care Baby Unit). It was to be several more years, several unsuccessful "Star Chamber" bids and a national initiative before this would become universal screening.

By the year 2000, both the Audiology Department and the ENT Department, now under the supervision of Mr. D. J. Premachandra and Mr. P. R. Prinsley, had outgrown the space provided and ENT moved out to Suite 1 at the front of the hospital and the Hearing Aid Department moved up to the space vacated by the ENT Department, to become the Audiology and Hearing Aid Department. In addition, the Department was given an extra room for a dedicated vestibular test room. The Audiology Team had also changed and grown. Robert Shepheard and John Middleton had left and Gary Osborne and Kevin Martland had joined as senior members of the Team, with Sue Sinden as a Trainee Audiologist. They were subsequently joined by Christopher Tovell as the number of patients seen continued to increase. The move also necessitated the use of a Receptionist and Jill de la Lynde took on this role.

In early 2000, the Audiology Department applied to be a First Wave site in the Government's initiative of Modernisation of NHS Hearing Aid Services (MHAS). The Department was successful in its bid and became one of 18 research sites. The project was funded by the Department of Health to evaluate the introduction of leading-edge digital signal processing (DSP) hearing aids across the NHS. The project partners were the Royal National Institute for the Deaf, NHS Supplies and the MRC Institute of Hearing Research. The aims of the project were to evaluate the costs and benefits of the introduction of DSP aids – which included evaluating Behind-the-Ear (BTE) and In-the-Ear (ITE) hearing aids – also the benefits of fitting unilaterally or bilaterally. The project also evaluated the costs and benefits of innovations in service delivery and reviewed supply arrangements. The project spanned 2000/2001 and 2001/2002. Four million pounds was made available nationally in the first year and six million pounds for the second year. The study's report gave much valuable information about future hearing aid service investment and service delivery changes.

Undertaking such a project brought with it positive and negative changes for the Department. On the positive side, through the development of MHAS, patient information was to be held electronically on a purpose-built database. This was to revolutionise the Department in that over 10,000 patient records were held on paper with all the difficulties that brought. As the Department was unable to recruit the recommended number of additional Audiology staff due to a national shortage of Audiologists, funding was used to employ data-input clerks to rationalise the number of patients known to the Department and to put active patients onto the database. The Department was then fully computerised with a networked computer in every consulting room.

It was a steep learning curve for the Audiologists with the introduction of the new database, new computer-based technology, digital signal processing hearing aids, new patient protocols and pathways and Audiologist-led clinics. This, coupled with undertaking research for the MRC as part of the project and the inability to recruit permanent staff, led to innovations in the way the Audiology team worked to ensure the best service for the patients and the staff alike. Part of this was to employ additional secretarial staff – Rosemary Whitmill and Verna Swan and subsequently Lyn Rowe – to relieve the Audiologists of administrative tasks that would free up much needed clinical time.

As MHAS was a national initiative, this prompted an unprecedented rise in demand for the service, which resulted in increased waiting lists and waiting times. However, with changes in working practices and employing long-term locums – Eldres Buekes and Mariana Kruger – five years on, what was new practice has become embedded service and wait times have decreased to enable us to achieve some of the best waiting times in the country.

In the second year of MHAS, the Department applied to become a second-wave site for Modernising Children's Hearing Services (MCHAS). The Department, with input it previously had from Jacqueline King, Audiological Scientist, had already developed Audiology-led

Paediatric Assessment Clinics and Paediatric Hearing Aid Clinics and that, coupled with the excellent ties it has with the Consultant Community Paediatrician, Teachers of the Deaf and Social Workers for the Deaf, set the Department in good stead to become a fourth-wave site in 2004 for another national initiative; this time for universal neonatal hearing screening.

The James Paget, Great Yarmouth PCT and Waveney PCT submitted a Tri-Trust bid to introduce Universal Newborn Hearing Screening (NHSP) as a Community Model. The screening of neonates is undertaken by the Health Visitor in the home at the first visit (day 10). Any "refers" are tested by the Local Screening Coordinator within a week. Referral to the Audiology Department for diagnostic testing is made by 4 weeks of age, thus reducing the age of detection of permanent sensorineural hearing loss from a mean age of 2.3 years to 3 months. Sally Howard was taken on as a part-time Clerical Officer to input data into the national screening database and the local child health database.

As the Audiology Department grew, so did the demand for Hearing Therapy services. Hearing Therapy initially had been funded regionally, which was then devolved to the Audiology Centre in Norwich to supply Hearing Therapists on a part-time basis. However, by 2004, it was felt that the Department would benefit from having its own permanent Hearing Therapist, so Michael Horwood was employed on a full-time basis. This meant that the Department could offer more counselling and rehabilitation as well as Tinnitus counselling and vestibular rehabilitation sessions. Due to the shortage of trained Hearing Therapists, the James Paget supplies Hearing Therapy for two sessions a month to the Queen Elizabeth Hospital in Kings Lynn.

In 2005, the Audiology Department joined with De Montfort University, Leicester, to take B.Sc. clinical placement students for a year of practical experience in their third year. Previously, Audiology Departments had taken on their own students and trained them. The last trainee Audiologist, who trained in the traditional manner, was Leanne Calver, and she graduated just prior to this new system starting.

By the end of 2005, the demand for the Department's services had grown so great, especially for the "drop in" open repair clinics, that the decision was made to change it to a booked repair system. The open clinics had become unmanageable, with up to 50 to 70 people turning up at each two-hour repair session. The waiting area was always packed and it was difficult for both patients and staff. In April 2006, after four months of raising awareness, the Department launched its booked system with templates allowing patients 15-minute appointments and with clinics being held throughout the week. Now the clinics are much easier to manage, it is known how many patients are on each clinic and they can be staffed accordingly. The waiting area is virtually empty as patients are seen on time and appointments are offered either on the day of request or within a couple of days. The only downside is that the telephones never stop ringing!

The last 25 years have seen changes that would not have been anticipated in 1982, including the ever-increasing demand for the service and the rise in staff numbers. In 1982, the staff whole-time equivalents stood at:

Senior/Chief Audiologists	1 wte (supplied by Norfolk and Norwich Hospital)
Student Audiologist	1 wte
Secretary	1 wte
Total staff	**3 wte**

On average, there were 3,500 patient contacts per year.

In 2007, the staffing consists of:

Head of Audiology	–	0.46	
Deputy Head	–	1.0	
Band 7	–	2.0	
Band 6	–	0.4	
Band 5	–	2.0	
Vacancy (Band 5/6)	–	1.0	Locum in post
Vacancy (Band 5/6)	–	1.0	To be appointed
3rd Yr Clinical Placement	–	1.0	
Clerical Staff	–	2.25	
Receptionist	–	0.5	
Total Staff	–	**11.61wte**	

Now, on average, there are 18,500 patient contacts per year.

So what does the future hold for the Audiology Department? Currently, the most pressing issue is to achieve the new diagnostic targets of six weeks from referral to test by the end of March 2008. Thankfully, the Department is starting from a good position of having some of the lowest wait times in the country. However, there is still some way to go and this means looking at more innovative ways of working; for example, one-stop assess and fit clinics, reducing the number of face-to-face follow-ups, different skill mixes and other ways of reducing waiting times. In the longer term, the Department is looking at new innovations in advanced audiometry with Auditory Steady State Response Audiometry, which is still in its infancy. In addition, the team will be developing complex needs clinics for patients who, after aiding, still have residual problems with their hearing. On the immediate horizon, there are Quality Assurance visits for Newborn Hearing Screening and later on for Adult Hearing services.

On a national scale, Audiology is in a state of flux, with very long waiting lists across the country. The Government has procured 300,000 independent sector patient journeys to reduce waiting times and there is a move to provide services "closer to home", so Audiology clinics may even end up on the High Street instead of being a hospital-based service.

This is an amazing story of how a much-needed service has developed from a total of three clinics a week shared between Yarmouth and Lowestoft and has blossomed into a highly successful and efficient Department serving over five times as many contacts a year with less than four times an increase in staff. In the last 25 years, the Department has taken the lead nationally in participating in ground-breaking studies and has extended its investigations and treatments. It is also interesting that the student audiologist who moved into the new Department for the first clinic on 4th January 1982 has been Head of Audiology for 20 years and she wishes to thank "the loyal and dedicated Audiology team past and present, which has made the events of the last 25 years possible".

Physiotherapy and Occupational Therapy Departments

These two Departments have much in common in trying to rehabilitate patients after operations, strokes and other conditions which bring people into hospital so it is sensible for the two departments to work closely together. The Physiotherapists also assess and prepare certain patients for theatre and help with their postoperative recovery.

Since February 2005 the therapists have worked together in specialist teams led by one Team Leader of either profession. They have found that the integration of Occupational Therapy and Physiotherapy encourages improved patient care, co-ordinated treatment programmes, shared learning and better communication. At the same time they integrated the roles of Occupational Therapy Assistants, Physiotherapy Assistants and Technical Instructors and introduced Therapy Assistant Practitioner and Therapy Assistant roles at the beginning of March 2006. These have now been assimilated into the various teams: Acute Medicine, Cardio/Respiratory/Surgery, Orthopaedic and Stroke Teams.

Community Paediatrics

From information from Dr. Ajit Verma

Dr. Ajit Verma was the first Community Paediatrician to be appointed and for many years he did on-call duties with the Paediatricians at the James Paget. His colleagues are Dr. Jane Mawer and Dr. Tony Goodwin. Their base is the Newberry Centre, which was built on the site of the small hospital in Gorleston which carried out elective orthopaedic surgery for the District. It is named after Dr. Roger Newberry, who was the District Medical Officer at the time of the opening of the District General Hospital.The Newberry Centre provides a co-ordinated service for children with neurodisability involving various agencies. There are multidisciplinary assessments and therapy and it is regarded as a centre of excellence. There is an Autistic Spectrum Diagnostic Forum, which again is multidisciplinary, and helps in the diagnosis and management of autism. The Attention Deficit and Hyperactive Disorder Services work in close collaboration with the child mental health team. There is a named Paediatrician and Nurse for Child Protection helping in the training and implementation of policies for child protection.

School Nurses are more involved with child mental health and public health issues and the Outreach Nursing Team provides services for children with chronic health problems in the community. A named Paediatrician is involved in training and advising on childhood immunisation.

The Newberry Centre has a very committed and hardworking group of professionals in Community Paediatrics which, despite limited resources, has been able to establish many good practices and has led to the improvement in childhood healthcare in the District.

Information Technology Department

Based on informations from Kim Turner

One of the major developments over the last 25 years has been the increasing use of computers. Although the hospital had a Patient Administration System in the early 1980s, it was not until the end of that decade that personal computers (PCs) started to be seen and, even in 1992, there were less than 20 PCs in the whole hospital. Kim Turner, who was one of the first to work in the IT Department, and is still there, has recorded the developments in that department over the last 15 years. She calls it the IT Timeline.

1992 2 staff, 1 student, less than 20 Personal Computers (PCs) and LOTS of typewriters.
Patient Administration System (PAS) was 10 years old.

1994 Moved to current PAS, which included Radiology.
IT Staff increased to 8, 1 student, 80 PCs, lots of dumb terminals and still 15–20 typewriters.

1996 Staff increased to 10. Two to three PCs installed on each ward as Nursing staff admitted, transferred and discharged patients on PAS, produced care plans and performed electronic criteria for care scores and Waterlow assessments (for pressure areas) regularly on the Nursing Information System.

1997 IT staff 10. New pathology system, allowing staff to access results throughout the Trust. IT team starts to develop in-house databases to support reporting requirements.

1998 The last typewriter leaves the building!! IT staff 12. New Pharmacy system installed, 100 PCs.

1999 Staff move into the electronic era and numbers of memos, etc., reduce. Email and internet are made available to staff.

2003 15 in team. Radiology system CRIS procured and implemented. Interfaces developed between CRIS and PAS and demographic feed to Pathology system. Staff throughout the Trust trained on email systems.

2004 A&E clinicians and clinicians in theatres get their chance to use new technology. 400 PCs throughout the Trust and many staff using email and internet.

2005 IT staff 15. Basic IT training offered to all staff.
11th December: PAS not working because of Buncefield Oil Disaster. Many a candle was burnt (wax, not oil) and systems were restored a few days later.

2006 IT staff 15. JPUH move into the 21st century – PACS implemented (enables X-ray images to be viewed anywhere in the hospital where there is a screen connected to the main computer) with major clinical benefit to clinicians. There are 500 PCs throughout the Trust.

What does the future hold for JPUH?

2007 is going to be a very busy time for the IT Department. New technologies being rolled out include wireless communication badges, wireless email access, Radio Frequency ID asset tracking, new email system, etc.

April 2008 New PAS (iPM) will go live.

Mid-2008 Order comms (iCM) – electronic ordering and results reporting will go live.

Admissions Department

Based on an account by Liz Brown

Patients are admitted to hospital either as an emergency – when they are admitted via the Accident and Emergency Department or sent in directly to one of the wards by their GP – or as an elective admission, when a patient has an appointment made at the time he or she is seen in the clinic or is sent an appointment later. The majority of medical patients are admitted as emergencies, whereas many surgical ones are elective. Since the hospital opened, there has been an admissions office for finding beds for the emergency admissions. The office also sends out details to patients requiring elective admissions.

Initially, the office was run by clerical staff. In 1990, the admissions office took on the management of the hospital beds, which became known as the Bed Bureau, and the office was led by two nurses: Paul Brewis and, later, Roy Young. Until that time, the Consultants had their own designated beds and if another Consultant wanted to borrow an empty bed he would contact that Consultant and agree on the length of time for which he could have the bed. Alternatively, if a Consultant needed to get a patient in for an operation and he had no empty beds, he would borrow one from one of his colleagues or see if one of his patients could go home earlier. The introduction of the Bed Bureau was not popular among most Consultants as they would find that patients were being refused admission due to lack of beds. This was being done without the Consultant being informed of the decision and often the patient who was postponed needed the admission more than others who were admitted. When this happened it caused distress to the patient and their relatives and played havoc with previously planned operating lists. It also meant the employment of more staff to run the Bed Bureau for a job which was previously done by the Consultants.

Prior to this, general surgical admissions were arranged through a clerical officer working with the Consultants' secretaries. Initially, this was Pat Giller, then Carmel Westgate until 1992, when Liz Brown took over. As more Consultants were appointed and the work increased, Sally Bracey helped with this work.

The main admissions office was originally at the front of the hospital on the left of the main entrance, with its own reception desk open to the public. Janet Hepworth was the supervisor, with six or seven part-time staff and, from 1990, Paul Brewis and then Roy Young joined to run the Bed Bureau. Several times a day, checks were made on the occupancy of the beds and the desire of some nurses to get a patient into a bed sometimes tested their honesty when reporting their ward's bed state. Later, the bed state became the responsibility of the ward clerks and the details were entered directly onto the wards' computers, rather than the Bed Bureau telephoning or visiting each of the wards several times a day.

About 1996, the admissions office was moved to the opposite side of the hospital foyer into a newly built office. Paul Brewis had moved to another hospital; Roy Young joined the Information Technology Team, to help develop the new computer system; and Andrew Fox became the new Manager for a short time before Marina Gibson took over. That same year, medical admissions were taken away from the office and Sue Garwood took on medical bed management.

In December 2001, the staff dealing with surgical admissions moved out to join Pre-operative Assessments, which were done in the old social workers' offices at the back of the hospital. There were three staff dealing with General Surgical and Orthopaedic admissions under the guidance of Sister Michelle Thompson, who runs the Pre-operative Assessment Clinic.

In 2005, it was decided to put the management of the medical beds back into the Bed Bureau and the Operational Centre was born. All the admissions work was taken out of there and is now done by a team of six under the management of Liz Brown. All specialties are covered, with the exception of ophthalmic patients, who are arranged by the Eye Surgeons' Secretaries.

There have been many changes in the way in which the bed state and the admissions are arranged. Now the bed state is recorded by the ward clerks on the ward computer and all admissions for up to 30 Consultants, except for eye patients, are arranged by the Admissions Department.

Medical Records Department

Based on information received from Elaine Sparkes

The Medical Records Department is open 24 hours a day, seven days a week and provides a complete health records service to the James Paget University and all outlying hospitals, which include Beccles, Lowestoft, Patrick Stead, Southwold, Northgate and the Newberry Clinic. There are an estimated 250,000 sets of case notes stored within the Department and a further 6,000 sets of notes of deceased patients are stored in the James Paget Warehouse. The notes are archived to optical disc four years following discharge.

Ann Rix was the first Manager of this Department from 1981 to 1993 and she was followed by Stephen Cox from 1993 to 1996. In 1996 to 1998, Elaine Sparkes took over and then from 1998 she shared management with Kim Harris and Sue Ives. The management team changed from three Managers to two in 2002, when Sue Ives changed her role within the Trust. Elaine Sparkes left the Trust in 2006, leaving Kim Harris as the sole manager. Many of the staff work part-time and, in total, there are 44 whole-time equivalents.

The Registration Department receives all GP referral letters and patient details are checked and updated. This information is then entered onto the computerised outpatient waiting list and the letters are delivered to either the secretary or department concerned, so that a date for an outpatient appointment can be made.

All requests for notes are dealt with by Reception. Computerised lists of requests are printed and the notes are obtained from filing before being collected by the requesting department or being sent by transport if they have been requested by another hospital. The Department has systems in place for dealing with requests for notes for emergency admissions, pre-booked admissions and outpatient clinics.

Each day, notes are collected from all round the hospital and are returned to filing in the evenings. It is the responsibility of any member of the hospital staff who handles case notes to file letters and results which are received when they are in their care. However, some of this paper does not catch up with the notes until the case notes have reached filing, so this task has to be done by the filing clerks.

Four years after a patient has been discharged, the notes are scanned onto optical disc and the notes are destroyed. If this information is needed or the patient is seen again, then the notes can be brought back to hard copy if required. This process saves a great deal of storage space and is much more efficient than the system used in the earlier days of the hospital when notes were microfilmed.

The notes of patients who are frequent attendees at the hospitals can become very large and run into four to five very fat folders. This makes it very difficult to transport the notes and to handle them in clinics and on the wards. To overcome these problems, such notes are culled and ward documentation and investigations prior to two years previously are removed from the notes and stored in the Medical Records Department.

Over the years, there have been many changes in the Department to help manage the increased workload. A computer system was installed in 1982 which recorded the demographic details of all the notes in the Department. Later, microfilming of old notes enabled them to be destroyed to free-up space for the ever-increasing number of new notes. In 1992, computer scanning equipment was installed, so allowing microfilming to be replaced by storage on optical disc. In 1995, an electronic system was installed for tracking case notes, whereby each time a set of notes is received in a department its barcode is scanned and this information is held on the central computer, which is accessible to anyone wanting a set of notes through their own personal computer. This has revolutionised the finding of notes.

Another innovation in 1995 was the installment of a mobile racking system for the case notes. This enabled more notes to be stored in the same amount of space.

When the hospital was opened, the Department was housed in the south-east corner of the hospital and, in 2003, when discussions were taking place to build an Emergency Assessment and Discharge Unit, this was the obvious site to put it. Clearly, work could not start before alternative space could be provided for the Records Department and, because of the urgency, it was decided to construct a 'Tesco' style building which would be much cheaper than the usual type of hospital construction and could be built quickly. Such was the urgency and commitment that, within a week of the decision, the builders were on-site and the building was completed within six months. The Department moved into the ground floor of its new building in 2004 and throughout the process maintained its full services without interruption.

Some statistics of the work done annually by the Department include:

- 20,000 new patients registered.
- 260,000 notes for 13,732 outpatient clinics.
- 45,500 sets of notes sent to the wards for pre-booked and emergency admissions, as well as for minor operations.
- 50,000 GP letters dealt with.
- 15,000 sets of notes scanned to optical disc.
- 80 patients provided with information under the Data Protection Act.
- 1,300 requests from solicitors for clinical information dealt with.
- More than 300,000 case notes are returned to filing.

The ideal for the future is a complete electronic patient record system, which would save on storage, filing and transfer of notes, but attempts at trying to implement this at other hospitals is proving to be difficult and creates enormous problems when the computer crashes!

The Department produces an excellent service for the hospital and it is extremely rare for notes not to be available for a clinic, which is a measure of its great efficiency.

Complaints and Legal Services Department

Based on information supplied by Mike Deavin

Originally, the work of dealing with complaints and liaising with solicitors was carried out by David Stevens, who worked from Great Yarmouth and Waveney Health Authority Headquarters based in Havenbridge House, Great Yarmouth. In 1992, the Department was brought to the James Paget and Christine Eagle was in charge, with Tracey Garner as her assistant. They worked from an office near the Library. Stephen Cox took charge in 1996, to be followed by Mike Deavin in 1999 with the new title of Complaints and Legal Services Manager. He has a deputy and a part-time administrative assistant and the office is now in the administrative corridor.

The Department has three functions: dealing with complaints; managing legal claims; and giving training and advice. On receiving a complaint, the people involved are asked to put in writing their views, from which a report is written and sent to the person making the complaint. In many cases, this is the end of the matter. In others, it is helpful to have a meeting of all concerned. On average there are about three hundred complaints a year.

Approximately 50 legal claims are made annually. These are passed on to a solicitor specialising in this type of legal work, who makes an assessment and requests reports from those involved. In the early years, John Chapman, who worked for a Norwich law firm, performed this function, until a legal firm in Peterborough took over the job in the late 1990s. From 2006, John Chapman, who has retired from full-time work, has been re-employed by the Trust and spends a day and a half each week in the office. Fortunately, a number of these claims are not proceeded with, some are settled and it is only rarely that they proceed to a court hearing.

The public is now much better educated about medical affairs, with daily information in newspapers and magazines as well as on radio and television. They are faced with advertisements encouraging them to complain and make claims and are told that this can be done with no cost to them. Unfortunately, the public's expectations about the whole healthcare system are not matched by the reality of the service available and these factors lead to an increasing number of complaints. The investigation of complaints is time-consuming and expensive and can be extremely upsetting for all concerned. However, it can demonstrate where there are faults in the service and then every effort is made to make sure a similar problem does not arise again.

One of the major causes of complaints is due to lack of communication and increasingly all staff are being made aware of this and they now spend more time explaining what is to be done and emphasising what is not possible. Unfortunately, in busy clinics or wards and where individuals are working under pressure, it can be difficult to devote enough time to a patient or a relative, but this time must be made. Without doing so, complaints will continue to rise. Pro-active rather than re-active information giving is essential. If patients and the local community as a whole do not know what can be done, how quickly it can be done and what are the limitations of the various services, the hospital should not be surprised if patients and their relatives continue to complain.

Part of Mike Deavin's time is spent talking to different groups in the hospital, informing them what are the causes of complaints and how they can be avoided. Hopefully, this will help in reducing the number of complaints.

Patient Advice and Liaison Service (PALS)

Based on an account by Liz Barber

The NHS Plan set a target that by April 2002 a Patient Advice and Liaison Service (PALS) would be established in every Trust. The aim of the service is to provide a quick response to concerns raised by patients, relatives, carers and members of the public.

Guidance from the Department of Health stated that PALS and complaints should not be connected or managed in the same way.

The Patient Advice and Liaison Team answers questions and queries from patients, visitors and the public about the services the Trust provides. If patients or their relatives and carers are unhappy with aspects of their care, but do not wish to make a formal complaint, PALS will meet with them and, with their agreement, set up a meeting with the appropriate nursing or medical teams.

PALS can also be called by members of staff for support within their area. This could be for advice or support when dealing with patients and their relatives. If concerns are not resolved, PALS will provide details of the Complaints process or how to contact advocacy services.

PALS is responsible for the importance of Customer Care training on the Corporate Induction days. The team contributes to various corporate meetings and projects, which include: the National Survey of Patients, Code of Valued Behaviours, Improving Working Lives, Patient Environment Assessment Team (PEAT), Corporate Image and Communications Board, Information Governance and the maintenance of Corporate Policy Folders. All activity is captured on the PALS database within the Safeguard System. The service is headed by Liz Barber.

To contact PALS, there is a telephone in the foyer of the hospital which connects directly to the office. Alternatively, the service can be contacted by telephone or via email: pals@jpaget.nhs.uk. PALS is open Monday to Friday and urgent out-of-hours enquiries are dealt with by the site manager.

Social Work Department

Based on information from Sue Barnes and Jim Small

The Social Work Department provides an effective and efficient secretarial and administrative support service to the Social Work Team based at the James Paget, to enable the social work staff to carry out their professional function. Sue Barnes has been the Office Manager for the last 23 years and has been job-sharing with Caroline Nightingale for the last two and a half years and before that with Janet King for three years.

When the hospital opened, there were only two social workers and one secretary, but within a year the team had grown to a Team Leader, five Social Workers, one Administrative Officer and one Secretary. Over the years, the Department has continued to grow and is made up of NHS staff, Social Work staff and three Community Liaison Nurses from the Primary Care Trust. The NHS staff consist of an Office Manager and three whole-time equivalent Secretarial staff. The Social Work staff from Norfolk County Council consist of a Team Manager, who is Jim Small, two Assistant Team Managers, 10 Social Workers, four Assistant Practitioners, 1.5 Community Assistants and two Referral and Reception Workers.

When the hospital opened, the Department had three offices but, as numbers of staff increased, the Department moved to a suite of rooms which is now occupied by PALS and the Complaints Team. A further move was made in about 1990 to where the Pre-operative Assessment Clinic is housed at the back of the hospital and the last move in October 2002 was into the first floor of Southside, the Portacabin-type building on the south of the hospital. A bonus was the provision of brand-new furniture for the first time!

Originally, all records were handwritten. Now the Department is on its third different computer system for recording this information. It was the first team in Health and Social Care in the Eastern District to use the new Electronic Single Assessment Process.

Initially, the Social Work Team dealt with both children and adults but, during one of the many Social Services Re-organisations, a Child Care Team was created to work with all children. Now the team at the James Paget is an adult-only team.

There is a greater awareness of Adult Protection issues, which has resulted in many more conferences taking place and a major change is the taking of minutes for Vulnerable Adult Strategy meetings.

One of the functions of the Department is to assess a patient's needs and to make arrangements for some to be looked after having been discharged from hospital. Many years ago, the patient's family took on this role, but now families are smaller, have moved away or are all out at work. Consequently, this role is being taken on by the local authority and this is made worse by the increasing age of the population and the decreasing number of long-stay beds and old people's homes. In addition, the local authorities are frequently short of money for this service and all these factors lead to increasing delay in these patients leaving hospital.

Social Services play a large role in the recently opened Emergency, Assessment and Discharge Unit in trying to prevent unnecessary admissions to acute hospital beds. This is important, for, once a patient has been admitted to a ward bed, it can be a long process finding accommodation for him or her outside hospital.

There is an increasing need for social workers to meet the demands of an ageing population which, in many respects, seems unable or unwilling to help itself. An efficient Department is essential to help the hospital's patients and to minimise delay in patients leaving hospital.

Her Majesty's Coroner's Office

Based on an account by Mr. Brian Sweales

The Coroner's Office is run by two of Her Majesty's Coroner's Officers. First appointed was Mr. Brian Sweales, who became Coroner's Officer in 1978 as a serving police officer and worked on his own covering Great Yarmouth General and Northgate Hospitals until the opening of the new District General Hospital. As it had a larger catchment area, as far as the Coroner's District was concerned, Mr. Geoffrey Peake was appointed as the second Coroner's Officer. He was also a serving police officer. In 1986, Brian Sweales retired from the police force and he was appointed as Coroner's Officer in a civilian capacity. The same year, Geoffrey Peake retired and was replaced by Christopher Dann, another serving police officer. He returned to the Police Force in 1993 and was replaced by John Gibbs, a retired police officer. He retired in 1999 and was replaced by Mr. Stephen Turner, a retired police Sergeant. Brian Sweales took early retirement on health grounds in July 2006 and his position was taken by Mr. R. Adams.

Initially, there was a small office in the mortuary, one wall of which was glass, so that anyone in the office could see the postmortems being carried out. After two years, the office was moved to the rear of the Haematology Department, with access from the main hospital corridor. Although it was some distance from the mortuary, it did allow, for the first time, some privacy to see and interview relatives and other people. Four to five years later, there was another move to a room in a corridor in Haematology, near to the Photographic Department. Eventually, in

1996, following extensive alterations to the mortuary, the H.M. Coroner's Office moved back to a room in the mortuary.

The functions of the Coroner's Officers are to investigate and to report to Her Majesty's Coroner, Mr. Keith Dowding, all unnatural and suspicious deaths. They need to complete Inquest Files and, where necessary, to arrange a venue and run the court proceedings. In all cases, they need to keep the families and relatives informed of the findings.

Until July 2005, when the Histopathology Department moved to Norwich, there had been little change in the work of the Office. This move meant that, instead of postmortems being carried out on a daily basis, they were done only on a Tuesday, Wednesday and Friday. Until that time, most relatives had to wait for 24 hours or at the most 48 hours for the results of the postmortem examination and the issue of documents which allowed them to carry out their funeral arrangements. Now, for example, if a person dies on the Friday a postmortem will not be carried out until the following Tuesday and, if Histology is required to determine the cause of the death, tissue samples will have to be taken to Norwich for examination. These tissue samples then have to be transported back to the James Paget and returned to the diseased before the body can be released. This can take over a week and obviously causes further stress and trauma to the relatives who are trying to arrange the funeral. This is in striking contrast to pre-2005, when everything was done on-site and completed in 24–48 hours.

Coroner's Officers are usually ex-policemen and are employed by the Norfolk Constabulary who, in 2005, approached H.M. Coroner to see if the workload of the Coroner's Officers could be reduced so that only one Officer was needed at the James Paget. Mr. Dowding refused to allow this as it would lower the standards of the service.

Brian Sweales feels he has been successful in his enquiry into a sudden death if he can help friends and relatives of the deceased understand the reason for the death and, in the case of inquests, how and why it came about, to help them come to terms with their tragedy. An indication as to how successful he has been is that he has received hundreds of letters of appreciation and not one of complaint. He puts part of this down to the great deal of co-operation he has received from the mortuary staff, the Consultants and other members of the hospital staff who have always been extremely helpful, sometimes in very difficult circumstances.

There has been only one instance in which a body could not be identified. This was a man who had stowed away and was found dead in the hold of a grain ship. He had no identification on him, but some papers with him suggested that he may have come from Albania and boarded the boat in Greece. After numerous enquiries with Interpol failed to trace his origin, he was buried in the grounds of Gorleston Crematorium.

In the 1980s, a body was recovered by a fishing vessel in the North Sea. The body was skeletal and was wearing only a pair of Levi jeans, two socks and a shoe. On examination of the jeans, a small cloth tag stitched into the seam of the leg was found with a serial number on it. Levi in Scotland said it was a batch number and that batch had been sent to Holland to be sold. Interpol was contacted, and they reported that four seamen had gone missing in the previous nine months, two of whom had dental charts. The charts were requested and from these the man was identified. He had been reported missing from a vessel travelling from Hull to a port in Holland. Although this was a tragedy for the family, the Coroner's Officers had the satisfaction of returning their son to them for the funeral.

Dealing with death is never easy, but the Coroner's Officers are full of praise for the enormous help they receive from the Mortuary staff, who will often carry out postmortems at inconvenient times to help them and the families of the diseased. Similarly, the Accident and Emergency Department staff have never failed to help even when they have been extremely busy and stressed carrying out their own duties.

Hospital Mortuary

Based on information from Iain Johnstone

The Hospital Mortuary provides a place for postmortem examinations, a chapel of rest, storage facilities and Home Office forensics. Its services need to be available at any time of day or night for the Hospital, the Coroners of Great Yarmouth and Lowestoft Districts and for the wider communities. In addition, it provides expert information to fellow colleagues both within and outside the Trust, allied to the Department, regarding death, bereavement and associated matters.

The first Mortuary Manager was John Schofield, who brought the Department from Lowestoft in December 1981. He was a legend in his life time and tragically died in 1993. He was a large man with a great sense of humour. He was succeeded by Iain Johnstone, who continues in charge. Daryl Bourn is his Deputy and there are three others in the Department, two of whom are females. There are 3.53 whole-time equivalents, compared with two in 1981. During this time, the number of bodies passing through the Department has increased by 20%, but the real increase in workload is the amount of work completed for each diseased person, to reflect changing quality care standards and the standards expected from an ever-increasing knowledgeable public.

There have been many structural changes to the Department, starting in 1993, when two postmortem suites were amalgamated into one. Three years later, there was a total refit and reconfiguration of the Department, with upgrade of the entire postmortem suite and internal refrigerators, plus the provision of new refrigerators. The Coroner's Officers were brought back into the Department and a new office and rest room were created.

In 1999, more refrigerators were installed to raise the capacity from the 39 in 1981 to 58. The Northgate Mortuary was upgraded in 2002, increasing the number of refrigeration spaces from 12 to 21. In 2005/2006, the postmortem tables at the James Paget were upgraded to comply with manual handling regulations and a fourth postmortem table was installed. There have been many changes in equipment over the years, such as replacing the hydraulic hoists four times; the installation of the Department's own washer disinfector and the technical equipment for use at postmortem examinations has been changed three times.

The work carried out in the Department is now much more involved than it was 25 years ago. There are more checks and such issues as audit, awareness of risk, health and safety, manual handling, etc. This has created a mountain of necessary paperwork to ensure safety and audit for all that is done in the Department.

Two members of staff have received JPH excellence awards and a further three have been nominated. Surely, there is no other department which has had such a high percentage of its staff so recognised. In 1995, Iain Johnstone collected the Community Health Council Annual Award for services to the community in recognition of the garden of remembrance which he and his staff created. It also attracted the Health Promotion Award for innovation. With such dedicated staff, it is not surprising that there has been only one complaint and investigation and this was created by a locum member of staff.

This is a small but efficient Department of dedicated people who continue to show a great example to the rest of the hospital. In spite of the changes brought about by the transfer of the Histopathology Department to Norwich, Iain Johnstone thinks the future is exciting, with new laws and regulations shaping the Department and its practices. He feels that a new rebuild will be needed within 10 years to meet the demands resulting from an older and larger population.

Portering and Security Department

Based on information from Richard Allen

Like most departments in the hospital, there have been many changes in the functions and methods of working in the Portering and Security Department. Initially, it dealt with Portering only, then took on the role of hospital security, managing the car parks and moving clinical waste.

The first head of Department was Lou Saunders, who came from the Yarmouth General Hospital. He was a typical, old fashioned Head Porter, who hated modern technology. He was succeeded by Brian Millington from 1985 to 1987, when Lou Lewis took over in September of that year. He was an extremely popular person and was always willing to help. Unfortunately, he died suddenly on 17th January 2002 and an indication of the loss felt by the hospital staff and the community was seen at his funeral, where the church was packed and overflowing into the church grounds. Richard Allen, who had worked in the Department for many years, took over in January 2002 but, after five years, he decided that he had had enough of managing his Department and his successor is Mr. Keith Wilson, who took over in March 2007. Richard Allen continues working in the Department as a Supervisor.

When the hospital opened, there were approximately 23 Porters but, with increasing responsibilities, the number has increased to 35.

There is one Portering and Security Coordinator, four Supervisors, 26 Porters, two Clinical Waste Porters and two Car Park Security Porters.

The Porters transfer patients between the wards, outpatients clinics, Accident and Emergency, X-ray, Central Treatment Suite, the chapel, etc., as well as moving deceased patients to the Mortuary. They transport specimens to the laboratory and deliver Pathology reports. They change gas cylinders, deliver milk around the hospital, move hospital furniture, attend fire alarms in the hospital and residences and attend helicopter landings. They collect all soiled linen, refuse and clinical waste, bale all cardboard and dispose of confidential waste.

They collect 1,760 bags of linen weekly, push on average 1,175 beds each week and deliver 531 pints of milk each week to wards and departments.

The staff attends all security incidents, such as dealing with people showing threatening behaviour, break-ins and theft. They monitor the closed-circuit television cameras around the hospital site. They patrol all car parks and hand out warnings and fines for illegally parked cars, as well as dealing with the intercom for the car parks. They order and record all taxi jobs for staff and cover a multitude of other activities.

There are over 1,300 car parking spaces on the hospital site, with an additional one adjacent to the Burrage Centre which can be used when there are special meetings or functions taking place. The turnover of cars per day for each space averages three, with the highest capacity being on a Wednesday and Thursday. In June 2006, 25,984 vehicles went through Car Park A, which has 250 places.

Along with their increased responsibilities, there has been an increase in the amount of paperwork to cope with risk assessments, reporting of violence and aggression and adverse incidents. Induction training is now mandatory and there is the need to attend various training courses.

On a lighter note, there has been the change from the old-fashioned uniform to a more patient-friendly, modern polo shirt and no longer do they have to drive a security van to St. Nicholas Hospital in Great Yarmouth to search for and bring back patients' notes in the middle of the night.

The Portering and Security Staff are generally a happy and helpful group of people who are essential to the smooth and efficient workings of the hospital. They can be very good at allaying the worries and fears of patients, relatives and visitors and they will be one of the first to know of any news items in the hospital.

Electrical Engineering Department

From information supplied by David Adams

The Department is responsible for electrical design and maintenance throughout the hospital. Since 1997, David Adams has been the Senior Electrical Engineer. The Department also has an Assistant Electrical Engineer, six Electricians and two Electrical Assistants. These numbers have increased over the years to meet the increased physical area of the hospital and the increasing amount of new technology.

In 1999, the hospital suffered some power cuts due to the increased demand for power, but since then the electrical capacity has doubled and this should cope with the continuing increased demand for the foreseeable future.

On Millennium evening, there were fears throughout the world that vital services would stop. David Adams was on-call and sober. Fortunately, everything went without any undue event!

Environmental and Logistics Department

Based on an account by John Applegate

The Environmental and Logistics Department has developed from the Postal and Transport Department and comes under the auspices of the Estates Department. Mr. Ken Brewer had been the Transport and Postal Supervisor/Team Leader of the Commercial Transport Department for many years and his successor in 1998 was John Applegate, whose title is now Environmental and Logistics Manager. He began with nine members of staff – four transport and three postal staff – and since then the Department has nearly doubled to 17 people, covering many more areas within the Trust. Working with him is a Logistics Supervisor, 3 Postal Staff, 8 Transport Staff and 3 Distribution Staff.

The Department serves a wide range of clients, which include various departments and sites within the Trust as well as many external locations, such as GP surgeries, other hospitals, Primary Care Trusts and Health Centres. In addition, it provides the logistical link to other hospitals in East Anglia and countrywide as needed.

Environmental and Logistics encompasses transport services, postal services, receipt and distribution, estates store, pool cars, warehousing, community deliveries and environmental, energy and waste management. These activities are managed on a daily basis by the Environmental and Logistics Manager, responsible to the Head of Estates. There is a multi-skilled team of staff consisting of nine full-time and eight part-time staff.

Transport Services

The main role of Transport Services is to provide the logistical link between the James Paget University Hospital and all its customers. All locations as far as Woodbridge in the south, North Walsham in the north and west to Norwich are covered. Currently, there are six dedicated transport schedules which operate from the James Paget University Hospital on a daily basis. The vehicle fleet comprises one Ford box transit van and five Ford transit connect vans. Currently, over 100 locations are visited on a daily basis and of the many tasks performed some are listed below:

- The collection and distribution of all Health Service mail between the James Paget University Hospital and all its clients, such as GP surgeries, Primary Care Trusts, Health Centres and other hospitals.
- Collection of all specimens within the District on a daily basis and this is combined with the collection and delivery of all clean and dirty HSDU instruments and sterile packs.
- For Medical Records there is a collection and delivery service of all patient notes and records for all locations and outreach clinics.
- For Supplies there is a delivery service for all items and goods ordered in and also the onward delivery of goods from NHS Logistics in Bury St. Edmunds.
- For Pharmacy there are deliveries which include vaccines and controlled drugs to all outside locations.

The Department also provides a service for the moving and transfer of equipment both within and outside the Hospital. *Ad hoc* work is also done and this may consist of any demands that are of an urgent nature. Some examples here include the delivery and installation of electric recliner chairs into patients' homes for Palliative Care and delivery and installation of beds and any other equipment directly into a patient's home.

Transport services also manage all the other owned vehicles within the Trust, which include four vehicles allocated to Estates, two to Medical Photography and one permanently allocated to the security porters.

Pool Car Service

The Pool Car facility is operated from the Environmental and Logistics office for all staff who require a car for official hospital business. There are four Pool Cars available, ranging from a Ford Fiesta to a Vauxhall Astra Estate.

Distribution

There are two full-time members and one part-time member of staff whose duties include handling, receipting, processing and delivering of all goods within the hospital and other locations. They are also responsible for sorting and delivering NHS Logistics from Bury St. Edmunds on a daily basis to the various wards and departments within the hospital. On a typical day, around 1,000 to 1,500 items are processed, transferred and delivered.

Postal Services

There are two full-time postal operatives whose key responsibilities include sorting and delivering external and internal mail throughout the hospital. Each day, the Royal Mail delivers approximately 2,500 to 3,000 items, which are sorted before 10 am and delivered to the appropriate departments. In addition, they deal with the internal mail between departments and all the outside locations. On a usual day, around 7,000 to 8,000 items are processed, transferred and delivered by the postal staff. The Department has a franking machine which processes all the external post going to the Royal Mail. There is a part-time person on duty between 1330 hrs and 1800 hrs who is the main operator of the franking machine.

Approximately 10,000 items per week are processed and sent out via Royal Mail. These can range from a 22p letter to a £10 recorded overseas parcel, and the cost annually is approximately £110,000.

Warehousing

There is a new warehouse which replaced the old one in Bells Marsh Road. It is located under the new Education and Training Centre and is for the short- or long-term storage of items from all departments within the hospital. It also houses all the archived notes which the Trust must retain for specified time periods as well as litigation and legal documents.

The Department also manages the disposal of obsolete equipment from the hospital and outside locations. Any items that can be reused or could be of use to the Third World are recycled and donated to Upper Room Christian Fellowship, which sends vehicles to hospitals in Romania, Bosnia and other locations.

Waste Management

Since 2003, Environmental and Logistics has overseen all waste management issues, ranging from how the waste is segregated at ward and department level all the way through the process to the correct disposal of each waste stream. This includes domestic waste, clinical waste, sharps, hazardous waste and any other waste that the Trust may produce.

In less than 10 years the Department has grown from just dealing with Transport and the Post to managing the distribution services, taking on the waste management for the Trust and handling all environmental issues. To cope with these increased activities, the number of staff has almost doubled, and John Applegate is confident that the Department will expand even further.

Supplies Department

Based on an article written by Janet Papworth

The functions of the Supplies Department are to provide a full procurement service to the James Paget University Hospital's NHS

Foundation Trust, including the outlying clinics and Lowestoft Hospital. The work includes Capital Equipping for new departments, refurbishment of old departments and providing new equipment. The Department is also involved in Tendering and the Materials Management Service to wards and departments, which involve topping-up, ward stocks and putting away whilst maintaining agreed stock levels.

Eleven staff work in the Department. They are:

- 1 Supplies Manager.
- 3 Buyers, one of whom is part-time.
- 1 Assistant Buyer who is part-time.
- 2 Purchasing Assistants who are part-time.
- 1 Materials Management Supervisor.
- 3 Ward Inventory Staff.

The numbers have not really increased, apart from when Materials Management was introduced in 1998, despite there being many more areas and departments to service.

Between 1982 and 1994, the Service Managers were Paul Ruthven, Sue Peters Corbett and Stewart Parker. Jane Gomes took over in 1995 and Janet Papworth followed her in 1998 and continues in charge. Between 1993 and 1994, Andrew Podd was Head of Procurement.

In the early days, the Department worked for the Great Yarmouth and Waveney District Health Authority, which also covered Beccles, Patrick Stead and Southwold Hospitals, as well as those in Great Yarmouth, Gorleston and Lowestoft. The office and stores were housed in the old Ruymps building, an old builders' merchants in Estcourt Road, which previously had been a chapel. Everything was processed manually and there was no computer until 1982. The administrative staff were later moved into Astley Cooper House in the grounds of Estcourt Hospital and then transferred to the back of the James Paget in 1987, where they remain to this day.

In the late 1980s, all purchasing was taken away from the hospital and centralised in Bury St. Edmunds for three years. This was not a success, as the staff in Bury had no local knowledge of the hospital or the staff and much of the time was spent in trying to correct the mistakes which were made. In 1993, all staff in the Department were transferred to the NHS Supplies Authority and were contracted back to work for the hospital. This arrangement lasted for six years, when the staff were transferred back to the James Paget.

In recent years, there has been much expansion of the hospital and among the projects the Department has been involved in have been:

- Maternity Outpatients.
- Hyperbaric Unit.
- Dermatology Unit.
- Day Care Unit.
- New Intensive Care Unit.
- Emergency Assessment and Discharge Unit.
- Education and Training Unit.
- Refurbishment of Burrage Centre.
- Southside.
- Endoscopy Suite.
- Renal Unit.

The biggest changes in the way the Department works and purchases equipment are the introduction of computers, fax machines and emails. Although they have their benefits, their use has curtailed the personal callers and phone calls, so the Department does feel more isolated than in the past. The team is very proud in making sure that all the equipment has been ordered and arrives on time when a new department opens and it likes to respond to any emergency in a timely and efficient manner. An index of their job satisfaction is that there is not a high turnover of staff and most have worked in the Department for many years. Janet Papworth has worked there for over 25 years.

Hospital Sterilisation and Disinfection Unit

Based on an article by Tony Grice

Hospital Sterilisation and Disinfection Unit is responsible for the provision of a whole hospital's sterilisation needs, including the processing of complex rigid endoscopic equipment, theatre instruments and disinfection of ventilators and anaesthetic equipment.

In 1968, two new Maternity Units were established at Norfolk and Norwich and Northgate Hospitals, incorporating small areas for centralised processing of sterile packs for their respective units. Prior to 1968, pre-packed dressings were undertaken in a small way at Norwich and Great Yarmouth, most of these packs being packed at ward level, placing demands on nursing time, deflecting them from their prime function of direct patient care.

Between 1968 and 1974, the Sterile Supply Service expanded to include the hospital wards, Casualty and Maternity Departments. At the same time, theatre pre-set trays were developed mainly for obstetric and gynaecological operations in both Norwich and Great Yarmouth.

Although the main Central Sterile Supply Department (CSSD) was based at Norfolk and Norwich, the original processing rooms at Northgate remained operational until 1978, during which time the service expanded to include sterile supplies to Community Nurses and Midwives and some General Practitioners in the Great Yarmouth and Waveney Health District.

Following reorganisation of the Health Service in 1974, it was the policy of the then Great Yarmouth and Waveney Health District to have as many as possible of its support services, including CSSD, based at District level and to become less reliant on the Norwich Health District for services supplied. Therefore, plans were drawn up to build a CSSD on the Estcourt Hospital site. This opened in 1978 and from then on all sterile supplies for the District came from here.

It was planned that as well as undertaking the workload of the then CSSD at Northgate and the transfer of the work from Norwich, new tray schemes would be introduced to the operating theatres within the Health District, so that all surgical procedures were catered for on an individual pre-set tray basis. This enabled the staff within the operating theatres and in the CSSD to become conversant with the new systems before moving to the new hospital at Gorleston in January 1982. This enabled any problems that arose during the interim period to be ironed out before the 'moving in' date.

With the opening of the District General Hospital, the Sterile Supply Department at Estcourt Hospital continued to supply the Great Yarmouth and Waveney Health District, but its Theatre Sterile Supply Unit production line was transferred to the new hospital. The Estcourt SSD closed on 2nd April 1993, when the HSDU extension at the James Paget was completed.

The HSDU at the James Paget undertakes disinfection and sterilisation of reusable items used in the suite of 8 Theatres, the Eye Theatre, Central Delivery Suite, Central Treatment Suite, Accident and Emergency, Outpatient Clinics, ITU, X-ray and special procedure sets for wards and departments. It 'tops up' wards and departments on a daily basis on Mondays to Saturdays.

In addition to servicing the James Paget, the Department supplies ward and Accident and Emergency sets for other hospitals, packs for Community Nurses, General Practitioners and undertakes work for other outside contractors and customers.

The total staff complement is 30.5 whole-time equivalents, including managerial and secretarial staff. Approximately 12,000 sterile packs are processed weekly, including on average 430 major operating sets. This compares with 1968, when the Sterile Supply Department opened at Northgate Hospital and the average turnover was 314 sterile packs weekly. The financial turnover is over a million pounds annually.

Hospital Catering

The Hospital Catering team consists of 90 staff, many of whom work part-time, so there are 49 whole-time equivalents. The Catering Manager is Andrew Head, who joined the Trust from the University of East Anglia in June 2005. His Deputy is Nigel Whale and Steve Brown, the Head Chef, oversees the work of eight other chefs.

Each day, the kitchens provide 2,000 freshly prepared home-cooked meals for the patients as well as services to the staff and visitors through the staff dining room (now called Aubergine), Paget's Pantry and the hospitality service. There is a budget of £2.70 per patient per day to provide a plated meal service.

The Staff Dining Room offers hot meals, snacks, sandwiches and beverages. Paget's Pantry, near the main entrance of the hospital, offers food and beverages for visitors and patients.

In a week, the patients and staff consume:

- 736 loaves of bread.
- 2,900 pints of milk.
- 403 kilos of fresh meat.
- 247 kilos of potatoes.

Linen Services

James Paget Linen Services provides linen to the James Paget site, Lowestoft Hospital and Medicom. The service is managed by Sally Hughes. Initial Services used to be the laundry supplier until it closed on 30th April 2006. Since then, there has been a contract with Synergy Healthcare. Until April 2006, the Trust bought its own linen and paid just for the laundering, replacing its condemned linen with a monthly top-up. With Synergy, there is a part rental service and the Trust no longer purchases main items of linen.

The Linen Room is open seven days a week and nine staff handle 34,000 items a week as they arrive clean from the laundry. The staff check the linen for quality, appearance, etc., and there are two seamstresses who make alterations to uniforms and other items.

Domestic Services

Domestic Services are managed by John Smith and his team includes 145 (69.44 wte) Domestic Assistants to provide high quality cleaning services to the James Paget Hospital and several clinics in the Great Yarmouth area. The team operates 24 hours per day.In 1999, the team won the Golden Services Award for the best cleaned premises by an in-house team and it was runner-up in 2004.

Residential Accommodation

There are 200 units for the housing of hospital and visiting staff. The accommodation provides single rooms to students and nurses, shared accommodation and family houses. The units are managed by the Accommodation Officer, Coral Blowers. At present, negotiations are taking place to transfer the accommodation to a Housing Association, with all the staff being seconded to the Association.

Hospital Switchboard

The Switchboard is the nerve centre of the hospital and through it communication is possible within the hospital and with the outside world. Frequently, it is the first contact that someone outside the hospital has with the James Paget and the Trust is fortunate in having a group of understanding, helpful and sensitive telephonists. There have been four supervisors: Joyce Seaman, Joy Mantripp, Jason Kay, who tragically died suddenly in November 2001 after he had been in post for only a few months, and Elaine Smith, who remains in charge. There are 11 Switchboard Operators and eight Trust Call Operators, which is a District Nurse Paging Service. In 1992, the old plug-in switchboard was replaced by computerised screens, which made the service much more efficient and increased its capabilities. Workload has increased by taking on calls for Northgate and Lowestoft Hospitals and by the continued expansion of the James Paget.

The ladies on the switchboard are on the front line and they are the first contact for many people getting in touch with the hospital. They are always calm, helpful and pleasant. They can also see the humorous side of life as is illustrated by a series of events sent in by June Northcott.

A caller, asking for the GUM (Genito-Urinary Medicine) Clinic, was transferred to the Dental Clinic.

Caller: "Can you tell me how to spell Leukaemia please?"
The Telephonist does so.
Caller: "Thanks, because my husband and I are doing a crossword and I knew he had spelt it wrong."

Caller: "Can I speak to Mr….. secretary please?
Telephonist: "Sorry but no secs. available in the hospital on a bank holiday."
Caller: "What, no sex!?"

Caller: "I would like the aids clinic please"
Telephonist: thinking this person sounds rather mature for the AIDS clinic and asks "Are you sure you want the aids clinic?"
Caller: "Yes, my eyes are not too good."
Telephonist: "Your eyes?"
Caller: "Yes, my dear, I need an appointment with the low visual aids clinic, please."

Caller: "My doctor says I need to exercise but in cold air because my breathing is bad so can I jog round your corridors in the winter time? Also, as I am on benefits can I travel in by patient transport as my neighbour is up your place twice weekly for treatment."

Telephonist pauses –
Caller: "So can you ask permission from the big boss and don't give me the middle man as middle men are always trained to say no!!"

Caller: "Can you test my water please as there is something wrong with it. I have been to the Council and the water board and they are no use."
Telephonist: "What's wrong with it?"
Caller: "I think it has got algae in it."
Telephonist: "You have algae in your urine?"
Caller: "No, not my urine, my tap water."

Caller: "It's not June is it?"
Telephonist: (whose name is June) "Yes it is" but did not recognise the caller's voice.
Caller: "Oh– it's May." (Sounded like 'me')
Telephonist: "Is it?"
Caller: "Oh, I don't know what months it is. Goodbye!"

Switchboard is often used as a general information centre as is illustrated by the following questions:

- "When is high tide as I will be taking my boat under Yarmouth Bridge today?"
- "Do you know where the nearest Avon Rep is?"
- "When does the Pleasure Beach open?"
- "Can you tell me the cinema times and when will 'So and so' film be showing?"

Union Office

Most of the health workers in the hospital who belong to a union belong to Unison, which has its office in a Portacabin at the rear of the hospital. Its branch secretary was David Clarke from 1993 to 2004. He was succeeded for six months by Iain Johnstone until March 2005, when Les Wilson took over. The Union plays a vital role in representing its members and negotiating with management and to some extent is responsible for the generally good relations between staff and management. Over the last year Unison has become involved in Life Long Learning and has opened a Learning Centre for the use of staff, their family and friends.

Les Wilson used to work with young offenders before he joined the Trust to work in the Operating Theatres. Apart from being Union Branch Secretary, he is the Staff Side Secretary, which involves meeting monthly with the Staff Side Representatives covering the 14 Unions in the 'recognition agreement'. The Staff Side is involved in the consultation of all Trust policies and meets with the Management Team every two months. Each month, he meets with the Chief Executive, the Director of Finance and the Director of Human Resources. He was elected a Governor of the newly formed Foundation Trust in 2006, which has extended his role and influence.

Department of Medical Staffing

Based on information from Pat Mullen

The Department provides a complete personnel service to all medical staff and guides and assists management and medical staff in all Government initiatives relating to doctors. It makes sure that there is compliance with regulations and recruits all substantive and locum medical staff to meet the service needs.

Initially, the Department was manned by one person, Frank Smith, who transferred from the Yarmouth District Hospital, where he was the hospital's Deputy Secretary. He was replaced by Audrey Balls as manager from 1983 until 1986 and her successor was Geoff Woodall. Pat Mullen took over in 1987 and Ginnie Stevens has been helping her run the Department since 2004. Now, there are four other people in the Department, making a total of six. Each increase in numbers has been in response to Government initiatives and workload shifts.

The first office was in an area which is now the Gynaecological Clinic. Since 1984, the Department has moved six times and in 2001 moved into its present offices in Southside, which is a Portacabin-type of structure. Over the years, the computer has replaced the typewriter.

Originally, the Department dealt mainly with the recruitment of junior medical staff and the provision of locums. Senior Medical Staff were dealt with by Region until the late 1980s, when gradually all matters associated with them were devolved to individual hospitals.

In the last 20 years, there have been an increasing number of initiatives and directives which have added to the work of the Medical Staffing Department. These have included Achieving a Balance, Junior Doctors New Deal, European Working Time Directive, Modernising Medical Careers, New Consultant Contract, Hospital at Night, etc. The Department ensures compliance with all these regulations as well as the terms and conditions governing Medical Staff.

In more recent years, the Department has become more involved in pastoral care, helping people to achieve work-life balances, and there has been more involvement in performance issues.

The Department achieved 100% compliance with the Junior Doctors New Deal and is proud of its ability to recruit Consultants to specialties which have been hard to fill nationally. Its staff work well together and have an excellent relationship with the medical staff at both junior and Consultant level.

Medical Staffing Committees

When someone talks of 'Medical Staffing', one immediately thinks of Christine Eagle, who has been intimately involved with the majority of Medical Committees since shortly after the hospital opened. She commenced work as Medical Secretary to a Consultant Psychiatrist at St. Nicholas Hospital, Great Yarmouth, in February 1974 and transferred to the Great Yarmouth and Waveney Health Authority headquarters at Havenbridge House, Great Yarmouth, in March 1983.

When the hospital opened, 'Medical Staffing' covered Human Resources and Medical Committee Administration; but in 1983 it was decided to split medical committee administration from Medical Staffing Human Resources. Christine Eagle took over the running of the many committees involving Medical Staff. This involved not only taking the minutes, but writing letters and chasing up actions decided by the committees. In the early days, the committees included Medical Staff Committee, Private Patients, Study Leave, Surgical Division, Medical Division, Paediatric Division, Hospital Drugs Formulary Working Party, Research Ethics, Control of Infection, Patient Services, Psychiatric Division, GP Forum, Radiation Safety, Cardio-Pulmonary Resuscitation, as well as several others.

Medical Staff Committee

The Medical Staff Committee is open to all Medical Consultants in the District and in the 1990s Associate Specialists were invited to attend as well. Meeting once a month at 5.30 pm on a Monday, it enables the Medical Staff to learn what is happening in the hospitals and District and to discuss what actions should be taken in promoting patient care and in the running of the hospital, outlying hospitals and clinics. The various committees and sub-committees should be encouraged to report to the Medical Staff Committee so that, by attending these monthly meetings, a Consultant is kept informed and up to date. In the 1980s, there were few Hospital Managers and the Medical Staff Committee was a powerful body; but with the introduction of a Chief Executive, more Managers, the Hospital Management Team and an increasing number of Clinicians taking a role in management, many decisions were being made outside the Committee. Sometimes, this did have a disheartening effect upon the Consultant body, but many times their views have been listened to and appropriate actions have been taken.

The Chairman was normally elected for a year starting in April, having served as Vice-Chairman for the previous year to learn some of the ropes. However, Dr. Kingsley Branch was appointed for a second year to cover the move to the new hospital and Hugh Sturzaker, Willy Notcutt and John Studley were requested to stay on for a second year for various reasons. By the Millennium, it was felt that there was much to be gained by the Chairman serving two years as for much of the first year they were learning the job. Only two ladies have taken the chair – the first being Maggie Wright – but in a Committee which is largely male that is hardly surprising. Both did the job supremely well and it is to be hoped that it will not be long before another lady follows them.

The Chairmen of the Medical Staff Committee have been:

1979	Dr David Wayne
1980/1981	Dr. Kingsley Branch
1982	Dr. Wolf Grabau
1983	Mr. Graeme McLean
1984	Mr. Julian Sansom
1985	Dr. Stuart Hishon
1986	Mr. Peter Black

1987	Dr. Vinod Kumar
1988	Dr. David Ellis
1989	Dr. David Blundall
1990/1991	Mr. Hugh Sturzaker
1992/1993	Dr. Willy Notcutt
1994	Mr. Andy Pozyczka
1995	Dr. Richard Stocks
1996	Dr. Robert Graham
1997/1998	Mr. John Studley
	Dr. Maggie Wright
2000/2001	Dr. Peter Forster
2002/2003	Mr. Ali Amanat
2004/2005	Miss Jane Preston
2006/2007	Dr. Nigel Huston

Research Support and Governance Committee

Based on a report by Christine Eagle

Research into new drugs and procedures can result in serious side effects and consequences for patients, so for many years each Health District has had its own Committee to look into all applications for research projects. These used to be called the Local Research Ethics Committee (LREC) and Geoff Woodall was the Administrator for this Committee when the hospital opened. Christine Eagle took this on in 1983 and the Committee looked at the Research and Development as well as the ethics side. In 1995, a Research Support Group was established, in addition to the LREC, and later it became the Research Support and Governance Group. Dr. Ellis was the original Chairman of the James Paget Research Support and Governance Group from 1995 to 1996. Jerome Pereira took over in 1997 to 2000, to be followed by Mr. Premachandra from 2001 to 2004. Willy Notcutt became Chairman in 2005. The Group reports its activities to the Trust Board. The Research Support and Governance Committee is responsible for research activities in the Trust and offers guidelines, information and encouragement to staff. Information is available on the Trust intranet for individuals interested in research activities in the Trust. The Committee meets every month to fulfil its duties, which include consideration of research projects and their subsequent approval and monitoring. The Committee also provides the necessary advice and guidelines for researchers. The Great Yarmouth and Waveney Local Research Ethics Committee was merged with Norwich LREC at the beginning of 2005. There is a Trust strategy that outlines the responsibilities of the researchers to the Trust, indemnity and the importance of carrying out research after formal and proper approval by the RS&G Committee and Local Research Ethics Committee.

The Trust's Research Support and Governance Committee is part of the East Norfolk and Waveney Research Consortium. Other members of the Consortium are the Norfolk and Norwich University Hospital Healthcare Trust, Norfolk and Waveney Mental Health Partnership NHS Trust and Norwich Primary Care Trust. The University of East Anglia and Institute of Food Research are associate members of the Consortium. The Consortium has an infrastructure to help researchers, ranging from developing grant applications to statistical assistance. There is also a website under construction.

There are active researchers within the Trust in the Departments of Anaesthesia, Medicine, General Surgery and Urology, Haematology, ENT Surgery, Genitourinary Medicine and Pain Management. In the pain management area, Dr. Notcutt is participating in major cannabis trials. The Trust is part of the Norfolk and Waveney Cancer Research Network and is actively participating in a number of national cancer studies. The Medical Students started undertaking research in 2006 and it is expected that one third of the students will do their research at the James Paget.

At the beginning of 2005, the Trust Board agreed to take on the role of Sponsor for Research. The Trust has systems allowing it to consider case by case whether to sponsor individual studies and the Research Support and Governance Committee has taken on this role.

A new National Health Research Strategy is being introduced which sets out goals for Research and Development over the next five years. Research funding levels for NHS organisations will also change.

The Research Support and Governance Committee reviewed 35 protocols during 2006 and its key objectives are to work closely with the consortium in the implementation of the new National Health Research

Strategy, to work closely with the Cancer Research Network and to encourage and support staff to participate in research activities.

Further changes are afoot and in 2007/2008 Comprehensive Local Research Networks will be established and the James Paget will be in the Norfolk and Suffolk Network based at the Norfolk and Norwich University Hospital.

Clinical Ethics Advisory Group

This Group was established in 1998 in recognition of the difficulty and loneliness of making good ethical decisions. Initially, the membership included:

- 8 Senior Hospital Doctors.
- 2 General Practitioners.
- 1 Hospital Chaplain.
- 3 Senior Nurses.
- 1 Member from professions allied to medicine.
- 1 Trust Chief Executive.
- 1 Lay Member from Community Health Council.
- 1 Administrator/Secretary: Christine Eagle.
- Experts in particular fields being co-opted as necessary.

The functions of the Group are to:

- Hold case consultations – where the continuing management of a patient causes ethical dilemmas to the Consultant in charge of the patient or another Healthcare professional.
- Provide a forum where ethical dilemmas can be discussed.
- Help in developing Trust Guidelines.
- Educate the members of the group and the members of the hospital at large.

The group meets every two months for formal sessions and whenever required if a quicker response is needed. It reports to the Trust's Clinical Governance Committee.

~ 4 ~

Medical Education

In 1972, a committee of Consultants and GPs was formed to organise Postgraduate Medical Education. Prior to this, there was some teaching. This was mainly on ward rounds and there were some tutorials, but at that time there were few juniors to teach and there was little formal teaching. Gradually, this started to be rectified. Dr. David Stuart, a GP in Great Yarmouth and a Hospital Practitioner in Dermatology, had set up a GP Training Course in November 1972 which consisted of two years of hospital posts at SHO level with six months in Obstetrics and Gynaecology, General Medicine and Paediatrics, plus an optional post. These posts were held at Yarmouth General and Northgate Hospitals and a third year was held in General Practice. This proved highly successful and attracted many excellent doctors who needed training in the hospital, and a large number of them stayed in the area to become local GPs. Dr. Paul Davies took on organising this in 1977 until 1998.

Postgraduate Medical and Dental Education on the coast were done under the direction of the Norfolk and Norwich Institute of Medical Education until the Coastal Medical Education Centre (CMEC) was established in 1973. Mr. Bill Costley was appointed Clinical Tutor and he set about building a Postgraduate Centre at Northgate Hospital. It was a Portacabin-style building and cost £15,000. It had a library, seminar room, two study rooms and an office. It was staffed by an Administrative Secretary, Miss Christine Jones, and a Librarian, Christine Lynch (now Thompson), and regular meetings were held there for the District until the new hospital opened at Gorleston.

CMEC was opened on 4th October 1975 by Sir John Butterfield, OBE, DM, FRCP, Regius Professor of Physics at Cambridge University.

It was his first official duty in that post and at the time he was still Vice-Chancellor of Nottingham University. In fact, he did not take up his Cambridge post until January 1976. Also attending the ceremony were Mr. Christopher Parish, Postgraduate Dean of Cambridge University and Regional Director of Postgraduate Education; Dr. G. D. Duncan, Regional Medical Officer; the District Administrator, Mr. A. E. Rhodes; members of the Area Health Authority and of the District Management Team; the Clinical Tutor from Norwich; and doctors and dentists.

Dr. David Wayne took over as Clinical Tutor in 1976 and was concerned that the planned education rooms in the centre of the new hospital would not be adequate. A small committee was therefore set up to look into the feasibility of having a separate building for education. In the end, it was decided that it would be too costly and there was some doubt as to whether it would be used sufficiently. However, about the same time, the Area Health Authority decided to abandon its plans to provide a social centre for the hospital staff. Hugh Sturzaker suggested that, as both the social club and the education building would require toilets and a bar, it would be reasonable to erect a building which could be shared. Eventually, the Burrage Centre came to be built.

With most of the Medical staff being brought together on the Gorleston site, it was much easier to organise Medical Education. In the Education Section of the hospital there was the Breydon Hall, which was not much more than a large room in which 60–70 could be seated; two other smaller rooms, which could be used as seminar rooms, or places for holding committee meetings; and a Library. The Headquarters of CMEC at the District General Hospital was an office and a storeroom in the corner of the Doctors' Mess. It moved from there to Southside in January 2000 and then into the Education and Training Centre in January 2005. With the opening of the Burrage Centre in 1987, three further rooms were available for education, and for large meetings the Sports Hall was available. Later, with the building of the Celebration Suite at the Burrage Centre, there was a large venue for bigger meetings and symposia.

Over the years, the amount of education being delivered has increased and Consultants have to demonstrate the amount of time they spend on keeping up to date by reading journals, going to courses and conferences. Attending these courses and conferences is expensive, but the hospital reimburses each Consultant by up to about a £1,000 per year. For most Consultants this covers only part of the expenses, but at least it is considerably more than many other hospitals pay.

As the amount of education increased for Doctors, Nurses and other professionals, it was obvious that there was inadequate space for it and this was going to be worse with the imminent arrival of the Medical students from the University of East Anglia. The Trust, therefore, paid for the Celebration Suite – a multi-purpose hall for lectures, dinners, dances, fashion shows, concerts, etc., at the Burrage Centre – to be refashioned and upgraded with state-of-the-art projection facilities. Shortly afterwards, the Medical Records Department was about to be re-housed in a brand new building which looked like a hangar or industrial building near the helicopter pad and nothing had been planned for the first floor. It seemed prudent to make this a new education area and plans were quickly drawn up for making the first floor an education and training centre. It was opened by Professor Shirley Pearce, Director of the Institute of Health, University of East Anglia, on 18th January 2005. This allowed the education rooms in the centre of the hospital to be used for other purposes, but the Library remains in its original place.

In the past there used to be regular evening meetings for GPs and Hospital Doctors. Unfortunately, these are nearly a thing of the past. However, twice a year there are GP Refresher Courses which last three days. There is a great deal more formal teaching for Junior Doctors, along with assessments, and there is a large programme of teaching for the Medical students which takes place around the hospital and in the Teaching and Educational Centre. Along with this there is a great increase in the amount of teaching which is organised for nurses. It is to be hoped that teaching for other health professionals and other people working in the hospital will increase.

In the last few years, National Examinations have been held on a regular basis at the James Paget for the Royal Colleges and these examinations have been for the MRCP, MRCS, Eye Examinations and Paediatric Examinations. This has enabled the examiners and candidates to see the facilities at the James Paget and puts it on the national map. In fact, many candidates come from other countries for these examinations.

The Paget Club has been running for over two years, every three months, in which Junior Medical staff have the opportunity to present a paper to their peers and senior medical staff and there is a small prize for the winner. There is also a talk by a member of the senior hospital staff and it ends with a buffet supper. Since it started, there has been an improvement in the standard of presentations and subsequently many have been given at Regional or National Meetings or been written up in the journals.

Over the years a number of Clinicians have taken the lead in Education as Clinical Tutors. They are:

Clinical Tutor	*Specialty*	
Mr. Bill Costley	Obstetrics & Gynaecology	1973–1977
Dr. David Wayne	Medicine	1977–1983
Dr. Terry Mitchell	Haematology	1983–1987
Dr. Anne Gerken	Microbiology	1987–1991
Dr. Wolf Grabau	Medicine	1991–1994
Dr. Stephan Absalom	Pathology	1994–1998
Dr. Eirlys Davies	Anaesthetics	1998–2003
Dr. Peter Harrison	Medicine	2003–

Peter Harrison now has the title of Director of Postgraduate Education.

Managers of Coastal Medical Education Centre

Christine Jones	1975–1977
Sue Watts (nee Collier)	1977–1988
Linda Woods	1988–1989
Jean Brown	1989–1999
Irene Walker	1990 (Manager since 1999)

GPVTS Course Organisers

Dr. David Stuart
Dr. Paul Davies and Dr. Neil Statter
Dr. Statter and Dr. Andrew Bigg
Dr. A. Bigg and Dr. Liam Stevens
Dr. L. Stevens and Dr. Phil Moxon

GP Tutors

Dr. R. Devonshire
Dr. G. Mohan
Dr. R. Fleetcroft (current)
Dr. A. Eastaugh
Dr. P. Quilliam and Dr. A. Walker

Dental Tutors

Mr. David Tewson
Mrs. Jan Lindsay (current)

Sir James Paget Annual Memorial Lectures - Speakers

This Annual Lecture was suggested by Dr. Wayne, with a view to bringing a National or International figure to the James Paget Hospital, and over the years there have been some very well known and famous people who have accepted the invitation. The invited audience is a mixture of Clinicians, Managers, Board Members, General Practitioners and others. The evening commences with a pre-lecture drink and finishes with a buffet supper.

1988	Clinical Freedom	Sir Raymond Hoffburg President of the Royal College of Physicians
1989	Understanding Nephritis	Dr. C. M. Lockwood Senior Lecturer in Medicine Cambridge (in place of Professor K. Peters)
1990	Royal Operations	Professor Harold Ellis Clinical Anatomist, University of Cambridge
1991	Home & Colonial – Emporium & Emporiatics	Dr. S. Wright London School of Hygiene & Tropical Medicine
1992	Ballistic Injuries and their Treatment	Major General N. Kirby Senior Consultant in A&E, Guys Hospital

1993	Controlling the Immune	Professor Keith Peters Regius Professor of Physics, University of Cambridge
1994	Will We Need Vascular Surgeons in the Next Century?	Professor Averil Mansfield Director of Academic Surgical Unit, St. Mary's Hospital
1995	The Future of NHS Reforms	Professor Julian Le Grand, London School of Economics
1996	The Cochrane Collaboration	Dr. I. Chambers Director of UK Cochrane Centre, Oxford
1997	Clinical Freedom: Chimera, Holy Grail or Dodo?	Dr. Richard Smith Editor of *BMJ*
1998	Medical Research: Who needs it, who does it, and who funds it?	Professor Nicholas Wright Deputy Principal for Research, Imperial College School of Medicine, Hammersmith Hospital
1999	"Eastern Promise – 25 Years of Medicine in East Anglia"	Dr. David Wayne Consultant Physician (retired) James Paget Healthcare NHS Trust
2000	Live or Let Die	Professor Sheila McLean International Bar Association, Professor of Law and Ethics in Medicine, Glasgow
2001	The Environment and Human Health *This lecture was cancelled*	Professor Roy Fox Director of Nova Scotia Environmental Health Centre, Canada
2002	Futuristic Surgery	Professor R Darzi Professor of Surgery, St Mary's Hospital, London
2003	Good Evidence, Bad Evidence, No Evidence	Mr. Andrew Moore Executive Editor of the *Bandolier*, Medical Journal
2004	2020 Vision:	Professor Sir Graeme Catto,

		President of the GMC
2005	Educating the Healthcare Workforce: Current Needs and Opportunities	Professor Shirley Pearce, CBE Pro-Vice-Chancellor, University of East Anglia. FutureVice-Chancellor, Loughborough University.
2006	Evidence Based on use of ICT in Medical Education	Dr. Martin Valcke Professor of Instructional Sciences, Ghent University, Belgium.

Mr. Bernard Ribeiro, President of the Royal College of Surgeons of England, is due to give the 2007 Lecture.

Sir James Paget Library

Based on an article by Christine Thompson

Prior to the opening of the new District General Hospital at Gorleston, the Medical Education Centre and Library were housed in a Porta-cabin at Northgate Hospital, with each of the hospitals in the District having a small satellite library. With the prospect of a new and enlarged library, Dr. Wayne, the Clinical Tutor, and Christine Lynch (now Thompson) felt that the library should have a name which symbolised Healthcare in the area and as Sir James Paget has been the most eminent doctor from the area it was decided that the library should be named after him and so it was from the day it opened.

A ground-breaking development on moving to the new hospital was the integration of the Medical and Nursing Libraries. At that time, Multi-disciplinary Education was not a concept which was accepted and requests were made that the two libraries should be kept as separate as possible, with the Nursing books at one end of the library and the Medical books at the other. In addition, there was a journal room for each. Over the years, full integration has taken place and has incorporated other Health professionals and Social Care.

The development which has had the biggest impact on the way in which the Library functions is the introduction of computers and Information Technology and, in 1985, the Library was one of the first departments in the hospital to have a personal computer. This brought challenges in learning how to use the computer, but it has also brought enormous benefits, and the following accounts indicate how computers have changed the working practices of the Library Staff:

Current Contents

This is a service whereby the Library sends out Contents pages of journals received in the library. The service was started prior to the move to the new hospital and has not really changed over the past 25 years. It has become more popular and currently approximately 400 pages per month are sent out. However, with the introduction of the Internet and the National agreement with Dialog/Datastar, this has been extended to enable readers to get an email alert via TDNet when a new issue of a journal title on the TDNet database becomes available on-line.

Individuals can register to receive the Contents pages of their selected journals from the list of journals available.

Selected Dissemination of Information

This was very similar to the Current Contents service. With this, readers told the Library what their subject interests were. As each journal came into the Library, the Librarian scanned the contents and added articles of interest to a database. Each week, a list of new articles on requested subjects was sent out to individual readers.

This was very time-consuming, but did lead to a comprehensive database of articles available within the library which could be searched by subject.

Bibliographic Searching

It is in this area that the greatest changes have taken place.

Who can ever forget Index Medicus (IM)? This consisted of monthly volumes which listed articles published and was produced by the National Library of Medicine. This was arranged by Mesh Terms (Subject Headings). Carrying out a Literature Search with Index Medicus was very laborious, especially towards the end of the year, when there were 12 individual volumes to search before the Annual Cumulated Volume was available.

Articles were listed only by author, title and source (no abstracts). Monthly issues were invariably late and the Annual Cumulated Volume usually arrived about May the following year. Index Medicus could never be up to date, due to the time taken for articles to be cited and the volume to be published and distributed. Interestingly, IM Cumulated ceased publication in 2000 as a direct result of technological advances.

Inter-library Loans

There has always been a very good network between the Libraries within East Anglia. Consequently, journal articles can be requested from elsewhere within the Region. A hard copy of the Union Catalogue of Journals holdings was published so that it was known where certain journals were held.

Requesting articles was a case of typing the request into a word processing document and then sending it via snail mail, or in the case of requests to Cambridge, via the Blood van twice a week. This cycle took about a week, so quick access to articles was not a possibility.

The introduction of the Internet has considerably improved the situation. The Union Catalogue has been uploaded to a website from which holdings can be viewed and ordered directly via email. Next day delivery is usual and a faxed article may be requested if the article is required urgently.

All the Library Managers are administrators of the site and so can amend the holdings for their site, which means that the holdings are always up to date. With the printed version it could never be current, due to collation and printing of such a document.

A museum was set up in the old Nursing Journal room in 1986 and was run Mr. Buddery, a dentist, for many years, until the room was required for computers and teaching. The budget for the Library, excluding salaries, was only £11,000 and Journal subscriptions were cut because of lack of funding. The inter-library loans increased each year from 1,399 in 1987 to 2,772 in 1990. In 1990, the School of Nursing moved to the Claydon Centre, taking their books with them, which were returned in 1995 when Claydon shut.

In 1991, CD ROM with Medline was purchased and the following year a word processor was available in the Library. Charges were introduced for making photocopies. In 1999, the Internet was introduced into the Library, along with the hospital intranet, which had been developed by Christine Thompson.

The Library has remained in its original position at the centre of the hospital. The biggest changes over the last 25 years have been the development of the personal computer and information technology. Fortunately, the Library staff have been at the forefront of these developments, to the great benefit of the hospital staff, and Christine Thompson masterminded the introduction of the Hospital Intranet.

Medical Photography and Illustration Department

Based on an account by Madeleine Borg

Medical Photography started in the Great Yarmouth and Waveney area with Madeleine Borg, a camera and a cupboard in 1975. The cupboard was in the newly erected Porta-cabin which was the Coastal Medical Education Centre at Northgate Hospital and she used this for taking photographs. Films were developed in the kitchen and she thought she was busy if she saw seven patients in a week. The preparation of text slides required using a special typewriter named the Executive. Once each text slide was typed, it was photographed on a special copy-stand with lights set at 45°. The film was then processed and dyed. Each slide was then mounted individually.

A few years later, the "Department" moved to a two-up/two-down house on Deneside, near the General Hospital. Business was "non existent", as no-one at the General had had such a service on their doorstep. Gradually, the news spread and enough work was generated to ask for additional staff. The first trainee was Annette Tovell, who travelled to London once a week to study for the City and Guilds 745 Scientific Photography Course. The first YTS trainee was Simon, who later went on to become a successful press photographer. Later, Shaun Eardley began his YTS placement.

In 1981, the new hospital was ready for occupation and, at last, Medical Illustration and Photography would have a proper, well-equipped Department. Two darkrooms, a large studio, a proper reception, large art room, two toilets and a changing room were a real improvement on the draughty house in Deneside.

Annette, Shaun and Madeleine began to lay the foundations of what the Department has become today.

In 1983, the Department was joined by Derek Rogers and Hugh Barber. Sadly, Hugh died in 2003, having coped with Spina Bifida and the complications of early 1960s surgery for so many years. He was always cheerful and never complained about his problems.

The Department slowly grew and when Hugh retired, Linda Wright was appointed as Clerical Officer. Later, Linda helped to administer the Diabetic Retinal Screening Service, which commenced in December 1987.

Thousands of 35 mm slides were produced, which formed the visual contribution to hundreds of medical lectures, seminars and Thursday Grand Rounds. Thousands of prints were produced, which are held in the patients' medical notes for record or comparison purposes. Everything was very labour-intensive and very little was automatic. Colour printing was farmed out to a local commercial firm, but all other processes were carried out in-house. The Nursing School situated just round the corner became a regular customer for presentations, teaching aids and exhibition material and there was not a computer in sight.

During the late 1980s, Paul Chapman joined as the fourth photographer, later to be replaced by Jerome Powers and then again by Douglas Middleton.

The YTS scheme developed into the NVQ and over 15 young trainees worked in Medical Illustration until the late 1990s, when workload became so intense that time for teaching trainees became impossible. The Institute of Medical Illustration introduced the Diploma in Medical Illustration as a basic entry qualification, which has now been replaced by the degree. The position of Trainee Medical Photographer began to become a rarity. The Institution began the fight to obtain proper recognition for the career of Medical Illustrator/Photographer with the long-term aim of State Registration, which should arrive by 2009.

The new Millennium brought with it the digital age and now the Department is fully digital, awash with computers and specialised software. The darkrooms have gone and, instead, a Diabetic Retinal

Screening Call Centre has been created to service the increasing number of diabetic patients requiring the service.

The services of the Department cover five main areas: patient photography, support to training and teaching, research, provision of photographs for litigation and morbid photography. The department also offers staff a passport photograph service and bus pass photographs.

Patient photography makes up the biggest workload of the Department and involves taking either clinical photographs or videos to provide visual documentation of internal and external disease. Frequently, these are 'before and after' comparisons, such as breast reconstruction, skin diseases and orthodontics. Apart from taking photographs in the Department, many are taken in clinics, on the wards or in the operating theatre.

In the past, the Department produced the majority of slides used for teaching and lectures. This involved many hours producing the artwork, photographing it and developing the film, which was followed by mounting the slides. With the introduction of the computer and software programs, such as PowerPoint, most medical staff, nurses and others produce their own presentations, although the staff in the Department is always willing to give advice and help. The Department also produces signs and large posters, which are increasingly being used at medical and nursing meetings.

The Department is occasionally involved in producing images for research and one such project is 'Age Related Macular Degeneration', by a Research Ophthalmologist in Cambridge.

Photographs are sometimes required for litigation purposes and the Department provides these for patients and solicitors outside the Trust, in which case it provides a source of income generation for the Department.

Morbid Photography involves the photographer working with the mortuary staff to take a series of photographs at postmortem. In addition, photographs may be taken of a dead baby for the relatives to have a memento of their child to help them with the process of mourning.

A large part of the Department's work is the Diabetic Retinal Screening Service. This was started in 1987 by Peter Black, David Wayne and Madeleine Borg and initially was funded by charity money. It involves taking high-quality photographs of the retina (the area at the back of the eye which picks up the image and transfers it to the brain.) with a special camera. Diabetes can damage the blood vessels in the retina and regular photography can detect these changes, so allowing the patient to have treatment which can reduce the damage. The image taken by the camera is transferred to a central computer at the James Paget and the images are graded by one of a group of a dozen Diabetic Retinal Screening Service staff. Primary and secondary grading is performed by the technicians, but final grading has to be performed by an Ophthalmologist. Reports are sent to the GPs and a copy is posted to the patient. Any patient who is found to have a problem is sent an appointment for the Eye Clinic. This is a service which has grown and grown and now covers an area extending down to Ipswich. Now there are 23,000 patients requiring annual retinal screening.

Madeleine Borg has four photographers working with her – Derek Rogers, Douglas Middleton, Annette Tovell and Rachael Bolton – and she is also the Manager of the Diabetic Retinal Screening Service. Together with additional specialised Retinal Screeners, Graders, Administrators, Secretary and Call Centre Operators, the staff has increased to twenty.

The Department has a new Receptionist who replaced the Department's well-known Adrian 'Elvis' Locke, who brought a naïve kind of entertainment to the hard-working Medical Illustration staff. Much of the work requires tact, sensitivity, diplomacy and patience, as many patients are embarrassed or upset about their condition.

Madeleine still heads the Unit but, after 30 years, is looking to spend more time with her adopted family and her new grandson, Geoffrey. The next few years will see the gradual transfer of responsibility to her senior staff, who she knows will continue to provide a professional quality service which will meet the demands of the 21st century.

The Medical School

Based on a paper by Mr. Jerome Pereira

In 2000, the bid by the East Anglian Joint Venture Medical School to run an MB, BS course at the University of East Anglia was sanctioned by the Government. The partner members were the University of East Anglia,

Norfolk and Norwich University Hospital NHS Trust, James Paget Healthcare NHS Trust, Norfolk Mental Healthcare and General Practitioners in the area.

In September 2001, the course was commenced with 110 students forming the first cohort. To begin with, the James Paget Hospital was sanctioned five Consultant wte posts for provision of 10% of secondary care education. However, due to the high quality of undergraduate education provided by a group of enthusiastic and talented teachers, soon one third of the secondary education was provided by the James Paget. In order to backfill the increased amount of education delivered, the University increased the number of Service Increment for Teaching (SIFT) Consultant posts from the original number of five to 15 Whole-time Equivalents posts. The student intake to the Medical School has now increased to 168 per annum.

The success of the Medical School Venture at the James Paget was due to a number of reasons:

- Early establishment of an effective Medical School implementation group.
- Enthusiasm by senior medical, nursing and other professionals to provide high-quality education.
- Strong management and University support.

The success of the undergraduate programme resulted in the Trust Board making education and training a "core function" of the Trust. A large number of Consultants also took up key educational responsibilities at the University, influencing curriculum development and delivery.

The importance of education and training within the Trust was further demonstrated by the opening of the new multi-million pound state-of-the-art educational and training facility in February 2006. This has resulted in increasing academic activity, including the running of Observed Structured Clinical Examinations (OSCEs), clinical, communication and basic skills courses, among others.

Regular feedback from the students, University and the GMC were highly encouraging in the sense that the organisation and delivery of education were praised for its consistently high quality. Students find the James Paget friendly environment a factor that further promotes their learning experience.

In 2006, the James Paget became a University Foundation Hospital, bringing further challenges and responsibilities. Currently, senior medical staff, management and the University are working to develop the following areas:

- Promoting research by establishing a local research office and joint research forum at the University.
- Increasing involvement of James Paget staff at the University and encouraging academic presence from the UEA at the hospital.
- Increasing the number of joint academic appointments.
- Encouraging the establishment of more national (MRCS, MRCP, etc.) examinations.
- Increasing the number of courses and other academic meetings.
- Facilitating/supervising larger numbers of higher University degrees (M.Sc., MD, PhD).
- Promoting Nursing and PAMS involvement in education and research.

The benefits of implementing University Hospital status would be:

- Increasing excellence in clinical services.
- Improvement in staff recruitment and higher retention of staff.
- Improving staff satisfaction and morale.
- Stronger Trust with long-term sustainability.
- Increasing academic, research and training activities within the James Paget University Hospital will give the institution a higher regional and national profile.

The aim is to develop one of the best University District General Hospitals in the United Kingdom.

In recent years, many of the pre-registration housemen came from abroad. As from this August, all the Foundation 1 year (equivalent to pre-registration housemen) who have applied and been accepted are UK-trained. Their numbers will have increased from 16 last year to 26 this August and next year will increase to 30. This is one of the consequences and benefits of the Medical School. Hopefully, this will carry through to more senior hospital posts and general practitioners in the area.

~ 5 ~

Burrage Centre

The Burrage Centre was built as the Medical Education, Sports and Social Centre of the hospital. The plans for the District General Hospital included a multi-disciplinary education centre on the ground floor in the centre of the building. Dr. David Wayne, who was Clinical Tutor at the time, felt that these facilities were not adequate and set up a small committee to consider building a separate building for Medical Education. After several meetings, it was decided that the cost would be too great and there was a question as to whether it would be used sufficiently. About the same time, the Area Health Authority decided to withdraw the funding for the social centre which was to be built in the hospital grounds. Hugh Sturzaker suggested that it would be reasonable to combine an educational centre with a social centre, as both would require a bar and toilets, and he chaired another committee to look into the feasibility of this. There were some comments that such a scheme would not succeed and, if built, it would be a financial disaster.

The plan was to have an entrance and foyer in the middle of the building and leading off from this on the left would be three educational rooms and on the right would be a large bar which could be divided into two sections. Behind the bar was a small kitchen and toilets and at the back of the building was a sports hall which was big enough in which to play badminton, netball, table tennis, etc. The hall also had a stage so that lectures or symposia for large audiences could take place, as well as plays and concerts. Unfortunately, the committee had to work on the plans with the Architects' Department of the Regional Health Authority and the architect seconded to the project became rather carried away with her design and costs soared. Eventually, the project was rescued by the Regional Architect, who simplified the design, which brought down the price.

During the planning stages, we were fortunate that an ex-patient, Mrs. Lily Burrage, left her house and substantial grounds to the hospital Medical Staff Committee. There was discussion as to whether or not the property could be sold and the money put to the CT Scanner Appeal. Eventually, it was agreed that the money (£195,000) should go to the Medical Education and Social Club and consequently it was decided to name the building after Mrs. Burrage. The Health Authority made a small contribution to the cost of the building and the rest came from the Social Club, which had been raising money from various events since the hospital opened.

It was planned that the building would be erected on the north-east corner of the hospital grounds at the junction of Brasenose Avenue and Lowestoft Road. However, just before the site was to be made ready, it was announced that the layout of Lowestoft Road and access to the hospital would be changing, so taking over the site planned for the building. There followed visits around the hospital grounds looking for another site and eventually an area at the back of the hospital was agreed upon.

As the building had two functions – education and sports and social – it was decided that there should be a Board of Management to oversee the running of the building. The Board consisted of the Chairman and Vice-Chairman of the Social Club, the Clinical Tutor and a representative of the Medical Staff Committee. In addition, it was decided to invite Mr. Noel Johnson, the Chairman of the District Health Authority, to join the Board to provide a direct link with the Authority and to give it some power. The building was officially opened by Mr. Noel Johnson on 11th February 1987 and the Burrage Teaching Centre had an official opening on 30th April 1987.

Membership of the Social Club is open to all people who work for the health service in the local area. Associate Membership is open to others and their number is limited to 60% of the total membership.

Far from being a financial disaster, the building was a great success, with Val Huggins being part-time Office Manager and John Bilverstone being Bar Manager. Prior to this job, he had been a chef and he was given some rapid training in how to run a bar. The bar and its snacks proved popular, the education rooms were regularly used by hospital staff and GPs and the sports hall was in constant use. Val Huggins arranged trips to the theatre, London and mini-holidays abroad. The land in front of the Burrage Centre was converted into a bowling green and, as the Chairman of the Health Authority arranged for most of the cost of this to be paid for out of endowment funds, it was named the Noel Johnson Bowling Green and he officially opened it.

Subsequently, a Petanque pitch was built and regular games are held by a small group of devotees who also play matches with some other clubs. At the time there was only one other pitch in Great Yarmouth.

Over the years, the Social Club has paid for equipment for the hospital's football and cricket teams, but neither seems to be active in recent years. By contrast, the people playing Pool and Darts continue to run several successful teams and the Bowls teams are very active throughout the summer.

With its increasing popularity, expansion of the Burrage Centre was considered and a questionnaire was sent to all members asking what facilities they would like provided. Top of the list was a swimming pool. Other favourites were a gymnasium and a multi-purpose room for lectures, dinners, dances and other recreational pursuits. The Board of Management considered the options and thought that the capital and revenue costs for a swimming pool would be prohibitive and that in the first instance it would be better to build a large kitchen, a multi-purpose room and a pool room. It was thought that the revenue from this would help to pay for the capital cost and the running of the swimming pool. The cost of these additions was £250,000. The Burrage Centre had saved £150,000 over the years and the remaining £100,000 was borrowed from the Endowments Fund, paying it back with interest over 10 years.

By this time, the hospital had become an NHS Trust, which gave it greater independence, and Mr. John Wells, Chairman of the Trust, agreed to take over from Noel Johnson on the Board of Management. He opened the multi-purpose room, which was called the Celebration Suite, on 11th February 1994.

The National Lottery had now been instituted and it was decided to apply to it to help finance the swimming pool and gymnasium. At that time, applications had to be accompanied by architectural plans and these were provided by Lambert Scott and Innes of Norwich. The plans provided for a 25-metre swimming pool with a gymnasium on the first floor overlooking the pool. There would be wet and dry changing rooms and more toilets. Applications to the Lottery needed to have the full approval of the Local Authority and this was obtained after several meetings with the Authority's Sports and Leisure Committee. The application passed all stages of the process to obtain a grant but fell at the last fence as the Chairman of the Great Yarmouth Sports and Leisure Committee said that the Council had not given its approval. This decision was made without any consultation with the members of his committee and was a disaster for the Burrage Centre and for the Yarmouth Swimming Club, which was planning to use the new facilities.

Eventually, further meetings were arranged with the Sports and Leisure Committee and the Chairman and his committee agreed to back the scheme. Unfortunately, by this time the goalposts had moved and the Lottery required an independent survey to show that there was a need for a swimming pool in the area. The Lottery was not prepared to accept the Burrage's own surveys; consequently, the Burrage had to commission an independent survey. This supported previous work, but then the results of a national survey suggested that the provision of pools in the local area was surprisingly good. However, this covered many pools in holiday camps which were not open to the general public. This argument was not accepted and the application was rejected.

Further discussions with the Sports Council indicated that another application could be made, but the goalposts had changed yet again. A Swimming Development Plan was required, but Great Yarmouth Borough Council did not possess one, nor did it have either the time or the money to produce one. After some discussion, the Council did agree to assist with the production of a Development Plan and the Burrage Centre agreed to appoint and pay a professional body to produce the Plan. This took several months and when it was completed it was presented to the Council, who refused to accept it because it did not have the money to implement it. The Council was told that it did not have to implement the Plan. All it had to do was to accept it. Unfortunately, it refused to do this.

All this was extremely depressing for, after several years' hard work by a small number of people and a considerable amount of money raised from the local population, the Burrage Centre had failed in its three attempts to obtain a Lottery Grant. This was due to the Borough Council refusing to back the scheme after originally agreeing to do so and the Lottery changing the way applications had to be made on three separate occasions.

In the late 1990s, the bar area was refurbished, but there was not enough money to redecorate the whole bar. The next addition was a conservatory extension to the bar overlooking the bowling green which gave extra space for eating and drinking.

For many years there had been dissatisfaction with the design and decoration of the Celebration Suite and in 2002 there was much discussion about where the medical students could be accommodated. One suggestion was that at times the Celebration Suite could be used for seminars and major lectures. As these facilities were needed urgently, the Trust agreed to fund the modifications to the Celebration Suite which were designed by Lambert Scott and Innes. The Burrage Centre and the Trust now has a superb facility which is used for lectures, symposia, weddings, dances, fashion shows and even Farmers' Markets. It has the largest screen for projecting football matches in the area and was packed for the screening of certain matches in the football World Cup.

Soon after this, the Trust decided to build an Education and Training Centre on the first floor of the building erected for the Records Department. This has provided a much needed facility, but scuppered the long-term plans of having an educational block on the north side of the hospital which would link into the Burrage Centre.

In 2002, the Burrage Centre started discussions with Spencer McCormack and Paul Brice, who were looking for a place from which to run a Gymnasium. From the days of the application to the Lottery for funding a swimming pool and a gymnasium, it had been the intention to have a gymnasium for its members as well as non-members who worked in the hospital or community as health professionals. In addition, it was intended that the facilities should be available to the local community and provide therapy for those recovering from operations – particularly Orthopaedic ones – and those people who had chronic conditions such as arthritis, respiratory or cardiac disease. Both Paul Brice and Spencer McCormack were in favour of this concept and plans were drawn up to convert the Sports Hall into a Gymnasium on the ground floor. It was planned to put in a floor at first-floor level, so providing a large area for exercise classes, lectures, seminars, etc. Unfortunately, the price for this was much greater than was expected and a simpler design was developed without the upper floor but providing some first-floor gymnasium space on metal decking. This provided a much more attractive gymnasium, but it had the disadvantage of not providing extra space on a first-floor level.

The gymnasium was partly paid for out of the money raised for the swimming pool and gymnasium and which remained after paying for a swimming development plan. There was also money from a legacy left in memory of Sister Jean Sandford, who had been a nursing sister at Northgate. The remainder came from the Trust, after the benefits which would accrue to its staff and patients had been explained. Paul Brice and Spencer McCormack called the gymnasium Bodywellness and it was officially opened by David Hill, Chief Executive, on 21st September 2004.

Along with the re-design of the Celebration Suite and the conversion of the Sports Hall to a gymnasium, plans were prepared for the modernisation of the bar, conservatory and pool room. Again, the architects were Lambert, Scott and Innes. A great transformation has been achieved and this has been financed by a loan from a brewery.

In recent years, the income coming into the Burrage Centre has been less for various reasons. One of these is the reduction in the provision of refreshments for meetings, as the Trust stopped paying for refreshments at all hospital meetings several years ago. The one exception is the Grand Round, which is held at lunchtime on alternate Thursdays, but this is paid for by non-Trust funds. In addition, there used to be regular meetings in the evenings which were well attended by GPs and members of the hospital staff and at which a good buffet supper was provided. These have more or less stopped as GPs are now having educational meetings in or near their practices. This not only affects the Burrage's finances, but it reduces the contact among GPs and hospital doctors.

It was this worry about finances that influenced a hard core of smokers to vote for smoking to be allowed in certain sections of the Bar when the Hospital decided on a 'No Smoking' Policy within its buildings and grounds. They felt that this decision would encourage some smokers to use the Burrage Centre and bring in extra revenue, although some argued that more non-smokers would use the facilities if there was no smoking there. However, smoking will be banned in the Burrage Centre from July 2007.

For 14 years, Kevin and Tim held the franchise for the catering at the Burrage Centre. They were an extremely popular couple, but left in the early 2000s to cater for the Gorleston Golf Club. Their successor started off well but his performance was not maintained. After that it was decided that the Centre would employ its own chefs, with varying results. Eventually, Lisa Harding, who had been an assistant in the office, was appointed to supervise the kitchen, since when there was been a turnaround in the standard of the cooking and in its profitability. Lisa Harding is now the Manager of the Centre and the staff and members are delighted with the new chef. Much of the improvement in the finances has been due to the hard work of Sheila Howlett, who, since retiring as Senior Colorectal Nurse Specialist, has been studying the books and reorganising the office.

In spite of there being warnings of financial disaster when the idea of an Education, Sports and Social Centre was first suggested, the Burrage Centre has expanded several times in the last 20 years and provides many facilities for the staff and local community. When it was first built, it provided much of the educational needs of the Trust, but since the need for even more education and the building of the Education and Training Centre, the Burrage Centre has played a much lesser role in Education. Its future lies in it providing a social centre, sports facilities and a gymnasium for its members and it is interesting that the membership fee for full members has not increased since the day it opened. Hopefully, it will continue to provide facilities for the larger educational meetings and symposia and it provides an excellent venue for regional and national meetings.

~ 6 ~

Management

Management and Board Members

Management of the Hospital

Prior to the opening of the District General Hospital, the hospitals in the area were small, of less than 100 beds, and they were run by a hospital secretary or administrator and a number of senior nurses. The Consultant Medical staff of the District met monthly on a Monday at 5.30 pm as the Medical Staff Committee and discussed various matters, received reports and passed motions on an assortment of issues. In overall charge was the Great Yarmouth and Waveney Health District, which was responsible for the day-to-day running of the hospitals in the District. This body was based at Havenbridge House in Great Yarmouth. For the first year of its existence, the District General Hospital was run by Sally Cockrell, the Senior Nurse, and Peter Harrison, who was the Administrator and had been one of the Commissioning Officers while the hospital was being built. Frank Smith was Administrator of Staff Services, the forerunner of Human Resources. Pat Mullen and later Jackie Dawson shared the same office. The terms and conditions and financial matters for Consultants were dealt with in Cambridge at the Regional Health Headquarters. These services for all other staff in the hospital were based at Havenbridge House and did not transfer until the second phase of the hospital was opened in 1985.

On 1st April 1982, the Area Health Authority was abolished and the Yarmouth and Waveney Health Authority replaced the Yarmouth and Waveney Health District. Mr. Noel Johnson became Chairman of the new Authority and Alistair Roy, who was the Administrator of the Health District, became Administrator of the Health Authority. At the same time, the Area Health Authority was abolished. The Regional Health Authority would make policy decisions and monitor what was being done in the District Health Authorities, which would have much greater autonomy. The Great Yarmouth Health Authority covered an area from Winterton in the north to Southwold in the south, had a staff of 3,000 and an annual budget of £21,000,000. Today, the Great Yarmouth and Waveney Primary Care Trust has a budget of over £300,000,000 and the James Paget University Hospital's budget is over £120,000,000. Not allowing for inflation, this is an increase in spending power of over 40 times.

On 1st January 1983, the Unit Management Team was established, consisting of Sally Cockrell, District Nursing Officer; John Corson, Consultant General Surgeon; and Tony Wilson, Unit Manager. They met every Wednesday for an hour. In 1985, the second phase of the hospital was opened and a management team was formed for the hospital, consisting of Geoffrey Briggs as Administrator; Sally Cockrell as Director of Nursing; Elayne Guest as Director of Nursing and Midwifery; and Arthur Lawn, the Unit Estates Manager. Towards the end of 1985, the Griffiths Report was published, which introduced the concept of General Managers, and Andrew Butcher was appointed as from 1st April 1986. By this time, Peter Harrison had moved to Lowestoft and Tony Wilson had gone back to Northgate.

In 1990, discussions started about whether the hospital should become an NHS Trust. Many of the Consultants were against the idea and some of the local population thought that it meant privatisation. Mike Pollard was appointed Unit General Manager in 1991 and from that time on there was an increasing pressure to become a Trust. As 1991 was the third year in which hospitals and other health organisations had had the opportunity of becoming a Trust, the James Paget was known as a 'third wave trust'.

An NHS Trust is managed by its own Board of Trustees, instead of by the District Health Authority, giving it:

- Freedom of action – decision making at hospital level, taking into account the views of staff and the clinicians as well as the local population through the non-executive members of the Trust.
- Flexibility – allowing it to respond to patients' needs and to local employment conditions to retain and recruit highly qualified staff.

- Financial freedom – to take advantage of income generation opportunities, retain surpluses and borrow funds within specified limits

While all this was being discussed, new NHS reforms came into effect in April 1991, separating the roles of the District Health Authorities, Hospitals and other Health Services and this was known as the 'Purchase/Provider Split'. This meant that the District Health Authorities concentrated on finding out what the local population needed in terms of healthcare and buying the necessary services. This introduced competition which it was hoped would improve the health service and bring down costs. It was the task of Elayne Guest to produce the case for becoming a Trust and to sell it to the local population by writing articles and speaking at numerous meetings throughout the District.In reality, the theoretical advantages of becoming a Trust proved correct and the James Paget has increased its workforce, put up new buildings, improved the quality of its services and yet has always balanced its books.

The last change has been the winning of Foundation status. A Foundation Trust consists of three parts: the Membership Community, the Governors' Council and the Board of Directors. Membership is open to anyone working in the hospital who has been a patient or lives in a defined catchments area. The Governors represent the views of those who elect or appoint them. Seventeen are elected from the community, seven are elected from among the staff and nine are appointed from various bodies such as the University of East Anglia, Great Yarmouth Borough Council, Waveney District Council, Norfolk and Suffolk County Councils, the Great Yarmouth and Waveney Primary Care Trust and a Voluntary Sector Representative.

The Board of Directors includes the Executive and Non-Executive Directors and was previously known as the Trust Board. The purpose of a Foundation Trust is to make it more responsive to local opinion and to be more independent of the Department of Health, so allowing it to make decisions, act upon them and to have greater financial freedom.

Communications and Foundation Team

For many years, one of Elayne Guest's many responsibilities was communicating with the media. With her retirement the Trust decided to pass on her various responsibilities to different people and to set up a Communications and Foundation Team which would be more proactive in publicising the activities of the Trust and to deal with the matters relating to Foundation status. Heading this team, as Head of Communications and Foundation Secretary, is Rebecca Driver, who, after her nursing training, went into management and subsequently became Manager for the General Surgery, Paediatrics and Urology Directorate at Addenbrooke's. Her last post was managing the Norfolk and Waveney Cancer Network. Working with her is Ann Filby as Foundation and Communications Manager. She was Assistant to the Chief Executive of the Norwich PCT and its Communications Lead. She came to the James Paget in January 2006 to project manage the Monitor assessment process leading up to the authorisation of Foundation Status. Tracey Moyse is the third member of the team working as PA and Executive Assistant as well as being PA to the Medial Director and the Chairman of the Trust, in addition to several other responsibilities. Carole Reeve, Head of Graphic Design, plays an essential part in designing and producing newsletters, leaflets, booklets and 'Making Waves' for the Trust.

The Communications Team is responsible for all internal communications such as the monthly brief, Making Waves and developing the Intranet. It deals with all Department of Health and media enquiries and supports all opening ceremonies and official visits. It is also responsible for making sure that the public is aware of all that is happening in the various hospitals and, increasingly, it will need to 'market' the Trust. The Team oversees the Trust's Foundation responsibilities and liaises with Monitor, which is the independent regulator of NHS Foundation Trusts. The team runs the Board of Directors and Governors Committee meetings, arranges the election of Governors and manages the membership of the Trust.

Medical Directors

David Ellis was appointed first Medical Director of the James Paget Hospital NHS Trust in 1993, after being a Consultant for 10 years. A few years before, he had been Chairman of the Medical Staff Committee and could see the advantages of the hospital becoming a Trust. His appointment as the Medical Director was supported by the Medical Staff Committee and he developed the job from scratch. He worked closely with Mike Pollard, Chief Executive, who appointed him Chairman of the Unit Management Team, and he was an active member of the Trust Board. HisThe first major achievement as Medical Director was to design and implement the Directorate structure of management in the Trust and to develop the Clinical Directors for each specialty area. He supported the expansion of Consultant numbers in a number of specialties, including Urology, Haematology, Obstetrics and Gynaecology and Radiology. He retired from the post in 1998.

Graeme MacLean was the second Medical Director and he emphasises the excellent relationship between Medical Consultants and Managers in the Trust. He puts much of the credit for this down to Mike Pollard, who had a good understanding of medical matters and a total commitment to a quality service. He also feels it was important that there was a limit on the length of tenure as a Clinical Director or Medical Director for, if it became too long, the Doctor would end up being a Manager and risk losing contact with the 'Medical Tribe'. He found David Hill to have a superb understanding of medical matters and that he would give 100% support to any worthwhile scheme, but would not support any frivolous idea.

Wendy Slaney was the first Medical Director not to have a Medical qualification. She trained as a Dentist and ran the Community Dental Service and had been the Clinical Director of the Special Surgery Directorate and previously had been Director of Corporate Development for the old Anglian Harbours Trust. She had also obtained a degree in business studies. She was appointed Medical Director in April 2003 and took on the additional role of Acting Chief Executive after David Hill left and before Adrian Pennington started.

Trust Board

W. G. (Garry) Muter

Garry Muter was appointed Chairman-Designate of the Trust by the Secretary of State in October 1992. He had connections with Great Yarmouth going back to the 1950s, when he was Director of the old

Progressive Food Company in Sutton Road, which used to can herring and export them to Australia and many other places. In addition, he was involved in commissioning a fish processing factory in Lowestoft. Subsequently, he was Director of Imperial Foods. Within just a few weeks of the Trust being established in April 1992, he resigned a few days before the first Board meeting.

John Wells

John Wells was born in Cornwall but moved to Great Yarmouth in 1946. After leaving school, he started work in the National Provincial Bank in Gorleston High Street before being commissioned into the Royal Army Service Corps in 1952. On leaving the Army, he joined Palmers Department Store in Great Yarmouth and worked his way up to being a Director of the firm.

He had been President of the Great Yarmouth Chamber of Commerce, Chairman of the Round Table and he was a member of the Red Cross. He also had some medical connections, as his first wife was the daughter of a well-known GP and his brother-in-law was Bill Shipley, the fifth of a long line of Veterinary Surgeons in Great Yarmouth.

He was appointed a Non-Executive Director of the James Paget Hospital NHS Trust and was elected Deputy Chairman by the Shadow Trust Board in 1993. While driving with his wife near Cley, in North Norfolk, he received a telephone call from Garry Muter, the Trust Chairman, informing him that he had resigned and would John Chair the first Board meeting, which was due to take place in three days' time. So, unexpectedly, he started off as Acting Chairman, but he thought it was important that the post of Chairman should be open to competition and the Trust was the first in the country to advertise for a new Chairman. A number of short-listed candidates were interviewed in August and from this group Virginia Bottomley, Secretary of State for Health, chose John Wells, and his position as Chairman was ratified in October 1993. When he retired on Friday 31st October 2003, he had been re-appointed Chairman on two further occasions and he was the longest serving NHS Trust Chairman throughout the whole of England.

He was very keen to make certain that the Trust Board acted as a team and he made sure that the Executives and Non-Executives sat alternately around the Boardroom table, so that there was no feeling of "them and us". He also made sure that the meetings ended by 1 pm. He feels most fortunate in having Mike Pollard and David Hill as his Chief Executives, and it must be unique for a Trust to have only two Chief Executives over a period of 14 years. Both were extremely talented, but had different personalities. They worked together extraordinarily well with David Hill as Director of Finance and subsequently he was appointed Deputy Chief Executive.

John Wells is very much a "people's person" and he enjoyed nothing more than walking round the hospital and saying "hello" to all members of the staff. It probably reminded him of his days wandering around Palmers. He was well known and liked by all the staff in the hospital and having spent nearly all his life in Great Yarmouth he knew many people and they knew him.

He enjoyed raising money and was very good at it. He was actively involved in many of the charity-raising schemes run by the hospital, particularly for the Breast Care Unit, the Scanner Appeal and for the Intensive Care Unit. When it was decided to have a local committee to fund-raise for the Big 'C' Charity, he volunteered himself as Chairman of the group which raised over £130,000 in four years. In addition, he was a great supporter of the Burrage Centre and served on its Board of Management for nearly 10 years. It was most useful having his support and advice on many matters.

He very much enjoyed chairing the Appointment Boards for new Consultants, as it gave him the opportunity of getting to know them right from the outset. His main hobby is sailing and for nearly 10 years he organised an annual sailing weekend in the Solent for a group of Managers, Consultants and a few friends outside the hospital. Three to four yachts, taking a crew of six to eight people each, were hired from Friday to Sunday and, although it was a long drive down to Portsmouth, the sailing and camaraderie were well worth it. He organised the whole weekend superbly down to the last detail and nowhere was this more evident than in the arrangements for the Saturday night dinners at the Royal Corinthian Yacht Club.

His highlight was organizing the visit of Her Royal Highness Princess Anne to open the Intensive Care Unit. Although it was a rainy day, the Princess arrived on time and the arrangements in the hospital, which he had planned and overseen, were meticulous. It was a memorable occasion for all concerned.

At his retirement, he received a cheque from Jane Middleton, Assistant Manager of the hospital's WRVS shop, which brought the amount raised for the Intensive Care Unit Appeal to its target of £600,000. This was an extremely fitting end to an appeal which he had worked so hard to support and a great way to remember a great Chairman.

John Hemming

John Hemming graduated from the University of Leicester with an Economics degree and spent his first 10 years in the steel industry. He then joined Philips and, when that part of Philips was bought by Thermo Electron in 1996, he became Managing Director of UK Operations and a member of the Global Leadership Team. His forte was leading teams developing and manufacturing analytical instruments in the UK for sale in a global marketplace (the UK is less than 10% of the world market). The firm developed and marketed a range of spectrometers which were award-winning and financially successful. He is a past-president of GAMBICA, a trade association for the laboratory, instrumentation, automation and control industries. He retired from Thermo Electron in 2004, six months after becoming Chairman of the James Paget.

He was appointed a Non-Executive Director of the James Paget in 2001 and became Chairman of the Trust in November 2003. He thinks the highlights that have occurred since then have been:

- Building the Education and Training Centre.
- James Paget being the only three star Trust in East Anglia in 2004–2005.
- Achievement of Foundation Trust status on 1st August 2006; the first Foundation Trust in Norfolk and Suffolk.
- Development of the education activities in the Trust associated with the UEA School of Medicine, raising the proportion of UEA teaching from the 10% initially planned to over 30% at the start of the fifth year, culminating in University status for the hospital on the move to Foundation Trust status.

- Development of the new governance structure of a Foundation Trust, with a supportive Governors' Council and appropriate sub-committee structure, together with a communications and secretariat function.

He thinks that the further success of the Trust in the future will require continued development of the University links, teaching across the health spectrum, research and development, clinical networking across the acute trusts of Norfolk, and improved economic growth in Great Yarmouth and Waveney to sustain and renew the local population.

Chief Executives

Mike Pollard

Mike Pollard had been a hospital manager in and around King's College Hospital, South London, for eight years when he was appointed to the James Paget as Unit General Manager in 1991. At the time, there was talk about hospitals becoming NHS Trusts and the following account gives a good insight into the difficulties which had to be overcome for the James Paget to make a successful application. He was full of ideas and emphasised the need for quality in all aspects of the hospital's work. He was outgoing, was frequently seen around the hospital and was excellent at remembering people's names. He was very fortunate in having David Hill as his Director of Finance to sort out the finances of his various ideas. In 1999, he was seconded to be Chief Executive of Essex Rivers Healthcare NHS Trust in Colchester and after a few years moved to Jersey to run the health services there. He came to the James Paget at a pivotal moment in its history and played a large part in ensuring its successful future. Here is what Mike said of his time here.

"My time at the James Paget Hospital was for me life-shaping. I could not have taken on my subsequent role as Chief Executive of Essex Rivers Healthcare NHS Trust without the experiences gained there. Nor could I have taken on my current (and final) role in healthcare management here in the idyllic Channel Islands.

I commenced my appointment at the James Paget Hospital on 12th August 1991 – which, as one wag reminded me at the time, was the start of the shooting season. I had spent the previous eight years working at King's College Hospital which, of course, is a major teaching hospital set in inner London south of the river in "Only Fools and Horses" country: Peckham and Brixton. The training I received while in front-line management in London set me in the best possible stead for the rest of my career.

I was appointed as the 'Unit General Manager and Chief Executive (designate)' – looking forward to the year 1993 when there were proposals that the James Paget Hospital (JPH) should become a NHS Trust. The previous Unit General Manager (Andrew Butcher) had been 'seconded' to the Regional Health Authority (RHA) and I found the senior management team feeling at a loss as to what the future could or should hold. The 'threat or opportunity' of NHS Trust status over-shadowed everyone's thinking. Linked to this was what the consultants thought about the way forward, as opposition from some such circles was known at the time. The management vacuum needed filling; that was clear.

In my early weeks, David Hill was acting Financial Director and an early first step of mine was to appoint him to the substantive post of Director of Finance. Later, he was appointed Deputy Chief Executive – and the rest, as they say, is history.

The context in 1991 was that in April of that year Margaret Thatcher's internal market in the NHS had begun. It was hugely controversial and the medical profession was split locally, as it was nationally, by the onset of these reforms. There was an added frisson locally because the community and primary care services serving the population of Great Yarmouth and Waveney became a first-wave NHS Trust in April – to be named the Anglian Harbours NHS Trust (AHT). No-one (including AHT staff and senior management) quite knew what this meant for local people, and no-one was quite sure why this status had been conferred on these services. Even in the early days, the viability – really the un-viability – of the AHT portfolio of services was widely commented upon. The Great Yarmouth and Waveney Health Authority (GYWHA) had not been given the opportunity to give its views on whether the AHT should be formed as a 'first-wave' NHS Trust. This corporate feeling of marginalisation on the part of the GYWHA played against AHT throughout the latter's short life.

In the 1990s, the NHS had a fairly standard way of consulting on important changes – such as NHS Trust status – which I will now consider. One had to produce a consultation paper (incidentally, the JPH's consultation document was judged by the RHA to be the best of the 1993 cohort) and then one had to undertake a number of 'road shows' in public places. As to the latter, some of these were very low key and mundane events. Others were quite different. The public event in the Lowestoft Library was a mass meeting and was so anti and full of vitriol and opposition that I had to be escorted out of the building at the end of the meeting for my own safety. Bob Blizzard – then leader of the Waveney District Council and later to be the distinguished MP for Lowestoft – was a major critic of NHS Trust status for the JPH.

Within the JPH, the views were complex and varied about Trust status. At one end of the spectrum, there were a very few leading doctors who believed that the GYWHA would not survive as a local health policy-making body as it was too small. Thus, a Hospital NHS Trust with a high level of independence could maintain a strong local health service presence should the GYWHA be abolished and policy-making power shift to Norfolk and Suffolk Health Authorities. At the other end of the spectrum, some doctors believed that the creation of NHS Trusts was the first step to the privatisation of the NHS itself. Opinion amongst other staff groups varied also – and local GPs mirrored this wide span of opinion – but with probably a skewing towards me not applying for NHS Trust status. In the end, I gathered a strong feeling that opinion was so disparate that it was basically up to me to decide. The trigger for application was a conversation I had with Peter Forster, Consultant Physician. Unannounced, he came to see me and said, 'If you apply for NHS Trust status then we might not like it, but my colleagues and I will not oppose you.' I remember this one-to-one meeting as if it were yesterday.

In the autumn to early winter of 1992, the Regional Health Authority (the body charged with implementing the 'NHS Trust movement') began contacting me with the aim of establishing the Trust Board in its 'shadow form'. There was a strong view that all of the non-executives should reside in the JPH's catchments area and this was honoured with one exception – namely, the designate Chairman. In those days, the chairmanship of public bodies was highly political and undertaken on a 'who knows who' basis. The Chairman Designate was in the end a surprise – as no-one within the public services in the Great Yarmouth and Waveney area had ever heard of him. This was Garry Muter, a Norwich-based man who was the husband of a supporter of the local Conservative Party MP. Mr. Muter's appointment as Chairman Designate caused deep-seated friction between him and the other non-executives and represents a dark period in the history of the JPH. Eventually, Garry Muter resigned and the Deputy Chairman, John Wells, took over. John was confirmed as Chairman some months later. The rest – again – as they say, is history.

The James Paget Hospital NHS Trust came into being in April 1993.

The major strategic weakness of the JPH was the size of its catchment population. Even in the early 1990s, there was the strong view that a District General Hospital needed a much bigger population if it was to achieve the economies of scale, build the necessary infrastructure, and develop sub-specialisation. To add urgency to the debate was the size and status of the Norfolk and Norwich Hospital and – to a very much lesser degree – the Ipswich Hospital. These two hospitals were seen to be able to 'carve up' the GYWHA's catchment population between them. However, in the mid-1990s, these two institutions were not really a threat. The N&N was suffering a long-term crisis of management coupled with major financial problems. The management of the Ipswich hospital (which also became an NHS Trust in 1993) was not aggressive in its plans to extend its catchment population into Waveney – looking more to the west to take catchment from Bury St. Edmunds Hospital (which also became an NHS Trust in 1993).

In 1994, there came the biggest challenge to the JPH. The GYWHA had at its disposal a significant new tranche of money for waiting list reductions. An approach was made to me along these lines:

> *A significant number of new cases had to be operated upon and cared for within a year with new funding. If this workload was achieved at the JPH, then this funding would be recurring and thus built into budgets in the longer term. If the JPH did not want to do*

the work – or could not develop the operating capacity to do the work – then that caseload would be sent to Ipswich and the Norfolk and Norwich Hospital.

This was an opportunity – perhaps the only opportunity in the 1990s – to develop the internal capacity so that sub-specialisation could take place and critical mass be achieved. This risky strategy of agreeing to undertake the work, but building capacity *at one and the same time,* was called 'the Growth Agenda'. It began the process of expansion which sees the JPH today as a supremely successful institution. Agreeing to take on this huge challenge was one of the quickest and one of the best decisions I have ever, ever taken. The 'Growth' Agenda was achieved by overtime, extra sessions and a range of new appointments.

In 1995, it became clear that the AHT was not viable in that its services could be provided by other providers and large savings in overheads could accrue. The collapse of the AHT made headline news on the national networks. What followed was a cross between a Dutch Auction and a Beauty Parade, by which a number of providers competed for the prize of taking over the AHT's portfolio of services. In the end, it came down to a straight competition between the JPH and the Allington NHS Trust (the latter was based in Ipswich). Supported by the Norfolk HA, by the Great Yarmouth Borough Council and, *powerfully so,* by Great Yarmouth GPs, the JPH took over all community services in the Great Yarmouth area. In Waveney, the Allington NHS Trust took over all community and primary care services (including the three South Waveney community hospitals), with the exception of the Lowestoft Hospital, which the JPH took into its portfolio. As a result of these changes, the James Paget Hospital NHS Trust became the 'James Paget Healthcare NHS Trust' in September 1997.

Reflecting on the above, JPH has been favoured by very benign geopolitics. The early 1990s saw a growing realisation, amongst local political leaders, that, unless they moved to protect the JPH, then it risked being carved up, leaving local people with a journey to Norwich or Ipswich for their treatment. These feelings run deep in Great Yarmouth and Waveney and should never be under-stated. The feeling – often expressed to me – was that the JPH would be protected at all costs. The politicians were as good as their word.

The local GPs need to be mentioned. Great Yarmouth and Lowestoft GPs were – and clearly remain – powerfully supportive of the JPH. Dr. Adrian Penn deserves special mention for his powerful advocacy on behalf of the institution. There is a book to be written about this great man's achievements in this regard.

I left the JPH in July 1999 on secondment – in the first instance – to become the Chief Executive of the Essex Rivers Healthcare NHS Trust. About a year earlier, it was mooted that a Medical School might be located at the University of East Anglia (UEA). One day, I had a chat in a corridor with Jerome Pereira, Consultant Surgeon, and I indicated to him that the JPH would be willing to enter into a partnership arrangement with the UEA and the Norfolk and Norwich Hospital to establish the necessary clinical and teaching network. After my departure, David Hill was able to take this 'conversation' and make it a reality. For the third and last time, the rest is history!"

David Hill

David Hill was appointed Chief Executive in 1999 and led the Trust through seven highly successful years, during which the University of East Anglia Medical School was established with a third of the medical students being trained at the James Paget, three star status was awarded in three out of the four years, Government targets were met, the Trust balanced its books each year and this culminated in achieving Foundation Trust status on 1st August 2006. It was, therefore, a great surprise and disappointment to learn that the next day David Hill submitted his resignation to take up a post in Bermuda as Chief Executive Officer of the Bermuda Hospitals Board for the next five years. There he will be responsible for all secondary care health services and will oversee the building of a new hospital and train his successor.

After qualifying as an accountant, he spent from 1974 to 1986 working in a variety of Local Government Finance Departments across a range of public sector services, including Social Services, Education and Environmental Health. In 1986, he joined the East Norfolk Health Authority Finance Department and reported to the Health Authority's Director of Finance on a range of financial areas, including audit, projects and consultancy. During that time, he chaired the National

Audit Committee to establish audit standards across the NHS; he delivered a range of projects achieving substantial cost savings with no detriment to quality of care; and he worked on a project basis across a whole range of health financial issues, including appraisal of capital projects.

In 1991, he came to the James Paget to help launch the new organisation as an NHS Trust and establish the finance and performance function. This involved establishing a new comprehensive Finance Department, taking annual revenue and capital budgets to the Trust Board for approval and seeing that they were successfully implemented. He led on the resource allocation process and spent much time discussing and negotiating this with clinicians and, through benchmarking and reviews, ensured that all services were delivered on a cost-effective basis.

In 1996, he was appointed Deputy Chief Executive to Mike Pollard with special responsibility for financial performance, service development and delivery. One of the first projects he was involved in when he came to the James Paget was the building of a Breast Care Unit and he also oversaw the expansion of this unit to include outpatient facilities. In addition, there was the building of the Hyperbaric Unit, the installation of the MR Scanner and the replacement of the CT Scanner, as well as the building of the new Intensive Care Unit.

When Mike Pollard left in 1999, David was the natural choice to succeed him. During this time, he was a member of the Joint Venture Board responsible for establishing and running the new Medical School of the University of East Anglia. Initially, it was intended that the James Paget would have only a few new Consultant posts associated with the University, but when it was pointed out that a third of Medical Students were being trained at the James Paget, there was a corresponding increase in the number of Consultant posts paid for by the University.

In the early 1990s, it became increasingly difficult to maintain an adequate number of histopathologists in the Department. This was due to a combination of Dr. David Harrison retiring and Mark Wilkinson and subsequently Wayne Kinsey taking up posts at the Norfolk and Norwich University Hospital. In addition, there was increasing specialisation in histopathology and smaller departments throughout the country were having difficulty in surviving. Therefore, negotiations were started with Norwich. At the same time there was a great deal of unhappiness about the physical nature of the histopathology department in the new Norfolk and Norwich University Hospital. One solution suggested was relocating the Norwich Histopathology Department to the Cotman Centre, a research laboratory recently vacated and about a quarter of a mile from the Norwich Hospital. It was suggested that the James Paget might join in with this enterprise and David Hill was appointed Chairman of the Project Team. The idea did not find much favour with the James Paget Clinicians, but eventually a deal was done and the James Paget Histopathology Department transferred to Norwich in the middle of July 2005.

Apart from running the hospital, David Hill managed to keep a high profile in the community and with the Primary Healthcare Trusts. In addition, he was a member of the Board of Governors for the Great Yarmouth College and was a Tax Commissioner arbitrating on Income Tax appeals for the Inland Revenue. At the request of the Department of Health, he was a member of a high-level team advising the Mexican Government on acute hospital issues.

Throughout his time as Chief Executive, he made sure that all services, including the laboratories, were fully accredited, service targets were met and the Trust always stayed in budget. In 2005/06, the Trust achieved a £1.5 million surplus on a £120 million turnover and over the previous five years has attracted an inward capital investment of £54 million.

David Hill is grateful to his Non-Executive Directors who supported him but never interfered and he felt that one of the greatest assets was the great *esprit de corps* of the staff. The Staff Satisfaction Survey carried out by an outside body in 2006 ranked the James Paget tenth in the country. He feels that the Trust must continue with its core values and increase its involvement in research. He is disappointed that the plans for a new Treatment Centre have been downgraded to just a new Outpatient Suite, but the money saved will enable the much needed upgrading of all the wards to 4-bedded bays and more single-bedded rooms with other improvements included. During his time in charge, the Trust built a new Intensive Care Ward, a new Endoscopy Suite, an Emergency Assessment and Discharge Unit, a Day Care Unit, a complete Dermatology Department, an Education and Training Unit with a new Records Department, modified and updated the Celebration Suite in the Burrage Centre and some operating theatres have been upgraded. Other improvements include a new car park, more housing for staff, re-building the Accident and Emergency Unit, installing two CT Scanners and an MR Scanner, and enlarging the Renal Dialysis Unit. In addition, many offices and departments have been upgraded and numerous staff have been re-housed in the infamous Southside, which is a Portacabin-style building on the south side of the hospital.

With such achievements behind him, it is perhaps not surprising that David Hill was the successful candidate out of nearly three hundred applicants for the job in Bermuda, where he can exercise his passion for golf. It is interesting that Mike Pollard has also ended up on an island – Jersey. Perhaps Adrian Pennington, the new Chief Executive, should get out his atlas.

Adrian Pennington

Adrian Pennington is the third Chief Executive and officially started on 1st April 2007, although he was at his desk on Friday 30th March, when news broke about a deadly strain of Clostridium difficile which had caused an epidemic and had been associated with several deaths at the hospital. What a start!

Adrian Pennington was born in 1962 and was 45-years-old on his appointment to the James Paget University Hospitals NHS Foundation Trust. He started working for the health service at the age of 16 in various administrative and financial posts – Human Resources, Management Accounts, Salaries and Wages – rising from clerical officer to Director of Finance in less than 20 years. Initially, he worked for the Warwickshire Health Authority and obtained his first management post at the Christie Hospital in Manchester. Between January 1988 and April 1996, he worked in various departments and held specialty and directorate management posts at the George Eliot Hospital NHS Trust until being promoted to General Manager for Training and Education at that hospital in April 1996. It was here that he developed the first emergency/elective split of services which has since been taken up by most other Trusts in the country.

In June 1997, he took five months off to travel round the world before becoming Management Consultant to the Birmingham University Hospitals for four months, when he became Project Manager for the North Warwickshire NHS Trust until September 1998. His next posting was to Plymouth Hospitals NHS Trust, first as Directorate Manager, then as Divisional Manager. From there he returned to the Midlands as Deputy Chief Executive of Northampton General Hospitals NHS Trust. Within a year, he had been appointed National Director of the Coronary Heart Disease Collaborative of the Modernisation Agency and, from April 2005, he was Chief Executive Officer of the NHS Heart Improvement Programme.

During his time with the Heart Improvement Programme, he oversaw the delivery of over 5,000 service improvements within cardiac services in England, the delivery of embedding service improvement techniques within all cardiology teams within England, the establishment of a return on investment strategy for modernisation programmes and the development of a national Cardiac Network structure. In addition, he produced 35 national publications and delivered plenary speeches at over 50 national events in the United Kingdom. He has also lectured extensively in North America and Canada, including Harvard Business School, Stanford University, Cleveland and Vancouver.

He has been Advisor to the Ministry of Health in British Columbia, Canada, for all health care development, including performance framework, provincial service frameworks, modernisation and service improvements.

He has developed Discovery Interviews Training Programmes, which enables patients and carers to become actively involved in service improvement of healthcare. He introduced the first on-line service improvement information system, called Rapport, and developed an NHS-wide service improvement web-based solution for recording service improvement activity.

In 2004, he became Six Sigma black belt champion. Six Sigma is a very complex statistical-based improvement methodology which takes two years full-time to train and he has been a partner to the development of Sigma Fast.

Throughout all his many jobs, he has attended many courses in this country and abroad and has obtained the APSA (Association of Payroll and Superannuation Administrators), the AAT (Association of Accounting Technicians) and the CIPFA (Business and Financial

Management) as a Postgraduate at Birmingham University; so, like David Hill, he has a good grounding in Financial Management.

On his appointment, he said that he put patients and the community at the top of his agenda. He noted that the local community had supported the hospital for years and the award of Foundation Status enables the local population to become more involved. As far as the staff are concerned, he wants to ensure that everyone is developed to their full potential. They are the Trust's greatest and most important resource and, having looked after them, he intends to build the equipment and buildings around them to best serve the local population. He wants to see a greater focus on patient pathway development and service/process improvement activity to improve the capability in the organisation. Already he has instituted weekly sessions to which any member of staff can come to listen and bring forward concerns or suggestions for improving services.

He still considers that the most important part of his career was the foundation training he received during his first junior management appointment, when his team consisted of about ten matrons of the old school with an average age of 61. They insisted early on in his post that he would not be allowed to enter the wards, etc., unless he was prepared to learn the basics. He can still make a bed with the proper hospital corners.

Adrian Pennington brings to the James Paget an enormous experience of having worked in many branches of the Health Service and has been involved in the initiation and development of many new ideas which have been successfully introduced throughout the country. He has written extensively and spoken at many important meetings in this country and abroad. He has wide experience at national level from his recent appointments, so should have access to the seats of power, which could be useful in his new post. He is obviously a great achiever and high flyer and it is to be hoped that he will stay here longer than he has done in some of his previous appointments. He feels there is a bright and innovative future for the hospital and there is an opportunity, especially with Foundation Trust status, to develop services more quickly.

Having spent so much of his time in the Midlands and the West Country, why should he decide to come to the easternmost part of East Anglia? Obviously, there are many reasons, but certainly one influence was his wife's late grandmother, who trained as a midwife in Great

Yarmouth in the early days of the National Health Service. Her name was Hilda Keith. She was an inspirational woman in her day and influenced her family in health careers. Three of her grand-daughters trained as nurses.

He and his wife have twin eight-year-old girls and if he has any spare time he likes to spend it relaxing with a glass of wine, watching football (Liverpool Football Club) and walking the dogs. He likes to keep fit in the gym or swimming.

Present Trust Board Members

Executive Directors

Wendy Slaney

Wendy Slaney trained at the Royal Dental Hospital, London, and undertook hospital posts at the Royal and Guys before moving into the Community Dental Service in 1979.

In 1981, she attained the Diploma in Dental Public Health prior to moving to East Anglia. With the formation of the Great Yarmouth and Waveney Health Authority, she became District Dental Officer. With the creation of NHS Trusts, the role transferred to Anglian Harbours NHS Trust, where the emerging Clinical Director programme led to a Trust Board role as Director of Corporate Development (1992-1996). During this period she obtained an MBA with the Open University.

The services of Anglian Harbours transferred to the James Paget Healthcare NHS Trust in 1997 and Wendy undertook the role of Clinical Director for Surgical Specialities in 1999.

In 2003, she was appointed Medical Director and was interim Chief Executive from November 2006 until the appointment of Adrian Pennington in April 2007.

Julie Cave

Julie Cave grew up in Lowestoft and obtained her degree at Lancaster University. After this, she moved to London and joined the South-East Thames Regional Health Authority as a Regional Finance Trainee. From there, she moved to Maidstone Health Authority for three years before working for East Suffolk Health Authority in Ipswich. Next, she was appointed Deputy Director of Finance at the Norfolk and Norwich Hospital. She was appointed Director of Finance at the James Paget in 2004 and believes that the Health Service deserves the same levels of professionalism from its managers as it expects from nurses, doctors and other staff.

She enjoys travelling, drinking wine and relaxing with family and friends.

Nick Coveney

Nick Coveney comes from the north-west, just outside Wigan. Initially, he studied Geography and Third World Development at University, before training as a Cartographer. Then he changed course and went to the Dundee and Angus School of Nursing and Midwifery. Subsequently, he worked at Guy's and Lewisham Hospitals in London, working his way up to Charge Nurse in Medicine. After a brief spell at Bromley, he went to Kings College as Night and Bed Manager, Practice Development Nurse and Head of Nursing for Medicine and Accident and Emergency. Next, he moved to St. Mary's Hospital, Paddington, in general management and then to Ipswich for four years, where he was a general manager and Associate Director for Emergencies with a couple of spells as Acting Director of Nursing. He was appointed Director of Patient Care in September 2002.

He loves to travel and has a mission to visit active volcanoes in all parts of the world. He is keen on music and plays lead guitar.

Liz Cooke

Roy Haynes retired as Director of Human Resources and Operations in May 2006 and his Deputy, Liz Cooke, was appointed as Acting Director.

Non-Executive Directors

Rita Carter

Rita Carter has served two four-year terms as Non-Executive Director and has been appointed as Associate Non-Executive Director until

October 2007. She has lived in Lowestoft most of her life and is married with two sons. For 18 years she had her own store and was elected a councillor to Waveney District Council in 1988, representing a very deprived ward. This made her determined to try and improve the community. To achieve this, she served on the Planning, Policy and Housing and Environmental Committees. One of her concerns was Health and the ability of people to access services. She was elected to the Community Health Council and took part in many surveys at the James Paget, Lowestoft and Northgate Hospitals. In addition, she has been involved with many voluntary organisations.

She was Chair of the Housing and Environmental Committee from 1991 to 2000, when she became Chair of the Waveney District Council. She had been appointed as a non-executive to Suffolk Health in 1995 and in 1997 was appointed as a non-executive to the Trust Board of the James Paget NHS Trust. Here she is a member of the Risk and Safety Action Group, the Clinical Governance Committee and has taken part in PEAT inspections and the Clean Hands campaign. At one time she was the Complaints Convenor. She finishes her spell at the James Paget in the autumn of 2007 after many years of devoted service to the people of Lowestoft and Suffolk and to the staff and patients of the James Paget.

Jean Mason

She was appointed as a Non-Executive Director in April 2001. Previously, she was Chairman of the Community Health Council and a partner in a residential and day care establishment for older people. She was a member of the Suffolk Social Services Standards Unit Advisory Panel. She is Vice-Chairman of the Board and chairs the Healthcare Governance Committee.

Annette Stannard

She is a qualified and practising Solicitor (Commercial and Property Law Specialist), is a Member of the Law Society and is involved in local charitable work. She was appointed a Non-Executive Director of the Trust in January 2003 and is Chair of the National Service Framework for Children Steering Group. She has been a member of the Board of Management of the Burrage Centre since 2003.

Ken Gaylard

He qualified as a Chartered Accountant in London in 1967 and moved from private practice to work for a number of major industrial companies, including Esso, Thorn Electrical and Plessey. He travelled extensively in the Middle East, negotiating defence contracts whilst at Plessey, who were major suppliers of air defence equipment.

He moved to East Anglia in 1976 to work for a subsidiary of Plessey in the offshore oil and gas industry. After the sale of the subsidiary, he joined Hoseasons Holidays, the largest provider of self-catering holidays in the UK. He became managing director in 1990 and led two management buy-outs of the business, one in 1999 and again in 2003, after which he retired.

Although he qualified as an accountant, the majority of his working life has been spent in general management. He was appointed Non-Executive Director to the Trust in March 2004 and chairs the Audit Committee and the Charities Committee. He is also a member of Healthcare Governance and Information Governance Committees. He sees his role very much as advisor and guide and to give another perspective to the broader debate of the provision of better healthcare.

This is his first experience of the Health Service from a management point of view and he has been very impressed by the dedication of everyone in the team, not just the medical staff, to the care of patients and their passion for ensuring the highest standards of patient care.

He is a member of the Broads Authority Navigation Committee, Chairman of the Broads Hire Boat Federation, member of the Excelsior Trust Management Board, non-executive director of a European property investment company in London, and chairman of two small local charities. In his spare time he enjoys golfing and gardening.

Hugh Roberts

Hugh Roberts is a qualified accountant and was appointed a Non-Executive Director in October 2005. He coaches in business and consultancy (including marketing) and was previously Financial Director and Managing Director of a major UK independent brewer. He was Chief Executive of Sunderland Football Club.

David Edwards

David Edwards commenced his working life as an engineer with British Steel and GKN (Birwelco) Ltd., but after eight years he joined the National Health Service in the Midlands, where he had a rapid rise up the management ladder, becoming Chief Executive of the Queen's Medical Centre, Nottingham University Hospital NHS Trust, in 1991. In 1999, he was appointed Chief Executive of the Cardiff and Vale NHS Trust, which was the third largest in the NHS, and he retired in 2004.

Over the years, he has held many national and regional roles, including membership of: the National Consultant Contract Negotiating Committee; the Royal Colleges and NHS Confederation National Working Party on Emergency Admissions; the NICE Special Health Authority Guidelines Advisory Committee; the Specialist Health Service Commission for Wales Board; Centre for Health Leadership Management Board; the National Assembly for Wales Workforce Development Task and Finish Group; and UK member of Academic Medical Centres in Europe Group.

He was awarded the OBE for services to healthcare in 2005. He is a Companion of the Institute of Health Care Management and of the Institute of Management, as well as a Fellow of the University of Nottingham.

He is a Governor and member of the Council of the University of East Anglia, Chairman of the University Audit Committee and a member of the University Performance Management Group. He was appointed the UEA representative on the James Paget University Hospitals NHS Foundation Trust Governors' Council in July 2006 and was elected as a Non-Executive Director of the Trust in March 2007.

His interests include antique clocks and Victorian relief moulded jugs, classic cars, scuba-diving, squash, foreign travel, walking and music. No wonder he needed to retire from his Chief Executive post!

The Original Non-Executive Members

Noel Johnson

Noel Johnson worked tirelessly for the Health Service for over 50 years and was one of a group who fought for the building of a new hospital for the people of Great Yarmouth and Waveney.

He was educated at Eversley School, Southwold, and from there went to Gresham's School in Holt, North Norfolk, where he was a pupil at the same time as Dr. Ronnie Gibbs. He took a degree in Modern Languages at Pembroke College, Cambridge, before serving in the Second World War with the Royal Devon Yeomanry Artillery, reaching the rank of Acting Captain before being invalided out of the service. The injuries he suffered to his leg were to plague him for the rest of his life.

In 1945, he joined the family clothing manufacturing company, Johnson and Sons, as Company Secretary and later was the Managing Director. The firm employed approximately 600 people. In 1977, he began working for Yarmouth Stores, which was an old established company in the town.

In 1953, he became a member, then Chairman, of Lowestoft and then Great Yarmouth Hospital House Committees. In 1974, he was made Vice-Chairman of the Norfolk Area Health Authority and was appointed inaugural Chairman of the Great Yarmouth and Waveney Health Authority in 1982. He retired from that position at the end of March 1992, having served the Health Service for 39 years. With the establishment of the James Paget as a Trust, he was appointed a Non-Executive Director and he retired, reluctantly, because of his age, from the Trust Board in July 1995.

From the day the hospital opened, he was a frequent visitor and most days he would do his round of the wards and departments – usually between 7 and 8 am. He was known and loved by all the staff. He would bow to the ladies, raise his arm and kiss their hands. He was a good listener, would note all comments made and take them to the appropriate authorities. He served on the Board of Management of the Burrage Centre from the day it opened until 1993.

In addition to his business and his health service commitments, he was also Chairman of the Great Yarmouth Tax Commissioners and of the Lowestoft Magistrates for many years. He was made an MBE in 1987 and Deputy Lieutenant of Suffolk in 1988. He was a regular golf player and at one time was Captain of Aldeburgh Golf Club.

In his last few years, his health was not good and he required blood transfusions every two to four weeks, which necessitated him being admitted to the James Paget. Even so, he still retained his cheery smile and showed his concern for others. He died in the James

Paget ("his hospital") on 13th December 2005. It is doubtful whether anyone else has done more for the healthcare of the local people than he did.

Nicholas Brighouse

Nicholas Brighouse was a Chartered Accountant and had recently retired as the senior partner of his firm – although he continued to work for them as a consultant – when he was appointed as a Non-Executive Director of the Trust. He had been a member of the Waveney District Council since 1973, was Chairman in 1977–1979 and Leader from 1984 to 1986. He was elected Suffolk County Councillor in 1989. He was National President of the Mini Olympics for the mentally handicapped and President of the St. Raphael Club for the Disabled. He was Vice-Chairman of the Board of Visitors at Blundeston Prison, Chairman of the Denes High School Governors, and Governor at Lowestoft College and Elm Tree Middle School, Lowestoft.

Sir John Nicholls

Sir John Nicholls spent his life in the RAF and flew all the fighters from the Spitfire to the Tornado and ended up as Air Marshal. He flew Sabre jets with the United States Air Force in the Korean War and was a test pilot for the Lightning. He was Director in Charge of the British Aerospace contract team assisting in the support of the Royal Saudi Air Force in Riyadh. His Trust Committees included membership of the Remuneration and Audit Committee. He retired from the Board in May 1995 when he moved to Norwich.

Mrs Linda Handford

Mrs Linda Handford moved to Norfolk from Nottingham 18 years before she was appointed one of the first five Non-Executive Directors. She had worked for Norfolk Social Services for four years when she was based at the James Paget Hospital, working mainly with the elderly. She was a Magistrate, a member of the Great Yarmouth Probation Liaison Committee, a member of the Family Panel Court serving the Norfolk Courts and a Trustee of the Norfolk Conciliation Service.

~ 7 ~

Minibiographies

A Selection of People who have worked for the Hospital or still do

Sally Cockrell

Sally Cockrell was born in Halesworth and trained as a nurse at the Royal Masonic Hospital in London. She did her Midwifery training in Norwich and after several jobs in London moved to Wisbech, and then to Addenbrooke's Hospital, Cambridge. In August 1980, she started work as Senior Nursing Officer of the Great Yarmouth General and Lowestoft Hospitals, expecting to be in charge of Lowestoft and the community hospitals in the southern parts of the District when the District General Hospital opened. Much to her surprise, she was informed in October 1981 that she would be the Senior Nursing Officer of the new hospital which was opening in two months time. She was ideal for the job. She had a quiet manner, got on very well with the nursing and medical staff and not infrequently would be seen nursing some of the patients. In 1986, she felt she needed another challenge and was appointed Director of Nursing in Ipswich in January 1987. She is now retired and lives in Southwold.

Vanessa Wood

Vanessa Wood was appointed as Senior Nurse for Surgery and worked under the watchful eyes of Sisters Pritt, Scarles and Clements. She took over as In-patient and Nursing Services Manager when Sally Cockrell moved to Ipswich and remained in charge until she was appointed Director of Clinical Care Services at Addenbrooke's, Cambridge, in 1991.

Chris Smith

She was born in Great Yarmouth and worked for the Great Yarmouth and Waveney Health District since qualifying as a nurse. She became Sister of the ENT Ward when the hospital opened. She gained promotion in Specialties and General Surgery and was Service Manager for General Surgery following the introduction of Clinical Directorates. She was appointed Director of Patient Care in 1992 and was an Executive Director of the Trust Board. Her position also involved the management of the Hotel Services and providing a Quality Assurance system for the hospital.

Her achievements were expanding the nursing workforce by the recruitment and integration of overseas nurses and "Return to Practice" courses for nurses who had left the profession. She helped to retain nurses by providing education, professional development and support for expanding the role of nurses. This was important due to reduction in Junior Doctors' hours to ensure good patient care "out of hours". She supported the development of Critical Care Services to improve the care for seriously ill patients with the appointment of the first Nurse Consultant in the hospital and expansion of the critical care outreach team. She worked with the Medical Director and Clinicians of all professions to make Clinical Governance part of "the way we do things here" to ensure safe care for patients.

For relaxation, she enjoys the gym, swimming, reading and visiting her family in Australia.

She retired from the Trust in December 2001, but was elected to be one of the Governors when the hospital became a Foundation Trust in 2006.

Roy Haynes

Roy Haynes started work as Director of Human Resources on 18th January 1993. Initially, he worked in Personnel in Local Government for nine years, then joined Allied Dunbar for seven years. Prior to coming to the James Paget, he was an Assistant Director of Personnel and Training with the Prudential for seven years. He is a Fellow of the Institute of Personnel Management and a member of the British Association Psychological Type. He retired in 2006, but still does some consultancy work in Human Resources. He enjoys riding, gardening, jogging and the theatre.

Robert Guest

Robert Guest started his psychiatric nursing at Bexleyheath in Kent and in the 1950s did his general nursing at Queen Mary's Hospital, Sidcup, in Kent. He specialised in Accident and Emergency, then became Matron at Joyce Green Hospital. Between 1968 and 1974, he was Principal Nursing Officer of New Cross Hospital in Birmingham before being appointed District Nursing Officer of the Great Yarmouth and Waveney Health District. He was heavily involved in the efforts to establish a District General Hospital on the coast and with recruiting the nursing staff to run it. He retired in 1983 and died in 2006.

Elayne Guest

Elayne Guest started her general nursing training at University College Hospital, London, in 1962 and did her Midwifery training at Whittington Hospital, Highgate, London, in 1967. From 1968, she worked as a District Nurse and Midwife for Nottinghamshire County Council and did her Health Visitor training. In 1972, she became a Health Visitor for Great Yarmouth Borough Council. In 1974, she was appointed Nursing Officer for East Suffolk County Council, in charge of Community Midwifery, covering an area from Lowestoft to Halesworth, Beccles and Bungay. The following year she was invited to look after the Maternity Unit at Northgate Hospital and in 1978 she took over the community maternity services in the Great Yarmouth area as well, so that all of the Maternity Services became an integrated unit. Subsequently, she married Bob Guest, District Nursing Officer.

With the opening of the District General Hospital in 1981, Gynaecology and Paediatrics joined forces with Maternity and she became Director of Nursing and Midwifery. With the transfer of the Maternity Unit to the James Paget in 1985, she joined Sally Cockrell, Director of Nursing, and Administrator Tony Wilson in forming the Management Team for the whole hospital. Subsequently, her role in management increased and she was given many tasks, such as preparing the ground for the hospital becoming a Trust and later, a Foundation Trust, sorting out charges for the car parks, allocating accommodation in the hospital, dealing with publicity and the corporate image, taking minutes for the Trust Board meetings, editing *Making Waves*, Chairing the Arts

Committee, etc. In addition, she took on the position of Acting Director of Patient Care from December 2001 to October 2002. She retired in 2006, but continued with some of her Midwifery duties until March 2007.

Her leisure pursuits are gardening, swimming, singing in the church choir and organising church activities.

Arthur Lawn

Arthur Lawn trained as an engineer at Norwich City College and Luton College of Technology. After working in industry, he worked at Little Plumstead Hospital before working at St. Albans and Hitchin. He was appointed Senior Hospital Engineer in Great Yarmouth in 1978 and was Commissioning Officer to the District General Hospital during 1980. Frequently, he was to be seen cycling round the site and the hospital corridors on his bicycle. In the past he had been a successful racer of motorcycles and had competed many times in the Isle of Man TT races. In 1984, he became the Unit Estates Manager and a member of the Unit Management Board. He retired in September 1992 to spend more time fishing, caring for ponies and watching football matches.

Malcolm Brooke

Malcolm Brooke trained as a mining engineer and, after a spell in the manufacturing industry, joined the NHS. His previous appointments had included Assistant Hospital Engineer in Hull and Hospital Engineer at Heath Road Hospital, Ipswich. He was District Works Officer to the Great Yarmouth and Waveney Health Authority during the planning, construction and commissioning of the District General Hospital and subsequently became District Estates Manager. He became Director of Estates at the James Paget by the amalgamation of the former District Estates Department with the Unit Estates Services Department on 6th July 1992. He was a member of the Hospital Management Team and managed the capital planning, building and engineering design and construction activities and the day-to-day estate maintenance services. His other responsibilities included medical engineering services, Hospital Sterilisation and Disinfection Unit, telecommunications, linen services, transport and distribution.

He was also a member of the Department of Health Steering Group on Hospital Technical Memoranda, Regional Representative on the Council of the National Association of Health Estate Managers, Council Member of the Institute of Hospital Engineering and a member of the panel responsible for accreditation of Civil Engineering courses on behalf of the Engineering Council.

Claire Rooney

Claire Rooney started her RGN Nursing in Ipswich in 1974 and, having qualified, took a year out working as a nanny to twins in Long Island, New York. On returning to the UK, she commenced her Orthopaedic Diploma at the Royal National Orthopaedic Hospital in Stanmore. She started her Midwifery training at the Norfolk and Norwich Hospital in 1979, which led to a special interest and qualification in Special and Intensive Care of the Newborn but, after two years as Midwifery Sister, she decided to return to general nursing.

She started at the James Paget as Orthopaedic Sister on 1st August 1983 and in 1988 took on the role of Clinical Nurse Manager for the Orthopaedic and General Surgical Directorates. This awakened her interest in management and, after undertaking various management studies, she was appointed Clinical Services Manager for General Surgery in August 1992. From October 1994, she added the Special Surgery Directorate to her responsibilities, followed by Orthopaedics and Accident and Emergency in 1999. In 2005, she took over as Manager of the newly formed Elective Division of the Trust acquiring Theatres, in exchange for Accident and Emergency.

Andrew Fox

Andrew Fox worked his way up to being Charge Nurse of Ward 3 then went into management and now is Manager of the Emergency Division of the Trust.

Antony Grice

Tony Grice has overseen most of the development in Sterile Services in the Great Yarmouth and Waveney Health District since 1968. He joined the

Royal Army Medical Corps in 1963 and trained as an Operating Theatre Technician and, while at the Royal Herbert Hospital in Woolwich, he trialled the first 'Edinburgh' theatre instrument tray system in the Army Medical Services. He joined the NHS as Operating Department Assistant in the Maternity Unit at Northgate Hospital in 1968 and established the first Sterile Services Unit in Great Yarmouth. He became Deputy CSSD Manager at the Norfolk and Norwich Hospital in 1971 and in 1979 was appointed Sterile Services Manager for the Great Yarmouth and Waveney Health Authority. Over the years, he took on more responsibilities, e.g. commercial transport, linen services, postal services, residential accommodation, Supplies Department, car parks and public transport provision for the Trust. For the last few years before his retirement, he was Operational Services Manager for Facilities Management.

Not only has he played a pivotal role in the development of sterile supply services locally, he has played a major part nationally and was National Chairman of the Institute of Sterile Services Management (ISSM) from 1985 until 1988. He was a member of the Institute's Working Party which produced the "Guide to Good Manufacturing Practices in the NHS Sterile Services Departments", which was issued in 1989. He was Chairman of the East Anglian Branch of the ISSM from 1994 until 1998. He retired from the NHS in November 2002, when he was a Manager overseeing many departments besides the HSDU. He continues to work for the ISSM and in 2004 was appointed a Fellow of the Institute of Sterile Services Management which, in 2005, was renamed the Institute of Decontamination Sciences (IDSc).

He enjoys gardening and is a fanatic on railways.

Peter Harrison

Peter Harrison was Commissioning Officer of the District General Hospital (DGH). From 1971 he worked in the Health Department of the Great Yarmouth County Borough Council until 1974 when he transferred to the Great Yarmouth and Waveney Health District as Sector Administrator for Community Services. In 1976 he was appointed Principal Administrative Assistant responsible for Service Planning and for a short time worked at Lowestoft Hospital. He was appointed Commissioning Officer for the DGH in December 1979 and worked closely with Alan Price who was responsible for the appointment of nursing staff and ordering equipment and supplies.

After the DGH was built he was the Sector Administrator for a year-working closely with Sally Cockrell, the Senior Nursing Officer- before returning to Lowestoft Hospital. He masterminded a bid for Lowestoft Hospital and some Community Services to become a first wave NHS Trust – known as Anglian Harbours -and was appointed the Chief Executive. Unfortunately, it proved financially not viable and its services were divided between James Paget and Allington NHS Trusts.

Alan Price

Alan Price was the Senior Nursing Officer for Planning and Commissioning of the District Genial Hospital from January 1978. Prior to this he had spent four years as a Divisional Nursing Officer and three years as a Senior Nursing Officer in the South East Thames Region and had been involved in both Capital Planning and Commissioning. He was responsible for compiling and reviewing operational policies in conjunction with members of the appropriate department staff, making sure that the various policies interlocked. He oversaw the compiling of equipment schedules and decided which equipment needed to be bought and which could be transferred from other hospitals which were closing.

Subsequently he became deputy to Robert Guest, District Nursing Officer. When the latter retired in 1983, Alan Price took over most of his duties as Nursing Advisor to the Health District.

Arthur Harris

Arthur Harris spent his early years working for J. H. Moore, a building firm in Great Yarmouth. Here his mentor was John Clymer, a director of the firm and a future Mayor of Great Yarmouth. He joined the National Health Service in 1972 and was appointed District Building Officer to the Great Yarmouth and Waveney Health District in 1975. Since then, he has been intimately involved with the building of the hospital and its subsequent many changes, alterations and new buildings. He has extremely high standards and in all contract negotiations he has ensured the best deal for the hospital. His new title is Strategic Capital Advisor and Planner.

Stanley Cooper

Stanley Cooper grew up in Great Yarmouth and did his medical training at Edinburgh University. While there, he developed pulmonary tuberculosis which required a year away from his medical studies. In fact, he was one of three medical students in Edinburgh who developed TB in spite of being Mantoux negative previously and then being given BCG. Their cases were written up in the British Medical Journal.

In 1956 he became house surgeon to Mr. McDonald at the Yarmouth General Hospital and then did a house physician's job. After various jobs in Paediatrics and Midwifery he went into general practice in Wales for eight years before moving to a practice in Lowestoft in 1970. A year later he was invited to become a GP Assistant at Lowestoft Hospital and in 1973 he became a full time physician to the hospital. He became an Associate Specialist in Medicine and transferred to the new District General Hospital when it opened at the end of 1981. He retired from full time work in 1990. Since then he has done some GP locum work and continues to do various medical clinics at the James Paget one to two days a week. It is now 51 years since he started work as a House Surgeon in Great Yarmouth and Stanley is still working. He looks no older than when he retired from full time work 17 years ago.

He remains active in his allotment, walking the dog, playing golf and squash and, when he has the time, he like to sketch and paint.

Consultant Biographies

Information about the Medical and Nursing Consultant staff has been obtained by writing to all present staff and to as many retired staff whose addresses were known. Some requests were made more than once, as well as by email. When there was no response, information was gathered from various sources and the final draft was sent to each individual for correction or alteration. Most people, but not everyone, responded. Some mentioned their interest in their families but, so as not to embarrass those who did not do so, this detail has not been included!

Accident and Emergency Consultants

Ejaz Ahmed

Mr. Ahmed trained in Karachi and was appointed as the first Casualty Consultant to the coast in 1976 and was based at the Yarmouth General Hospital. He took charge of the Casualty Department in Lowestoft and oversaw the merger of both units to form the Accident and Emergency Department at the new District General Hospital. He retired in 1994.

Richard Franklin

Richard Franklin was appointed in 1988.

Chris Taylor

Chris Taylor was born in Germany and went to Bonn Medical School. She came to the United Kingdom after qualifying in 1982 and did Accident and Emergency Training in Manchester and Sheffield. She was appointed Consultant in the Accident and Emergency Department in 1994, but left a few years later.

Victor Inyang

Victor Inyang trained at the College of Medicine in the University of Lagos, Nigeria. After posts in Lagos, he came to England and joined the SHO Surgical Rotation at the James Paget. After further SHO posts in Anaesthetics and ITU in the West Midlands and a post in the Accident and Emergency Department in Norwich, he held Registrar and then Specialist Registrar posts at Ipswich, Addenbrooke's and the Norfolk and Norwich Hospitals, before being appointed Consultant in the Accident and Emergency Department at Ipswich and then the North Staffordshire Hospital. He was appointed Consultant in Accident and Emergency at the James Paget in 2003.

He has been the Trust Clinical Lead for the Emergency Care Collaborative and Chair of the Head Injury Committee. He set up the Emergency Department Management Team Group to plan medium- to long-term strategy and obtained educational approval for Specialist Registrar training. He introduced Emergency Department thrombolysis with the support of the Cardiologists. He teaches on the APLS and ALS courses and is the Medical Director of the local ALS course. He is a recognised teacher with the University of East Anglia Medical School. He is the Regional Programme Director for the Acute Common Care Stem Rotation.

In his spare time he works as a Medical Officer at Snetterton Race Track and serves on a voluntary basis with the Anglian Air Ambulance. He plays golf at national and regional level, as well as socially.

Duncan Peacock

Duncan Peacock was born in the north-east of England in Middlesbrough. He left school after taking his GCE "O" level examinations and went to work in an old people's home. He then started working for his "A" level examinations and was accepted by Dundee University to study Medicine in 1986. He used to spend his summer vacations and often other holidays working in the Accident and Emergency Department of the James Paget and attended rounds and clinics in other departments, particularly in General Surgery and Medicine. He picked up many of the student prizes during his training and after Surgical SHO Rotations in Dundee he was SHO in the James Paget Accident and Emergency Department. From there, he joined North-East Thames as an Accident and Emergency Specialist Registrar, working at the Royal London and University College Hospitals, among others.

It certainly seems that his early contact with the hospital as a medical student played a part in his deciding to apply for a Consultant post at the James Paget and it is hoped that the regular training of Medical students from the University of East Anglia Medical School will have similar benefits. He was appointed in 2003, at the age of 38, as Consultant in the Accident and Emergency Department.

He has been Chairman of the Resuscitation Committee since shortly after being appointed Consultant and is now Clinical Lead of the Accident and Emergency Department. Among other committees he sits on are the Point of Care Committee, the Vocational Trainee Scheme, Modernising Medical Careers and the Child Protection Committees. As relaxation he enjoys DIY, gardening, building and motor sport.

Anaesthetists

Neville Hicks

Neville Hick was appointed Consultant Anaesthetist to the Great Yarmouth and Waveney Health District with two sessions at the Norfolk and Norwich Hospital in 1961. He was appalled at the anaesthetic services when he started and soon relinquished his post in Norwich. He produced statistics which showed that the amount spent on medical care decreased exponentially with the distance from Cambridge. On transferring to the new hospital, he insisted on the largest room in the anaesthetic suite as his office, but David Turner feels that he had earned it. When he retired in 1983, the Anaesthetic services had been transformed and his room was converted to the Anaesthetic Department common room. He retired to the Isle of Man, but continued doing locum anaesthetic posts for many years.

David Turner

David Turner was appointed Consultant Anaesthetist to the Great Yarmouth and Waveney Health District in November 1969 at the age of 34 and he played a major part in building up the Anaesthetic Department and in the building of the James Paget Hospital. He qualified at Edinburgh University and, after two years of house officer jobs there, was Senior House Surgeon in Lowestoft before taking up Anaesthetics in Ipswich and East Suffolk Hospitals, finishing up as Senior Registrar in Edinburgh. He helped to unify the Coastal Anaesthetic Services, which were divided between Great Yarmouth and Lowestoft Hospitals as well as several other smaller hospitals, and with the building of the new District General Hospital he oversaw the development of a full anaesthetic service. He established the Pain Relief Clinic and had a major part to play in setting up an Intensive Care Unit.

He was on the Project Team and subsequently was Chairman of the Commissioning Team for the new District General Hospital from 1975 to 1981. He was Medical Staff Chairman in the 1970s, was the first Chairman of the Hospital Arts Committee and served on the Hospital's Ethics Committee. In the early 1980s, he was Chairman of the local BMA and of the Regional Anaesthetic Committee.

He retired from full-time work in 1996 at the age of 61, but continued as a part-time Consultant, doing two sessions weekly for a further six years.

For many years he has had his own boat, which he frequently sails. He has been Commodore of the Royal Suffolk and Lowestoft Yacht Club and he is an active member of his local church.

Kingsley Branch

Kingsley Branch did his medical training at the University of Birmingham. After pre-registration posts at Workington Infirmary, Cumberland and Stourbridge, he served for 16 years in the Royal Air Force. During this time his design for a nuclear decontamination centre was one of two designs adopted by Bomber Command. He was also seconded to the Royal Rhodesian Air force. On returning to the UK, he started his training in anaesthetics, during which he spent time at the Hammersmith and Addenbrooke's Hospitals, as well as time abroad in Germany and Cyprus. He was appointed Consultant Anaesthetist to the Yarmouth and Waveney Health District in 1974 at the same time that Barbara Castle became Minister of Health. There was much unhappiness in the Health Service and he resigned in 1976 to take up a post in Holland. Two years later, he returned to East Anglia to his old post, which had not been filled.

He was Chairman of the Medical Staff Committee for two years to cover the period of opening the new hospital in 1981/82 and for the following four years was on the District Management Team. He was heavily involved in the training of Operating Department Assistants and, with Dr. Turner, started the Epidural Service for the Maternity Unit. He was Chairman of the Resuscitation Committee which appointed the first Resuscitation Training Officer, Pam Cushing. He retired in 1997 and after four weeks returned part-time for a further five years.

Rachel Eirlys Davies

Eirlys Davies was born in Llanfynydd, Wales. She spent three years helping to run the family farm before starting medical student training at the Royal College of Surgeons in Dublin. She did her house jobs in

Map of hospitals and the Newberry Clinic in the Great Yarmouth & Waveney Primary Care Trust

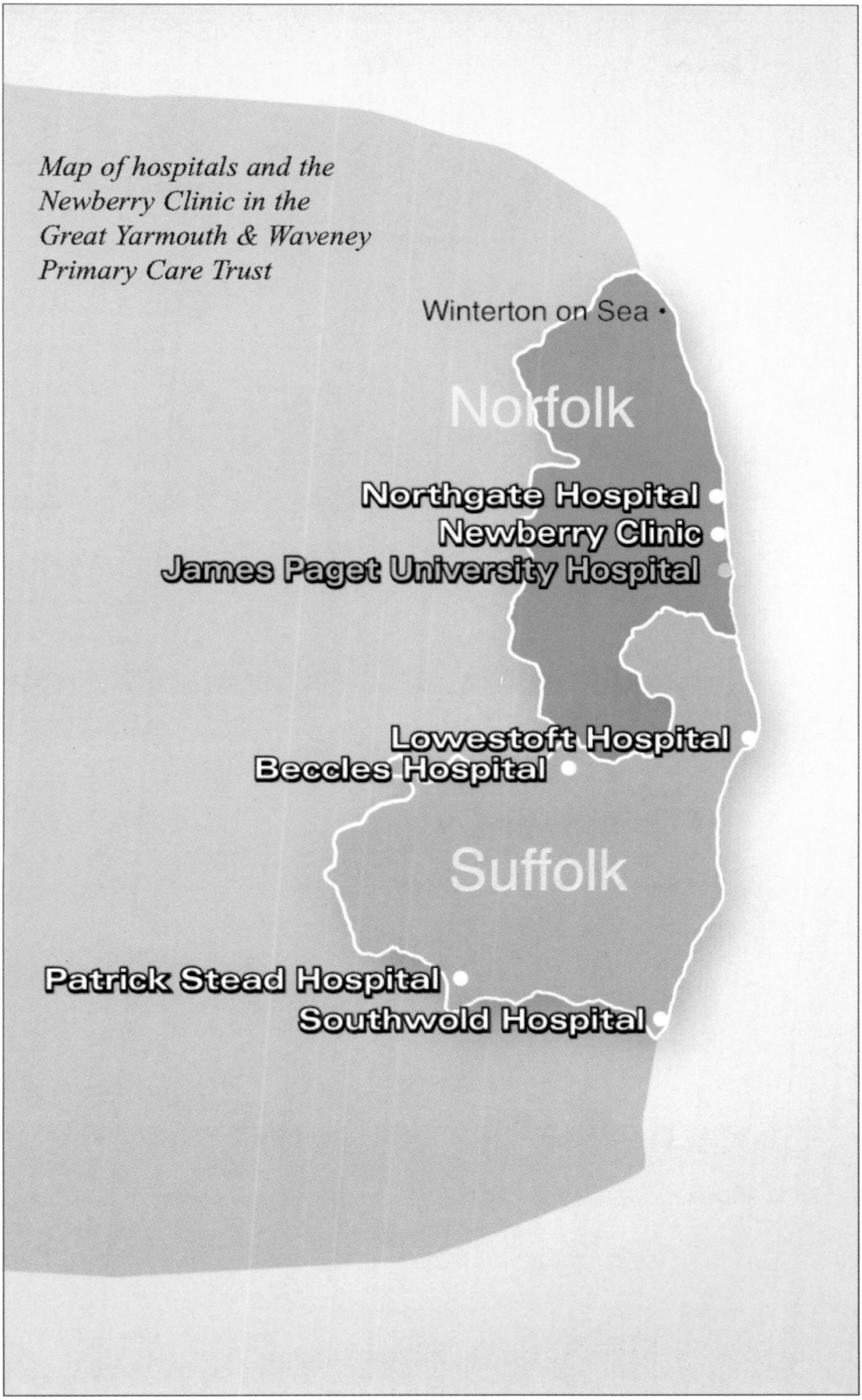

Winterton on Sea

Norfolk

Northgate Hospital

Newberry Clinic

James Paget University Hospital

Lowestoft Hospital

Beccles Hospital

Suffolk

Patrick Stead Hospital

Southwold Hospital

Yarmouth General Hospital

Gorleston Hospital

Southwold Hospital

Northgate Hospital

Beccles Hospital

Unveiling of sign indicating site of District General Hospital, Thursday 1st April 1976.
Left to right: Dr G A Bracewell, Mr R W C Guest, Mr A E Rhodes, Dr J T Dawson, Dr E H Back, Mr D G Farrow, Mr B J Hall, Mr M R H Cartiss, Mrs M Reynolds, Dr N J Ball, Mr J N Johnson, Sir Arthur South, Mr A G Sturrock.

Lowestoft Hospital

Unveiling sign after Foundation Status granted
Tuesday 1st August 2006.
Left to right: Hugh Sturzaker, Governor; Victoria Hunt, Governor; Julia Hunt, Matron of Emergency Division; David Hill, Chief Executive; John Hemming, Chairman; Bernard Brett, Divisional Director of Emergency Medicine; Patrick Thompson, Chair of Patient and Public Involvement Forum.

James Paget University Hospital sign

Logos Past...

... and Present

James Paget University Hospitals 

NHS Foundation Trust

Education and Training Centre with Medical Records on ground floor

Recent New Buildings

Education and Training Centre entrance

Southside office buildings

Burrage Centre with Bowling Green

Burrage Centre Bar

Body Wellness Gym

Celebration Suite, Burrage Centre

Dublin, then moved to Wales, ending up at the University Hospital of Wales in Cardiff as Registrar and Senior Registrar in Anaesthetics. It was here that she met her future husband, Graeme McLean, who was to become Consultant Obstetrician and Gynaecologist for the Great Yarmouth and Waveney Health Authority. She moved here with him and, after doing some Locum Consultant posts in Norwich and Great Yarmouth and having a baby, she was appointed Consultant Anaesthetist in December1980 at the age of 37. Her main task on appointment was to establish the Intensive Care Ward at the new District Hospital, which was to open in a year's time. Her other interest was in Obstetric Anaesthesia, but her main one was Education, and she was College Tutor from 1990 for six years and Clinical Tutor from 1998 (having been Associate Clinical Tutor since 1994) until she retired in April 2003 at the age of 59.

Apart from attending many Regional Committees, she helped set up the North Norfolk School of Anaesthesia at the University of East Anglia with her fellow College Tutors at the Norfolk and Norwich and Kings Lynn Hospitals, along with Professor Shirley Pearce from the University in the early 1990s. For many years she was the Secretary of the East Anglian Association of Anaesthetists, Editor of its Journal and President from 2001 to 2003. At the James Paget, she oversaw the moving of Education from the main hospital to the Southside Block and the establishment of a Skills Laboratory there. She also introduced Skills Testing for all new trainees at the James Paget and ran a course at the James Paget on "Teaching the Trainers to Teach"

She was a Council Member of the Age Anaesthesia Association from the mid-1990s until her retirement. Now she is doing an Open University Humanities Degree and is involved with Age Concern. She is a Governor of the Trust. In her spare time she enjoys gardening, sailing and going to the opera and ballet.

Jennifer Jenkins

Jenny Jenkins was born in London and qualified in Medicine at the Westminster Hospital. Later, she became Anaesthetic Senior Registrar on the Norfolk and Norwich and Addenbrooke's rotation. She was appointed Consultant to the Great Yarmouth and Waveney Health

Authority at the age of 34 and started working in May 1981, seven months before the District General Hospital opened. She has a special interest in Obstetric Anaesthesia, was Chairman of the Surgical Division and was Chairman of the Anaesthetic Department between 1992 and 1994 and between 1997 and 1998. She was Chairman of the Clinical Ethics Advisory Group from 2002 to 2006.

William Notcutt

Willy Notcutt was born in Ipswich and did his medical training in Birmingham. After house jobs in Birmingham and Stoke-on-Trent, he was a Flying Doctor in Maseru, Lesotho. He was a Senior House Officer and Registrar in Anaesthesia at Sutton Coldfield, before going to the University of the West Indies, Kingston, Jamaica, as Registrar in Anaesthesia. While there, he became Senior Registrar and Lecturer. Returning to the UK, he was Senior Registrar on the Nottingham Area Health Authority rotation until being appointed Consultant Anaesthetist at the James Paget in 1982, at the age of 36.

Since being at the James Paget, he has expanded the Pain Relief Service, started and developed the local Palliative Care Service and has been heavily involved in education and research. He introduced Patient-controlled Analgesia (PCA) to the hospital when the concept was new in this country. He introduced the Pain Management Service, was Lead Clinician for it for 19 years and remains Lead Clinician for the Back Pain Service. He was a founder member of the Anglian Pain Society and founder member and Chairman of the Philosophy and Ethics Group of the British Pain Society. He was Chairman of the Regional Palliative Care Working Party and Medical Advisor to the Macmillan Nursing Team. Much of his time is devoted to education of doctors, nurses and students in this country and abroad and he has been closely involved with the setting up and development of the University of East Anglia Medical School, of which he is an Honorary Senior Lecturer.

He has been Chairman of the Anaesthetic Department and the Medical Staff Committee. He was a founder member of the Local Clinical Ethics Advisory Group and in 2000 he started and still runs an "Introduction to Healthcare Weekend" for 6th form students.

His research and publications have included such topics as Endotracheal Cuffs, PCA, Pain Relief Services, Acute and Chronic Pain, Pain Philosophy and Cannabinoids. He is a reviewer for five journals. He is Chairman of the Local Research and Governance Support Group, is a member of the Norfolk and Norwich University Hospital Research Governance Group and is a Research Assessor for the Multiple Sclerosis Society.

In spite of all of this, he still finds time for other interests such as religion, skiing, Tai Chi, scuba diving, music and writing.

David Blundell

David Blundell did his medical training at St. Andrew's University and, after house jobs at Southport Infirmary in Lancashire, he joined the medical branch of the RAF. He was appointed Consultant Anaesthetist at the James Paget in 1983, at the age of 43. He was Chairman of the Medical Staff Committee and of the Anaesthetic Department and at one time he was in charge of the Intensive Care Unit. He retired in 2002.

He is interested in books.

Robert Mann

Bob Mann was born in Aberdeen and that was where he did his medical training. He was Senior Registrar in Anaesthetics at Ninewells Hospital, Dundee, before being appointed Consultant Anaesthetist at the James Paget in 1983, at the age of 32. He was Clinical Director of Critical Care from 1996 to 2002 and twice has been Chairman of the Anaesthetic Department. For many years he has been the Medical Staff Committee Representative on the Charitable Fund Committee and he is the Chairman of the Private Practice Committee. He has played a large part in running the Hyperbaric Unit. In the past, he has been the secretary and deputy editor of the newsletter for the East Anglian Association of Anaesthetists. He has been on the Committee of the Age Anaesthesia Association since 2004.

He is involved in teaching and examining medical students. Well known for having a beard, he was rather shocked to find that he was not recognised at a management meeting after having removed it for the first time in 20 years.

He enjoys sailing, surfing, outdoor pursuits and travel.

Richard Morgan

Richard Morgan was appointed Consultant Anaesthetist in 1985. He took over the running of the Intensive Care Unit before becoming Clinical Director of Anaesthetics and Operating Theatres in 1992. He developed the Early Warning Score, which highlights those patients who are deteriorating. He left for another post in Blackpool in 1996.

Maggie Wright

Maggie Wright graduated with an Honours degree in Pharmacology from the University of Dundee and, after a year of research, decided she would prefer working with people rather that test tubes. After graduating in Medicine from Dundee, she completed training posts in Scotland and at the Hammersmith Hospital in London. After several years of doing Locum Consultant Anaesthetic posts at the James Paget and raising her young family, she was appointed Consultant Anaesthetist in 1990. She had always had a passion for Intensive Care and has been Director of the ICU since 1992. She promoted the building of a new ICU and was an active member of the Fundraising Committee.

With Richard Morgan and Frances Wilkinson, she developed the Early Warning Score, which has helped in the early identification and treatment of patients who are at risk of developing critical illness. This score has been adopted and adapted across the UK and is now required by the Department of Health to be used in hospitals.

She was the first female to Chair the Medical Staff Committee and has been a member of numerous committees. A founder member and Past Chairman of the Clinical Ethics Advisory Group, she sits on the UK Clinical Ethics Network National Committee and in 2006 she organised their annual conference in Norwich on the theme “Ethics for the Vulnerable”. She has organised and chaired sessions on “Ethical dilemmas in ICU” for the Intensive Care Society.

She has been heavily involved with the UEA Medical School from the outset and functions as a Unit team member, a Problem-Based Learning and Consultation Skills Tutor, an adviser, lecturer and an examiner.

She has published articles on the early warning score, the intensive care unit and clinical ethics committees.

Her most important job is being a mother (aka taxi driver) to her three very sporty children. She runs marathons, plays cricket badly and loves to visit France as often as possible.

Michael Hooper

Mike Hooper held various jobs in Plymouth, Newcastle, New Zealand and Australia before becoming Senior Registrar in Anaesthetics in the West Midlands. He joined the hospital as Consultant Anaesthetist in January 1994 with a special interest in pain management.

He has an interest in growing Grapes, sea fishing and wood carving.

He returned to Australia in 1996. In 2003, he was reappointed to the staff of the James Paget, but he returned to Australia in 2003. Perhaps the Australian vineyards were too much of an attraction.

Stef Oosthuyson

Stef Oosthuyson was born in Cape Town and did his Medical Training at the University of Cape Town and his anaesthetic training at the University of Witwatersrand. After five years of Anaesthetic private practice in South Africa, he did a Locum Consultant post in Preston, Lancashire, and was appointed Consultant Anaesthetist at the James Paget in June 1994. His special interest is in Regional Anaesthesia, especially ultrasound-guided peripheral regional anaesthesia, and he introduced thoracic para-vertebral block for breast reconstructive surgery. He was College Tutor for the Anaesthetic Department for three years, and was a member of the Risk Assessment Group.

His interests outside medicine are sailing, gardening, traveling, sport and investing in the Stock Market.

He left for a post at the Norfolk and Norwich University Hospital in 2005.

Thinus Mostert

Thinus Mostert was born and bred in Johannesburg. He did his Medical studies at the University of Pretoria Medical School and after his internship he worked as a medical officer in the South African Medical Services and completed a course in aviation medicine. Later, he went into Private Practice as a Consultant Anaesthetist, before taking up his appointment at the James Paget in 1995.

His hobbies are ornithology, backpacking, gardening and distance running.

He left the Trust in 2001 to take up a post in London.

Ranjith Ganepola

Ranjith Ganepola was born in Sri Lanka, where he went to Medical School. Having been Consultant Anaesthetist and Senior Lecturer at Galle Teaching Hospital, Sri Lanka, he joined the James Paget Anaesthetic Department in 1995, at the age of 39. He has a special interest in Intensive Care, Technical matters and Information Technology. He enjoys teaching and training. Outside medicine, he devotes time to moral and political philosophy, computers and gardening.

Dean Millican

Dean Millican was born in Norfolk and has lived most of his life in Gorleston. After junior medical posts in Orthopaedics, Plastic Surgery and Accident and Emergency Medicine, he started his Anaesthetic training and was appointed to the James Paget in 1996, at the age of 37. He has a special interest in anaesthetising children and has shown an interest in management. He was Director of the Anaesthetic Department and so sat on the Unit Management Team. He has been involved with Risk Management. He has been an Educational Supervisor, College Tutor and has been Anaesthetic Advisor on external review panels. He is an Instructor for Acute Life Support, Acute Trauma Life Support and Acute Paediatric Life Support courses and is a Tutor for the University of East Anglia Medical School.

His interests outside Medicine are music, walking and cycling.

Patrick Blossfeldt

Patrick Blossfeldt qualified as a doctor at the University of Tuebingen, Germany, and did house jobs at the James Paget before returning to Germany for Anaesthetics Specialty Training. Fortunately for the hospital, his children preferred England to Germany and he was appointed Consultant Anaesthetist in January 1997, at the age of 36. He was Chairman of the Anaesthetic Department from October 2000 until July 2002. He has a special interest in Pain Management and eventually gave up his Anaesthetic duties to devote his time to Palliative Care and Pain Management in December 2004. With Dr. Notcutt, he helped to establish a multi-disciplinary Pain Management Service. He has been Lead Consultant for Palliative Care since January 2003 and has led the establishment of Hospice at Home Care Service with an £800,000 National Lottery grant. He teaches Medical students, Junior Doctors and General Practitioners and has a special interest in Acupuncture.

He has interests in psychology, spirituality and long-distance running.

Michael Gay

Mike Gay was born in Southampton but attended school in South Africa and obtained his medical degree from the University of Cape Town. He did his house officer jobs at the Groote Schuur Hospital, then spent some time in general practice doing GP locums in South Africa and in the United Kingdom, before starting a career in Anaesthetics. He completed his anaesthetic training at the Tygerberg Hospital, University of Stellenbosch, Cape Town, and was appointed Consultant Anaesthetist to that hospital in 1987. He had a year out as Senior Registrar in Anaesthetics in Leicester in 1994. He joined the hospital in 1997 as Consultant Anaesthetist, at the age of 47.

He is the Department's Linkman for the Anaesthetic Association of Great Britain and Ireland. He is the Anaesthetic Lead for ECT services and was a member of the Theatre Health and Safety Committee and Theatre Risk Management Committee.

He enjoys cycling, bird watching, music and photography.

Darell Tupper-Carey

Darell Tupper-Carey was born in London and did his medical student training in Birmingham. Later, he became Anaesthetic Specialist Registrar in the North Thames Region. He was appointed to the James Paget in 1999, at the age of 35. He is College Tutor for the Anaesthetic Department and is responsible for the training of the Junior

Anaesthetists in the hospital and the participation of the hospital in the National Audit and Research Centre's audit of the work carried out by Intensive Care Units. He has a special interest in infection control in Intensive Care Units and the influence that ICU design has on improving cross-infection.

He enjoys sailing and reading.

Hazel Stuart

Hazel Stuart was born in Great Yarmouth and is the daughter of David and Pat, two Yarmouth GPs. Prior to doing her medical training at St. George's Hospital Medical School, London, she worked for six months as a nursing auxiliary at the James Paget and returned to do this job periodically until she qualified. She did her Anaesthetic training at St. Georges and was appointed Consultant Anaesthetist in 1999, at the age of 36. She has a special interest in Intensive Care Medicine and was in charge of introducing the computer system for recording notes which abolished paper notes.

She was Chairman and then Clinical Lead of the Anaesthetic Department from 2003 until 2006 and is the Medical Staff Representative for Healthcare Governance and Information Governance. She teaches medical students about Emergency Medicine.

She enjoys sailing and wine tasting.

Herbert Koessler

Herbert Koessler studied medicine at the Universities of Freiburg and Tubingen. He did his Anaesthetic training at the Freiburg University Hospital and continued working there after he had passed the State examination and the examinations of the European Academy of Anaesthesiology. He was appointed Consultant Anaesthetist at the James Paget in 2001. He left the Trust in 2006.

Sharon Rhodes

Sharon Rhodes was born in Sheffield and did her medical training at that university. She was appointed Consultant Anaesthetist to the Norfolk and Norwich Hospital in 1994 and continued working there until she was appointed Consultant at the James Paget in 2002. She has special interests in Anaesthesia for Day Case Surgery and Obstetrics and is very keen on Audit. She is a member of the Labour Forum, the Maternity Services Liaison Committee, the Day Care and Pre-assessment Board, the Audit and Effectiveness Steering Committee and the Obstetrics Guidelines Committee. She is Vice-Chairman of the Surgical Division.

She is involved in teaching Medical students, Junior Anaesthetists and Midwives and her research interests include Obstetric Anaesthesia and Analgesia.

She is a member of the Beccles Choral Society and enjoys cricket, horse riding, films, the theatre and New Zealand, although she has yet to find a Hobbit.

Andreas Brodbeck

Andreas Brodbeck was born in Germany and did his Medical training at the Eberhard-Karls-University in Tuebingen. After holding resident posts at the Teaching Hospital in Tubingen, he became a resident in the Department for Anaesthesiology and Surgical Intensive Care Medicine. He did a PhD thesis on Clinical-Experimental Research into the Effective Use of Tobramycin and Gentamycin by the Help of Drug Monitoring. After further training in Anaesthesiology, he qualified and was offered a permanent post in 1995, which he held until June 2002. From February 1997 until August 1999, he was granted leave to work as a Medical Doctor in Mnero Hospital, Tanzania, with the German Development Service. He was involved in almost all clinical fields, including General Surgery, Gynaecology, Obstetrics and Public Health. A major part of his time was in administration, organizing and delivering anaesthetic training for the region and for six months he was Medical Director.

He was appointed Consultant Anaesthetist with a special interest in Intensive Care and Pain Management at the James Paget in 2002, at the age of 42. He has set up a hospital central venous catheter service and is a protagonist for the increased use of Ultrasound investigation and Transthoracic Echo-cardiograms.

Steve Wilson

Steve Wilson spent some time in the Navy as an Anaesthetist before being appointed Consultant Anaesthetist in 2001. He has a special interest in emergency operations and is the Chairman of the Blood Transfusion Committee.

Among his interests outside the hospital is keeping bees.

Nathalie Frayssinet

Nathalie Frayssinet was educated and did her Medical training in France. She held a training post at the Norfolk and Norwich Hospital before being appointed Consultant Anaesthetist at the James Paget in 2002. She made a great contribution in drawing up schedules for the pre-operative assessments of patients. She left for a post in Canada in 2005.

Pieter Bothma

Pieter Bothma was born in South Africa and trained at Cape Town Medical School and the Anaesthetic Department of the University of Witwatersrand, Johannesburg. Subsequently, he held Consultant Posts in South Africa with a special interest in Vascular and Trauma Anaesthesia. He also worked in Brunei before joining the James Paget in 2003, at the age of 50

He became Clinical Lead for the Anaesthetic Department in 2006 and Medical Director of the Hyperbaric Unit in 2007. His special interests are Intensive Care and Hyperbaric Medicine. He is Chairman of the Medical Mortality and Morbidity Review Committee and is a member of the Surgical Mortality Review Committee. He is the author of 'Critical Care Topics' in a book entitled *MRCS Picture Questions,*

Pieter is one of an increasing number of South Africans who have been recruited in recent years and continues to enjoy squash, sailing and travelling.

Mike Lundberg

After doing several locums, he was appointed to a permanent post as Consultant Anaesthetist in 2005.

Arnth Engel

Arnth Engle was born in Eckernfoerde, Germany, and was a medical student in Bonn, Germany. After working in York, Cork University

Hospital, Ireland, and Wismar City Hospital in Germany, he was appointed Consultant Anaesthetist at the James Paget, at the age of 39, in 2003. He has a special interest in Regional Anaesthesia and the Central Venous Catheter Service. Outside Medicine, he plays the harmonium, and enjoys Irish folk music and gardening.

Doug McKendrick

Doug McKendrick was appointed Consultant Anaesthetist in 2005, but left a year later.

Ajaiya Mull

Ajaiya Mull was a Red Cross Paramedic (the equivalent of compulsory military service in Germany) before doing his medical training at Johann-Wolfgang-Goethe University at Frankfurt/Main in Germany. He came to Britain in 1991, where he completed Junior Medical posts in Medicine and Surgery before commencing his training in Anaesthetics in the south of England. After various SHO and Registrar appointments in Anaesthetics, he returned to Germany for two years to complete his training. For the next seven years he worked in Bournemouth, first as a Staff Grade and then as an Associate Specialist in Anaesthetics. He was appointed Consultant Anaesthetist at the James Paget in 2006 and has a special interest in Obstetric and Regional Anaesthesia.

He plays squash and football and is a keen swimmer.

M. Karlikowski

Dr. Karlikowski was appointed Consultant Anaesthetist in August 2006 and has a special interest in intensive care.

Senthil Thiyagarajan

Senthil Thiyagarajan was born in Bangalore, India, and trained at the Stanley Medical College. He was a Specialist Registrar in Anaesthetics in East Anglia and was a Visiting Consultant at Washington University School of Medicine, USA, before being appointed Consultant Anaesthetist at the James Paget in October 2006. He has special interests in Obstetric and Regional Anaesthesia.

His main interest outside Medicine is travelling.

E. Lams

Dr. Lams was appointed as Consultant Anaesthetist in November 2006.

Dermatology

Robert Martin Graham

Robert Graham was born in Wolverhampton and trained at the Middlesex Hospital Medical School, London. After Dermatology Registrar posts at St. Thomas' Hospital and the Royal Berkshire Hospital in Reading, he became Senior Registrar and Honorary Tutor in Dermatology at the Royal Liverpool Hospital from 1985 until his appointment in 1988 as the first Consultant Dermatologist at the James Paget, at the age of 33. Since then, he has built up a high standard modern Dermatology Department. His main Dermatological interests are skin signs in systemic disease, skin tumours, contact dermatitis and paediatric dermatology and he has written several chapters in *Rook's Textbook of Dermatology* (1992, 1998 and 2004), as well as publishing many papers.

He was Chairman of the Medical Staff Committee in 1994. In the early 1990s, he became the BMA's Place of Work Area Representative and the local BMA Secretary. He was Regional BMA Secretary from 1995 to 2005. He served on the Local Negotiating Committee as Secretary and later Chairman. He was Programme Director and Regional Specialty Dermatology Advisor of the Royal College of Physicians from 1995 to 2003 and in 1993 was Chairman of Dermatology Regional Audit. He has been Honorary Senior Lecturer in Dermatology at the University of East Anglia since 2004 and took a Certificate in Medical Education in 2005. He is heavily involved in teaching Medical students and is an Examination Setter for the Specialist Registrar Exit Examination in Dermatology. Somehow, he manages to find time for flying, sailing, skiing, cycling, motoring and cooking.

Ingrid Althea Salvary

Ingrid Salvary was born in Trinidad and Tobago in the West Indies and went to Medical School at the University of the West Indies in Jamaica.

She did postgraduate training in Dermatology at the University Hospital of the West Indies in Jamaica. She worked as Senior House Surgeon in the Accident and Emergency Department, then as SHO in Dermatology at Grimsby District General Hospital. She then did a rotational appointment in General Medicine and Dermatology at Birchhill Hospital, Rochdale. She obtained a distinction in the Dermatology Diploma at the St. John's Institute of Dermatology in London and was appointed Consultant Dermatologist at the James Paget in 1996, at the age of 36. She has a special interest in Genital Dermatosis and Dermatopathology.
She was a member of the Great Yarmouth and Waveney Research and Ethics Committee from 1997 to 2005 and its Chairman from 2001 until 2005. She was Royal College of Physicians College Tutor in Dermatology from 1997 to 2000 and a member of the Regional Black and Ethnic Minority Committee from 2002 to 2005. She is a recognised teacher and Honorary Senior Lecturer of the University of East Anglia and is actively involved in teaching Medical students and Junior Doctors. Outside Medicine, her interests are ballroom dancing, jujitsu and netball.

Ear, Nose and Throat Surgeons

Anthony Couldrey

Tony Couldrey was appointed Consultant Ear, Nose and Throat Surgeon in the mid-1970s and had a joint appointment with the Norfolk and Norwich Hospital. He had been trained as a General Surgeon and enjoyed doing Thyroidectomies and Parotidectomies. He retired at the end of 1990.

Khushbal Singh Mangat

Khush Mangat was born and educated in Kenya and did his Medical training in Edinburgh, qualifying in 1962. He was appointed Ear, Nose and Throat Consultant in 1973 and held several sessions at the Norfolk and Norwich Hospital. His particular interest was Surgery of the Middle Ear. He retired in 1995 and continued working on an old farmhouse in France which he was restoring. Unfortunately, he developed complications following surgery and died in 2002.

Don Jayantha Premachandra

Prem was born in Sri Lanka and did his early training there before joining the Guy's ENT Registrar Training Scheme. He was appointed Consultant to the James Paget in 1991 at the age of 40 with a special interest in Head and Neck Cancer. His research included work on Chemo-sensitivity of Squamous Cell Carcinoma *in vitro* Cell Cultures and Matrix Metallo Protenoses in Squamous Cell Carcinoma and Thyroid Carcinoma. He has continued to publish on a wide range of topics and set up the Bernice Bibby Research Trust with a bequest from a patient. Fellows from this Trust are working with Mike Gleason, ENT Surgeon at Guys Hospital, on intracranial microsurgical techniques and producing many interesting papers. He is a member and advisor to the Anthony Long Research Trust.

With increasing specialization, many District General Hospital ENT Departments were becoming smaller or closing, but Prem was able to avoid this at the James Paget by arranging an amalgamation with the Norfolk and Norwich Hospital, which continues to work well.

He was Chairman of the Surgical Division in1993–1994 and Chairman of the Research and Ethics Committee from 2001 to 2004. He is Honorary Senior Lecturer at the University of East Anglia.

He has had many papers published on a wide range of topics covering his research: the damage caused by button batteries in the ear, nose and cervical oesophagus; the importance of examining the upper aero-digestive tract before biopsy of neck lumps; abnormal anatomy in the neck; thyroid and parotid disease; the use of epithelial cell grafts in mastoid cavities; as well as many others.

Peter Richard Prinsley

Peter Prinsley was born in Yorkshire and was a Medical student at Sheffield University. He did his ENT Registrar training at the Royal Free Hospital from 1988 to1992, before joining the Senior Registrar Rotation in Leeds Bradford and Hull. During this time he was President of the Association of Otolaryngologists in Training (AOT). He was appointed Consultant ENT Surgeon in 1996, at the age of 38, and has a special interest in Ear Surgery. He was Surgical Tutor for the James Paget, Regional Advisor for ENT and is Chairman of the ENT Regional

Training Committee. He is Honorary Senior Lecturer at the University of East Anglia. His Research interests include various clinical projects relating to Otology and training in Otology.

He is a member of the Britain–Bangladesh Ear Society and Britain–Nepal Otology Service, which involves short spells of operating in these countries. He enjoys camping.

Junaid Hanif

Junaid Hanif graduated in Medicine in Scotland and underwent specialised ENT training in Wales. He obtained a Master of Philosophy degree in 2001 and spent a year in Australia as a Senior Fellow in ENT. He has developed an interest in Otology and Rhinology and was appointed Consultant ENT Surgeon in 2005. He is hoping to develop a sleep disturbance service in the near future.

He plays squash, has a passion for reading and he used to have a private pilot's licence, which he hopes to regain.

Consultant General Surgeons

John George Corson

John Corson was born in Fareham, Hampshire. He did his Medical student training at St. Thomas' Hospital, London, after which he was House Surgeon to Mr. N. R. Barrett, leading oesophageal surgeon of the day. He was Surgical Registrar in Leicester before becoming Senior Registrar in Ipswich and at West Suffolk Hospital, Bury St. Edmonds. During this time, he spent a valuable year at Massachusetts General Hospital in Boston, USA, where he assisted in surveys into Peri-operative Biliary and Neighbouring Systems Surgery.

He was appointed to the Great Yarmouth and Waveney Health District as Consultant Surgeon in 1967, at the age of 41, working in Lowestoft and Great Yarmouth, having previously worked as a locum. He was associated with the planning and building of the new District General Hospital and, with its opening in 1981, he transferred all his sessions there. From 1983, he helped with the every-day running of the new hospital for five years. He retired at the age of 65 on 30th November 1991, but came back the following year to do a month's locum.

He was Chairman of the Medical Staff Committee for the Coastal Hospitals from 1972 to 1973 and Chairman of the James Paget Hospital Management Committee for five years. This consisted of a Nurse, Administrator and a Doctor and he was responsible for the running of the whole hospital. Although hospitals were smaller in those days, this arrangement is very different from the multiple and varied committees which run hospitals today. He was an Honorary Lecturer of the Cambridge University Medical School and from 1988 to 1991 he sat on the East Anglian Region Medical Advisory Committee.

He used to have a private pilot's licence, enjoys travelling and working on machines.

Paul Aukland

Paul Aukland was born in Fleetwood, Lancashire, and did his Medical training in Liverpool before working as a GP in Sheffield. From 1967 to 1969, he did Voluntary Service Overseas in Malawi for nearly two years before becoming a Senior House Surgeon in Blackpool. He then joined the Registrar and Senior Registrar Rotation on Merseyside, during which he spent a year at McMaster University in Hamilton, Canada. He was appointed Consultant Surgeon with a special interest in Vascular Surgery to the Great Yarmouth and Waveney Health Authority in 1979, at the age of 38, working mainly in Lowestoft. With the move to the new District General Hospital, he was able to develop Vascular Surgery further. He continued to have outpatient sessions in Lowestoft, Southwold and Beccles Hospitals and did minor surgery at Beccles. In addition, he saw patients at Blundeston Prison. He was a member of the Lowestoft District Management Committee and was Clinical Director of Surgery at the James Paget. He was a member of the Regional Pre-Registration Committee and an Honorary Lecturer of Cambridge University Medical School. His research interests were Vascular Grafts and direct access for patients to undergo hernia repairs.

He retired from full-time work in 1999 at the age of 59, but works part-time doing surgery for the Dermatology Department. This enables him to continue his passion for flying his own Tiger Moth and other planes, sailing his own boat in the Mediterranean and having some exotic holidays. He is now learning to fly a helicopter.

Hugh Gerard Sturzaker

Hugh Sturzaker was born in Lancashire and did his Medical training in Oxford and at Guy's Hospital, London, during which time he was Education Officer and subsequently President of the British Medical Students Association. After house jobs at Guy's, he was Surgical Registrar in Guildford before joining the Guy's Surgical Registrar Training Scheme, during which he worked at St. Mark's Hospital and Great Ormond Street Hospital for Sick Children. In 1979, at the age of 38, he was appointed Consultant Surgeon with a special interest in Gastro-intestinal Surgery to the Great Yarmouth and Waveney Health District and was based mainly at Great Yarmouth General Hospital.

He moved to the new District General Hospital when it opened and helped to develop Colorectal and Breast Surgery. He established the first Stoma Care Service in East Anglia and introduced Laparoscopic Cholecystectomy to the James Paget in 1990. He was associated with the foundation of several patient support groups, such as the Amputees Club, BRAS, Ostomy Support Group and the Ileal Pouch Group. He was Chairman of the Medical Staff Committee from 1989 to 1991.

He was a member of the Regional Committee for the Prevention and Management of Malignant Disease, the Regional Medical Advisory Committee from 1991 to 1995 and a member of the Regional Consultants and Specialists Committee from 1989 to 1991, as well as the Regional Training Committee from 1995 to 2005. He was Chairman of the Norfolk and Waveney Colorectal Cancer Network.

He was a Council Member of the Association of Surgeons of Great Britain and Ireland from 1997 to 2002 and was a member of the National Committee for the Examination of Post-Operative Deaths (NCEPOD), which produced its 2001 Report, "Changing the Way we Operate". He was Regional Advisor for the Royal College of Surgeons of Edinburgh from 1984 to 2005 and continues to be an Examiner for the College. In the last few years he has organised the Intercollegiate MRCS Clinical Examinations at the James Paget. He was Honorary Lecturer of the Cambridge University Medical School and Honorary Senior Lecturer of the University of East Anglia Medical School.

He succeeded in seeing that the District had its own Breast Screening Service and Breast Care Unit. The latter was paid for by raising money from a Public Appeal. In 1982, he suggested the building of a combined sports, social club and education centre and oversaw its construction. This became the Burrage Centre, in memory of Mrs. Burrage, who was the chief benefactor. He continued to be the Chairman of its Board of Management until he retired.

He did research on Collagenase and its association with malignancy and has written papers on Carcino-embryonic Antigen, Recurrent Sigmoid Volvulus in Young People and Gastro-intestinal Problems.

He retired in June 2005, at the age of 65, to tend his garden, travel and to see more of his children and grandchildren. He continues to teach and examine in this country and abroad and is a Governor of the Trust.

Julian Rupert Sansom

Julian Sansom was born in London and did his Medical training at St. Thomas' Hospital, London. After house jobs, he spent over a year as Medical Officer in the Antarctic. Later, he was a Surgical Registrar at the Queen Elizabeth Hospital Renal Unit in Birmingham, before becoming Senior Surgical Registrar on the Professorial Surgical Unit there.

He was appointed Consultant Surgeon with special interest in Urology in 1980, at the age of 40, and led the development of a good urological service with the assistance of his three colleagues. He had a special interest in Endocrine Surgery and did most of the Parathyroidectomies. Without doubt he was the fastest operator on the Coast. Initially, he was based in Lowestoft, but transferred most of his sessions to the new District General Hospital when it opened. He continued an Outpatients Clinic in Lowestoft for many years.

He was District Surgical Tutor for the Royal College of Surgeons of England from 1981 until 1992. He was Chairman of the Surgical Division and Chairman of the Medical Staff Committee. He was the first Clinical Director of the Surgical Division and served on multiple committees.

He was an Honorary Lecturer of the Cambridge University Medical School.

Among his publications was the "Outcome of 250 Cadaveric Renal Transplants", published in the *British Medical Journal* in 1975.

He retired in February 2005, at the age of 65, and now devotes his time to gardening, carpentry, reading history and cosmological theory.

John George Noel Studley

John Studley was born in London and trained at the Middlesex Hospital Medical School, London. He was Research Fellow in Surgery in 1979/1980 in the State of New York, Buffalo, USA, where he studied blood flow in the pancreas and this was the basis for his MS, which he obtained in 1986. Between 1987 and 1991, he was Senior Registrar in General Surgery on the Hammersmith Hospital and Royal Postgraduate Medical School/Northampton Rotation. In 1991, he was appointed Consultant Surgeon at the James Paget with a special interest in Upper Gastro-intestinal Surgery, at the age of 42.

Apart from being a good surgeon, he has a forte for administration. He was Surgical Tutor from 1992 until 1999 and a member of the Regional Training Committee, during which time he introduced many changes in the training and assessment of junior doctors. He produced an information booklet which is given to all junior surgical staff. He qualified as an Acute Trauma Life Support Instructor in 1996, a post which he continued until 2003. He was a member of the BMA Local Negotiating Committee from 1996 until 2001, being its Chairman from 1998 until 2000. He was Chairman of the Medical Staff Committee from 1997 until 1999. He became Clinical Director for General Surgery and Urology from 2000 until 2004. At that time, the management structure of the hospital changed and he was appointed Director of Elective Services. He continues in this post. He was a member of the Regional Consultants and Specialists Committee and he is the Trust representative on the Big 'C' Committee. He has sat on numerous committees and has been chairman of many.

He was heavily involved with the development of a new Endoscopy Suite and Day Care Unit. He was also the clinician in the group securing the finance for the development of a Treatment Centre but, due to changes in the Health Service, this plan has changed and a new outpatient build is planned, as well as modernisation of the wards.

He is the author of chapters in several surgical text books on topics such as Surgical Treatment of Tumours of the Liver and Bile Ducts, Thyroidectomy and Tumours of the Small Bowel. He has written multiple peer-reviewed articles. He continues to oversee several publications by his junior staff and has been the reviewer of articles for the *British Journal of Surgery* since being appointed a Consultant.

In his spare time he runs marathons (London in 2004, 2005 and 2007 and New York in 2005).

Jerome Pereira

Jerome Pereira was born in India and did his Medical training at Madras University. Between 1985 and 1988, he was Senior Surgical Registrar at the Luton and Dunstable Hospital before becoming Bernard Sunley Research Fellow at the Royal College of Surgeons of England and Honorary Senior Registrar in Plastic Surgery at the Queen Victoria Hospital, East Grinstead. Here, he did his research work on using muscle grafts for nerve reconstruction and their application in Leprosy. From 1990 to 1994, he was Visiting Research Consultant to LEPRA (UK), after which he was appointed Consultant Surgeon to the James Paget Hospital, at the age of 44.

He has been Chairman of the Surgical Division and the Research Support Group. He was a member of the Hospital Training and District Medical Education Committee, the Medical Manpower Committee and the Resuscitation Committee, as well as several others. He has been Chairman of the Norfolk and Waveney Breast Cancer Network and a member of the East Anglian Surgical Training Committee.

He was Chairman of the Medical School Implementation Group and has been instrumental in establishing the James Paget's links with the Medical School and the University of East Anglia. He is a Recognised Teacher, Honorary Senior Lecturer and a member of the Curriculum Development and Design Team. He was the first person to be awarded an MD by the University. He was appointed Chairman of the University Hospital Status Working Group in 1997.

On his appointment to the hospital, he became Clinical Lead for Breast Surgery and he was the first Surgeon in a District General Hospital in East Anglia to start Breast Reconstruction. Since then, he has established a National Audit on the procedure which has the backing of Breast and Plastic Surgeons and the work is being finance by NICE. Now he is the Lead Clinician of the National Mastectomy and Breast Reconstruction Audit. He has been involved in teaching Breast Reconstruction at the Royal College of Surgeons of England and has demonstrated the techniques at several hospitals around the country.

He contributed to a chapter in the British Association of Surgical Oncology/ Royal College of Surgeons Breast Course in 2000 and the MRCS STEP 2001. He has had over 30 articles published on Leprosy, Breast Cancer and Reconstruction and is a reviewer for the *Leprosy Review*, *British Journal of Surgery* and *European Journal of Surgical Oncology*.

Outside Medicine, he enjoys travelling, social work and research abroad and he is fundraising for a theological college in India.

Matthew Philip Armon

Matthew Armon was born in London and was a Medical student and houseman in Nottingham, where he became a Research Fellow. He was a Specialist Registrar in Nottingham, Johannesburg and Sheffield, before being appointed Consultant Vascular Surgeon at Norfolk and Norwich University Hospital and the James Paget. His special interests are in Aortic Aneurysms and Carotid Surgery. With increasing specialization, his time at the James Paget is taken up by doing clinics, seeing patients on the wards and doing mainly varicose vein surgery, amputations and debridement. He has developed a vascular service with strong links to Norwich and now all patients requiring major arterial work are transferred to Norwich, where he operates on them.

His research interests include Endovascular Abdominal Aortic Aneurysm Repair –whereby stents are inserted into the aneurysm through small incisions in the groins under local anaesthetic – and Thrombolysis for Deep-vein Thrombosis.

He plays golf, squash and tennis.

Hank Schneider

Hank Schneider was born in New Jersey, USA, and trained at Charing Cross and Westminster Medical School, London, where he was Captain of Boats. After house jobs, mainly at Charing Cross, he was Chief Medical Officer for Operation Raleigh, Queensland Expedition, before becoming an Anatomy Demonstrator at St. George's Hospital, London. After two years as an SHO in General Surgery and Urology at Medway Hospital in Kent (during which time he had won the Gerald Townsley Travelling Fellowship to study Trauma Management in the USA), he did a Residency programme at Portland in the USA. On returning to the United Kingdom, he was a Research Fellow at the Royal Marsden for a year before joining the Registrar programme of the South-East Thames Region. He was appointed Consultant Surgeon to the James Paget in 2001, at the age of 40. He became the Lead in Paediatric Surgery, joined the Colorectal Unit and participated in other aspects of general surgery.

He was Surgical Tutor and sat on the Regional Training Committee. He was a member of a number of hospital committees. He has contributed chapters to four books and has written a number of scientific papers, which have included Benefits and Complications of Laparoscopic Surgery and a review on Immunonutrition. He was Medical Officer to the Cambridge University Boat Club for the Boat Race from 1996 to 2001 and is interested in travel, music, photography, sailing, sculling, diving, skiing, fishing, shooting, riding and vegetable gardening.

In the middle of 2005, it came as a surprise when he announced that he was leaving the James Paget. Since then, he has undertaken a number of Locum Consultant posts in Burton-on-Trent, Dorchester and at the Chelsea and Westminster Hospital, London.

Vivek Chitre

Vivek Chitre was born in New Delhi, India, and did his Medical training at the Goa Medical College and, after Junior and Senior Registrar posts in Surgery, came to the United Kingdom, where he worked at the James Paget as Senior House Surgeon. He then became Specialist Registrar in Surgery on the Anglia and South Thames Rotation. He was appointed Consultant Surgeon with a special interest in Upper Gastro-intestinal Surgery and Laparoscopic Surgery in 2004, at the age of 41. He is Clinical Lead for Day Surgery and Pre-assessment. He is a recognised Medical Teacher of the Medical School.

Sarah Elizabeth Downey

Sarah Downey was born in Lytham, Lancashire. She trained at Nottingham University Medical School, was a Surgical Registrar on the Leeds Rotation and did research in Manchester. She was appointed Consultant Breast Surgeon in Bradford in 2002 and the Surgical

Department was delighted to attract her to the James Paget in June 2005, at the age of 39. Most Breast Surgeons nowadays want to do only Breast Surgery and no emergency work, so the James Paget is fortunate that she wishes to be involved with the Emergency Rota and to do Laparoscopic work.

Already, she is a member of the Local Negotiating Committee and is Surgical Tutor. She is on the Executive Committee of the Royal College of Surgeons of England Court of Examiners and helps with the Intercollegiate MRCS Examinations at the James Paget.

Roshan Lal

Roshan Lal was born in Bilaspur, India, and trained at the Indira Gandhi Medical College, Shimla, India. After Medical School, he had his early Surgical training at the Postgraduate Institute of Medical Education and Research, Chandigarh. During this training, he carried out research on peritonitis in rats for his MS. He was Surgical Registrar at the James Paget in 1995 for a year, followed by similar posts at the West Suffolk and Bedford Hospitals. In 1999, he was appointed Staff Grade General Surgeon at the West Suffolk Hospital and was promoted to Associate Specialist in 2003. He commenced work as Consultant Surgeon at the James Paget on 1st January 2006, at the age of 43, with a special interest in Colorectal and Laparoscopic Surgery.

Already, he is on the Surgical Mortality Review Committee, the Thromboprophylaxis Committee and the Resuscitation Committee. He is the Department's Lead for Paediatric Surgery. He is a member of the Regional Sarcoma Group. He has had papers published on Traumatic Haemobilia and Haemoperitoneum.

He enjoys swimming and watching international cricket.

Kevin Murray

Kevin Murray did his medical training in Ireland, and then joined the East Anglian Specialist Registrar Rotation in General Surgery. He spent the first two years of this at the James Paget. At the end of the rotation, he went to Australia to extend his knowledge and experience of Laparoscopic Colorectal Surgery. He commenced his post as Colorectal Surgeon at the James Paget in February 2006 and started setting up

Laparoscopic Colorectal Surgery. Unfortunately, after less than six months, he decided to return to Ireland.

Darren Morrow

Darren Morrow was born in London and did his Medical training at St. Bartholomew's Hospital, London. He was Senior House Surgeon at the Norfolk and Norwich and James Paget Hospitals before becoming Specialist Registrar in General and Vascular Surgery on the East Anglian Rotation. He then spent two years on a Fellowship in Vascular Surgery in Australia, before being appointed as Consultant Vascular Surgeon at the Norfolk and Norwich University Hospital, with sessions at the James Paget in 2006, at the age of 37. He has a special interest in Endovascular Surgery and a research interest in the application of information technology to surgery.

Outside Medicine, his interests are driving, dining and computing.

Achilles Tsiamis

Achilles Tsiamis has been appointed as Colorectal Surgeon and is due to start in September 2007. He has spent the last part of his training in Leicester and it is hoped that he will continue to develop Laparoscopic Colorectal Surgery at the James Paget.

Urological Surgeons

Gokarakonda Suresh

Gokarakonda Suresh was born in India and trained at Guntur Medical College, Guntur, and Nagarjuna University, Andhra Pradesh. He obtained his MS in General Surgery in 1982 at the Postgraduate Institute of Medical Education and Research, Chandigarh. He did much of his Urology training in Manchester and was Consultant Urologist in Cheltenham and Gloucester Hospital for two years, before being appointed the first full-time Consultant Urological Surgeon at the James Paget in 1996, at the age of 42. Since then he has expanded the extent and quality of Urology in the hospital. He is the Lead Clinician for Urology and the Urological Cancer Lead for the James Paget. He is an Examiner for the Intercollegiate MRCS.

Andrew Simpson

Andrew Simpson was born in Manchester and at Cambridge took a degree in Zoology. He did his clinical training at St. Bartholomew's Hospital in London. He did his house jobs there and in Newmarket. SHO posts were held in Oxford. During his Registrar posts in East Anglia, he did some research into Day Surgery in the Region and then he joined the higher surgical training programme with posts in Cambridge, Ipswich, Bedford and Norwich. He was appointed Consultant Urologist at the James Paget in 1999 and introduced Percutaneous Nephrolithotomy as part of his interest in urological stone management. He was Chairman of the Surgical Division and was involved in introducing a new computer system into the operating theatres.

He enjoys playing the piano and accordion, sailing and hill walking.

Unfortunately, he left in May 2005 for a post in Lincoln.

Genito-Urinary Medical Physicians

Mohammed Sulaiman

Mohammed Sulaiman ran the Genito-Urinary Medicine Department at Estcourt Hospital, but left shortly before the Bure Clinic was opened in the James Paget.

Nadarajah Balakumar

Nadarajah Balakumar was appointed Consultant in Genito-Urinary Medicine in 1991 to work in the Bure Clinic, which was transferred to the James Paget that year. Sadly, he died suddenly in 1995.

Tubonye Clement Harry

T. C. Harry was born in Nigeria and qualified as a Doctor at the University of Lagos. He came to the United Kingdom in 1984 and trained as a General Practitioner on the University of Liverpool Vocational Training Scheme, after obtaining the MRCOG on the Mersey Regional Obstetric and Gynaecology Scheme. He started his Genito-Urinary Medicine training as a Registrar in 1992 on the

Newcastle/Sunderland rotation and became a Senior Registrar in GU/HIV Medicine on the Sunderland/South Shields/Newcastle rotation. He was appointed Consultant in GU Medicine in 1996.

He has written numerous papers on topics connected with Genito-Urinary Medicine.

Outside Medicine, his interests are cycling and attending jazz music sessions.

General Physicians

Ronnie Gibbs

He was born in Norfolk and went to Trinity Hall, Cambridge, and St. Thomas' Hospital Medical School, before finishing his training at Addenbrooke's Hospital, Cambridge. He was appointed Assistant Physician (SHMO) to Lowestoft and North Suffolk Hospital in 1956, with four sessions weekly, and worked part-time with the Walker family. A few years later, he was upgraded to Consultant. In 1967, he was appointed Physician with a special interest in Geriatrics at Northgate Hospital as well and gave up General Practice.

The sessions at Northgate Hospital involved looking after the elderly. At that time, Drs. Whylie Beattie and John Adams, who were Consultant Geriatricians in Norwich, used to come to Northgate once a week to see the elderly patients. Other Consultant Physicians from Norwich used to visit the Coastal Hospitals for one or two sessions weekly. He was a member of the Norwich, Great Yarmouth and Lowestoft Management Committee and was an active supporter for developing a new District General Hospital on the Coast. At one time, he was Chairman of the Regional Merit Awards Committee.

With the opening of the new District General Hospital, most of his work was transferred there, but he continued some sessions in Lowestoft and at Northgate. He retired in 1986, at the age of 63. He continues looking after his farm, playing the piano and sailing. He was a father-figure to so many, particularly the Physicians. He is cultivated, urbane, erudite, well-read and was always generous of his time and advice.

David Wayne

David Wayne did his pre-clinical training in Oxford before moving to University College Hospital, London, to do his clinical training. After his House jobs in London, he did his National Service in the Royal Army Medical Corp between 1960 and 1962, serving in East and West Africa. He ended up as Captain.

After various house jobs and research posts in London and Glasgow, he joined the Medical Registrar Rotation at University College Hospital for three years, before becoming Senior Medical Registrar on the Cambridge/Norwich Rotation. In February 1974, at the age of 40, he started work for the Great Yarmouth and Waveney Health District as Consultant Physician in General Medicine with a special interest in Geriatrics. Later, he was to develop the specialty of Diabetes and Endocrinology. With the opening of the new hospital, most of his sessions were transferred there, although he continued working at Northgate Hospital. He retired in February 1998, at the age of 64, but continued work as Locum Consultant until September 1998. He was angry at the collapse of the medical 'firm' – an apprentice system of informal on-the-job training which kept all grades of medical staff on their toes.

He was Chairman of the Medical Staff Committee in 1979 and for many years was Regional Adviser to the Royal Colleges of Physicians of London and Edinburgh. He was a member of many Regional Committees, including the Regional Research Committee, the Regional Medical Specialties Advisory Committee, the Regional Geriatric Advisory Committee, the Regional Training Committee in Diabetes and Endocrinology and Chairman of the Regional "C" Awards Committee and a member of the "B" Awards Committee. He represented Cambridge University on the District Health Authority and was a member of the District General Hospital Commissioning Team and eight working parties. He suggested that the hospital should be named after Great Yarmouth's most famous citizen. He established the annual "Sir James Paget Lecture" to bring speakers of national and international importance to the hospital.

He was Clinical Tutor for six and a half years from 1977 and oversaw the transfer of Medical Library and Educational Services as an integrated service for all grades of hospital staff from Northgate to the new hospital.

He was Chairman of the Library and Postgraduate Educational Committees and a member of the National Association of Clinical Tutors.

He was leader of the Geriatric Services and Convenor of the Health Care Planning Team (Geriatrics) from his appointment and instigated the integration of Geriatrics into General Medicine. He developed the Diabetic Service.

In spite of all his committee work and a busy clinical timetable, he continued to publish widely. He was on the Planning Committee for the monthly medical journal *Hospital Update* and then on the Editorial Board from the first issue in October 1974 until its demise after the December 1994 issue. He was Editorial Advisor for books published by Reed Healthcare, Reed Business Publishing and Reed Elsevier Medical Publishing. He has been co-author on various medical and biological books, including *Lecture Notes on Clinical Medicine, Multiple Choice Questions on Lecture Notes on Clinical Medicine, Aids to Prescribing, The Clinical Manual, Human Form and Function, Health Science* and *The Heinemann New Family Medical Encyclopaedia.*

Wolf Grabau

Wolf Grabau trained at the Medical School in Liverpool and stayed on to do his house jobs and early Medical Registrar posts. He then moved to London to become Registrar in Cardiology and Medicine at Charing Cross Hospital and the National Heart Hospital before becoming Senior Medical Registrar at Guy's Hospital, London. He was appointed Consultant Physician and Cardiologist to the Great Yarmouth and Waveney Health District in 1978, at the age of 35, and in the early years he shared the work of looking after the elderly with his Consultant colleagues.

He was Chairman of the Medical Staff Committee in 1982, Chairman of the Medical Division (1982–85) and Clinical Director for the Department of Medicine from 1994 to 2000, during which time he oversaw the introduction of the Medical Admissions Unit. He introduced a Rapid Access Chest Pain Clinic (1995), opened a new Coronary Care Unit (1996), and initiated an Open Access Echocardiography and a Nurse-led Heart Failure Unit (1999).

He was Postgraduate Clinical Tutor from 1990 to 1994, during which he introduced Educational Supervisors for all members of the Junior Medical staff, and he made Grand Rounds a regular feature of the Education Programme.

Among other posts he held were Accountable Officer for National Service Framework for Coronary Disease, Clinical Governance Lead for the Medical Directorate and Clinical Lead for Cardiology. In the 1980s, he was on the Regional Manpower Committee and the Regional Cardiology Advisor Committee.

He is Honorary Lecturer of the UEA Medical School, a Medical Panel Member for Appeals Tribunals, Medical Liaison Officer for the Royal Medical Benevolent Fund and a Trustee of Norwich MIND.

He retired in April 2007, but is returning to do Locum Outpatient Clinics.

For relaxation, he enjoys opera, walking, travel and sailing.

Stuart Hishon

Stuart Hishon trained at the Westminster Hospital, London, and, after Medical Registrar posts at St. James's Hospital, Leeds, and the Central Middlesex Hospital, London, he entered the Norwich-Addenbrooke's senior registrar rotation in Gastroenterology. He was appointed to the Great Yarmouth and Waveney Health District in 1981, at the age of 35, as Consultant Physician with an interest in Gastroenterology and started work the same day as his wife, Dr. Jenny Jenkins, Consultant Anaesthetist.

At that time, all the gastroscopies and colonoscopies were done by the surgeons. With the move to the new hospital, seven months later, an Endoscopy room was set up in a room in the Central Treatment Suite. This was not adequate, and with money from the WRVS, he oversaw the opening of two rooms as a basis for an Endoscopy Suite at the end of the Day and Emergency Ward. He introduced the monitoring of patients during Endoscopy and started Endoscopic Retrograde Cholangio-Pancreatography (ERCP) in the hospital. His special interest was Inflammatory Bowel Disease and he had a good and close working relationship with the surgeons and the nurses in building up the Gastroenterology Department.

One of his funny stories was his first attempt to set up an endoscopy list. He borrowed instructions on fasting from a surgical colleague which said, "Do not have anything to eat or drink after midnight on Sunday." Unfortunately, Stuart's list was on a Thursday. A patient staggered in, apologising that he had had a cup of tea on Tuesday!

He was College Tutor for Medicine and was Chairman of the Medical Staff Committee. He set up the Region's Gut Club – which has continued to flourish and twice a year is the main regional meeting for gastroenterologists – and organised the first meeting in Norwich at which Sir Francis Avery Jones was the guest speaker.

Stuart had suffered from anxiety and depression since childhood. This proved a constant and occasionally debilitating problem during his career, particularly in times of stress. He decided to retire in 1994, with the hope that his health would improve. Unfortunately, it did not, and he spent his last years in very poor health. He died on 14th February 2005, at the age of 59.

David Ellis

David Ellis trained at the Medical School in Edinburgh and held various junior posts there. He developed an interest in Respiratory Medicine working for Sir John Crofton as a Senior House Officer. He was Senior Medical Registrar in Newcastle-upon-Tyne and was appointed Consultant in Respiratory Medicine to the James Paget in 1983, at the age of 36, and with his colleagues shared the responsibility of looking after the elderly.

He was Chairman of the Medical Staff Committee in 1988 and Consultant Representative on the James Paget Hospital Unit Management Committee (1990–93), before being appointed the hospital's first Medical Director, a post he held from 1993 to 1998. He was Director of the Great Yarmouth and Waveney Health Promotion Unit (1994–1997), Hospital Trust Research and Development Lead (1993–1999) and Chairman of the Risk Management Steering Group (1995–1998). In addition, he was the Trust's Clinical Audit Lead (1998–2000) and a member of the Clinical Governance and Clinical Ethics Committees.

He was Chairman of the East Anglian Medical Directors Group (1997–1998), a member of the Regional Health Authority Doctors in

Management Initiative Project Team (1992–1994) and a member of the Anglia and Oxford Palliative Care Steering Group.

He has been a main player in the development of Cancer Services, being the James Paget's Cancer Lead from 1993 until 2002. He was Vice-Chairman of the Norfolk and Waveney Cancer Project in 1996, until his appointment as Medical Director of the Norfolk and Waveney Cancer Network in 2002. From 1999 to 2002, he was Chairman of the Eastern Region Cancer Strategy Group, which became the Eastern Region Cancer Task Force. From 2001–2002, he was Clinical Cancer Lead for the Eastern Regional Office and was a Member of the National Cancer Dataset Working Group of the NHS Information Authority.

He has built up a strong Department of Respiratory Medicine with specialist respiratory nurses and developed many new procedures. He was Chairman of the Norfolk Respiratory Interest Group from 2000, was a member of the British Thoracic Society Lung Cancer Group from 1998 until 2003 and, since 2003, has been the Regional Specialty Advisor in Respiratory Medicine for the Royal College of Physicians and Regional Representative for the British Thoracic Society. He was President of the East Anglian Thoracic Society from 1997 to 2001.

In addition to all these commitments, he has been very active in education, being an Examiner for MRCP (UK) since 1997, when he was appointed Honorary Senior Lecturer of the University of East Anglia. In 1998, he was appointed Programme Director and has been Chairman of the Respiratory Specialist Training Committee of the Eastern Deanery from 2001. He is an Undergraduate Teacher and Examiner of the University of East Anglia Medical School and, since 2001, he has been Chairman of 'Clued up on Cancer' Campaign, which aims to educate the public about cancer.

Outside Medicine, he is keen on gardening, DIY and walking in Scotland.

Peter Forster

Peter Forster did his Medical training at the University of Birmingham and subsequently obtained his MD in 1983. After junior medical appointments in and around Birmingham, he was Research Fellow in High Altitude Medicine and worked at the United Kingdom Infrared

Telescope of the Royal Observatory Edinburgh in Hawaii and was Associate Clinical Professor in the Department of Medicine of the John A. Burns School of Medicine in Honolulu, Hawaii. On his return to the UK, he became Senior Registrar in Rheumatology in Edinburgh, before becoming Consultant Physician and Rheumatologist at the James Paget in 1986.

Within a year, he was Chairman of the Division of Medicine and then Clinical Director of Medicine and Elderly Services. As a result, he was a member of the hospital's Unit Management Team from 1991 to 1997. He was Chairman of the Medical Staff Committee from 2000 to 2002 and has been a member of the James Paget Clinical Ethics Advisory Group since 2001. From 1988 to 1995, he was District Representative on the East Anglian Regional Health Authority Locally Organised Research Committee.

He has been a member of the Joint Venture Medical School Implementation Group since 2001 and is very much involved in planning the curriculum, teaching and assessing the students. He is a Recognised Teacher, Honorary Senior Lecturer and Clinical Tutor for the Medical School and examines for the Membership Examination of the Royal College of Physicians. He has co-hosted the examination at the James Paget. He has been a member of the Regional Rheumatology Training Committee since 1996.

He continues to be a member of high altitude research expeditions to many exotic parts of the world, run by the Birmingham Medical Research Expeditionary Society. One just wonders why he chose to work and live in relatively flat East Anglia.

He has written a monograph on "Work at High Altitude: A study at the United Kingdom Infrared Telescope, Mauna Kea, Hawaii". He has written several book chapters on high altitude medicine, participated in a film on "Astronomers above the clouds" and has had over 30 papers published, mainly on rheumatoid disease and aspects of high altitude medicine. With his wife, Dr. Rosalyn Proops, Consultant Community Paediatrician in Norwich, he wrote "Domestic implications of a medical partnership" in *Your Career – Choice or Chance.* In his spare time he enjoys skiing, sailing or cycling.

Ken Rhodes

Ken Rhodes was appointed the first Consultant Physician with an interest in the care of the elderly in October 1994. He studied Medicine at Westminster Hospital, London. His initial interest was in Chest Medicine and he worked as a Consultant in the South Pacific, where he ran a bronchoscopy, gastroscopy and renal biopsy service for the country of Vanuatu. Returning from there, he became Senior Registrar in Care of the Elderly in Nottingham. He had interests in Orthopaedic Liaison and Incontinence. He brought in a number of changes in the management of the elderly, but left in 1997 for a post in Bromley, Kent.

Jin Kang

Jin Kang was born in Malaysia and received his Medical training at Birmingham University. After various Junior Hospital posts, he was appointed Associate Professor of Medicine in the National University of Singapore. He was appointed Consultant Gastroenterologist at the James Paget in 1995, at the age of 45, where he increased the role of therapeutic endoscopy and initiated regular gastroenterological meetings. He is very much research orientated and it was not surprising that he was appointed to St. George's Hospital, London, in 1999. Since 1995, he has published 64 papers in major journals.

Peter Harrison

Peter Harrison trained at Guy's Hospital Medical School, London, and, after further training, became Consultant Physician and Nephrologist in Bristol in 1981. He became increasingly involved in Acute Medicine and Medical Management and planned the development of Care of the Elderly and Rehabilitation within community hospitals during his three years as Clinical Director of Medicine. He left Bristol to develop transplantation in the Middle East. After doing a three-month locum at the James Paget, he was appointed to the permanent post of Consultant Physician with a special responsibility for the elderly in 1997. Since then he has overseen changes in the care of elderly patients within the James Paget Hospital and, more importantly, the four community hospitals in Suffolk, which, with the exception of Lowestoft Hospital, were facing closure. He identified the lack of suitable care for stroke patients and this led to the provision of a dedicated ward for stroke patients opening in 2006.

He has always been interested in education and has had a significant input into education at the James Paget and regionally and nationally. He was appointed Director of Postgraduate Medical and Dental Education in 2003 and Honorary Senior Lecturer at the University of East Anglia. In his Deanery role, he helped develop and has become lead faculty for Appraisal and Assessment within the Trainer Development Programme and is part of the core group developing the programme with the University of Bedfordshire.

He was elected to the Council of the National Association of Clinical Tutors in 2004 and appointed Assistant Secretary in 2006.

He has been Chairman of the Drugs and Therapeutics and the Local Negotiating Committees and continues to Chair the Trust Education Committee. Since 2004, he has been Chairman of the Joint Foundation Programme Committee for the Norfolk Hospitals and of the East of England Clinical Tutors.

He is a member of the Joint Committee of the Council of Heads of Medical Schools (CHMS), the Conference of Postgraduate Medical Deans (COPMeD) and the Foundation Programme Directors East of England Deanery.

His passion is gardening and his garden, constructed from scratch in 1998, has opened in the National Garden Scheme for a number of years. He is a qualified diver and rides large motorcycles too fast.

Kiruparajan Jesudason

Kiruparajan Jesudason was born in Ceylon and trained at the University of Ceylon. He was Medical Registrar at Queen Elizabeth Hospital, Kings Lynn, before coming to the James Paget in 1984. Subsequently, he was Senior Medical Registrar and Associate Specialist, before being appointed Consultant Physician with an in interest in Cardiology in 1997. He has been Deputy Chairman of the Medical Staff Committee and teaches some of the Medical students.

Nigel Huston

Nigel Huston was born in Liverpool and trained at Charing Cross Hospital Medical School, London. After various Junior Medical posts, he was appointed Consultant Physician at Thames Hospital in New Zealand in 1983, at the age of 32. He was appointed Consultant Physician with a special interest in Diabetes and Endocrinology at the James Paget Hospital in 1998. His special interest is to provide chronic care to patients with diabetes in the local area. He has been Clinical Director of Medicine, Chairman of the Surgical Mortality Review Committee and is the present Chairman of the Medical Staff Committee.

He is involved in teaching Medical students, Junior Medical staff and is an Examiner for the Membership of the Royal College of Physicians Clinical Examination.

He owns and races some old sports cars.

Tim Cotter

Tim Cotter was born in Cork, Ireland, where he did his Medical training and, at the same time, took a B.Sc. (Hons) in Physiology. He obtained his MD in 2003 for investigations of inflammatory mechanisms in asthma and the means by which corticosteroids influence them. After junior medical posts and two years as a Registrar in General and Respiratory Medicine in Cork, he was a Research Fellow in the Department of Respiratory Medicine at Kings College Hospital, London, for three years. He was Senior Registrar in General and Respiratory Medicine in Leicester for a further three years, before being appointed a Consultant in General and Respiratory Medicine in 1999, at the age of 36.

He has been Departmental College Tutor, Clinical Lead for Respiratory Medicine and for the Tuberculosis Service. He has been a member of the Eastern Region Education Committee for Specialist Registrar Training in Respiratory and Acute Medicine. He is involved in teaching Medical students.

He has written several papers on plasma volume and vasopressin, human mycobacterium bovis infection and tests for sarcoidosis.

His interests outside Medicine include mountaineering, hill walking and swimming.

Crawford Jamieson

Crawford Jamieson was born in London and did his Specialist Registrar training at the Royal London, Middlesex and other hospitals in the North-East Thames Region. At the age of 33, he was appointed to the James Paget Hospital in 1999 as Consultant Gastroenterologist. His special interests are Endoscopy, Nutrition and Education and he led the commissioning of the New Endoscopy Suite. He was one of the first people in this country to assess the value of Capsule Endoscopy, which involves swallowing a small capsule which transmits photographs of the gastrointestinal tract to a device attached to a belt. Unfortunately, he left to take up a post at the Norfolk and Norwich University Hospital in 2004.

Ian Beales

Ian Beales qualified in Medicine at St. Bartholomew's Hospital, London, and, after some junior medical posts, started specialising in Gastroenterology when he was a Registrar at the Hammersmith Hospital, London. He did some research there and at the University of Michigan in the USA and obtained his Doctorate, but realised he was missing Clinical Medicine. His next post was Senior Registrar at the Norfolk and Norwich and then as Clinical Lecturer in Cambridge. He started work as Consultant Gastroenterologist at the James Paget in February 2000.

Outside Medicine, his interests are music, the cinema, keeping fit in the gym and by swimming and watching or participating in a variety of sports. In 2001, he transferred to a post at the University of East Anglia and the Norfolk and Norwich University Hospital.

Abel de Kock

Abel de Kock was born in South Africa and received his Medical training at the University of Free State, before being appointed Consultant Physician at Tygerberg and Ernest Oppenheimer Hospitals in South Africa. After working for a year as a Locum at the James Paget, he was appointed Consultant in Respiratory Medicine in 2003, at the age of 45. He is Chairman of the Non-Invasive Ventilation Care Group and

Respiratory Health Local Implementation Team. He is helping with a Regional Enquiry into Asthma Deaths and with the Strategic Health Authority Respiratory Local Implementation Team. He has a special interest in Pulmonary Rehabilitation and Chronic Obstructive Airways Disease Management. He is a member of the Confidential Enquiry into Asthma Deaths and is a member of the Strategic Health Authority Chronic Obstructive Pulmonary Disease Group. He is developing the use of Thoracoscopy in the management of patients with respiratory problems.

He enjoys karate, inline skating and reading.

Bernard Brett

Bernard Brett grew up in Cleveland and did his Medical training at University College, London, where he took a B.Sc. in Pharmacology. After house posts in London and Northallerton, he held various senior house physician posts at Northwick Park Hospital. After being a Registrar at Edgware General Hospital, he moved to the Royal Free Hospital as a Registrar and Research Fellow (his research project involved the role of gastrin as a tumour growth factor), before moving to Oldchurch Hospital in Romford, Essex, as Specialist Registrar. He was appointed Consultant Physician and Gastroenterologist at the James Paget in 2002, at the age of 34.

He has been involved in many committees at the James Paget, which have included being Chairman of the New Ways of Working Committee, Lead for the Gastroenterology Ward Based Area and member of Junior Doctors Hours Working Committee and the Hospital at Night Working Group. However, his most important and time-consuming role is being Divisional Director of the Emergency Division and, no doubt, his interest in management developed when he was junior clinical manager while he was in his last post as Specialist Registrar at Oldchurch Hospital.

He is keen on education and has played an important part in developing the Gastroenterology course for the University of East Anglia Medical School. He has been joint author with three others on two books, *Update for the MRCP*, and has written Multiple Choice Questions for the internet. He has had several publications in various journals on pancreatic cancer and gastrin. He continues to enjoy a variety of sports, which include tennis, football and running and he frequently cycles to work. He enjoys eating out, travelling and going to the cinema.

Matt Williams

Matthew Williams was born in Essex and trained at the London Hospital Medical College. After Junior Medical jobs, he was appointed Specialist Registrar on the North-East Thames Gastroenterological Rotation. He was appointed Consultant Physician and Gastroenterologist at the James Paget in 2002. His special interests are in Oesophageal and Gastric Cancer and Inflammatory Bowel Disease. He has been Clinical Lead for Gastroenterology, Upper Gastrointestinal Cancer and Endoscopy since 2004.

He is involved in teaching Medical students at the University of East Anglia and Specialist Registrars in the Regional Endoscopy Training Centre.

His research interests are in Helicobacter Pylori, Pharmacological Acid Suppression and Palliation of Oesophago-Gastric Cancer and he has had many articles published on these topics. He is on the Editorial Board for Gastroenterology and Liver Diseases Specialist Library of the National Electronic Library for Health.

Outside Medicine, his main interests are fishing and gardening.

Guy Vautier

Guy Vautier was born in Hampshire and trained at the University of Southampton. He joined the Army Medical Services and was Senior Medical Registrar in Fremantle, Western Australia, from 2000 to 2001, when he was appointed Consultant Physician and Gastroenterologist at the Ministry of Defence Hospital Unit in Portsmouth. He was appointed Consultant Physician and Gastroenterologist to the James Paget in 2004, at the age of 39. His main interest is Hepatology and he has set up a unit to manage Hepatitis C. From September 2007, he will be the Consultant in Charge of the Emergency Assessment and Discharge Unit.

Anupama de Silva

Anupama de Silva was born in Sri Lanka and trained at University College London Medical School. Subsequently, he worked at the Royal London and Royal Free Hospitals and in the North-East Thames Region. He was appointed Consultant Gastroenterologist at the James Paget in 2004, at the age of 34. He has special interests in Inflammatory Bowel Disease and Endoscopic Retrograde Cholangio-Pancreatography. He is involved in teaching the Medical students and supports Tottenham Hotspur Football Club.

Abraham George

Abraham George was born in India and trained at Jawaharlal Nehru Medical College, India, where he did his MD in Internal Medicine. He did specialist training in Renal Medicine and was practising Renal Medicine prior to coming to the UK in 1995. Subsequently, he undertook Specialist Registrar training in General and Geriatric Medicine and was a Locum Consultant at the Borders General Hospital in Scotland. He was appointed Consultant for the Care of the Elderly at the James Paget in 2003. He is the Lead Consultant for the Falls Service Development and has recently taken on the role as a Stroke Physician, in addition to his General Medical duties. He enjoys reading and travelling.

Mohammad Al-Khafaji

Dr. Mohammed Al-Khafaji was appointed Consultant Cardiologist in 2004, but his wife and family remained in Scotland, so it was not surprising that he decided to leave in 2006.

Jo Randall

Jo Randall qualified at the London Hospital Medical College and was Senior House Physician in Southampton when she realised how much she enjoyed the specialty of Diabetes and Endocrinology. Subsequently, she was Specialist Registrar in Bath, Norfolk and Norwich, Addenbrooke's and Southend Hospitals, before being appointed as Consultant Physician in Diabetes and Endocrinology at the James Paget in January 2007. Apart from the ward and outpatient work, she is involved in the Joint Antenatal Diabetes Clinic and the Joint Adolescent Diabetes Clinic.

She enjoys travelling and playing the piano.

Alison Tarnya Marshall

Tarnya Marshall was born in Edinburgh and trained at the Middlesex Hospital, London. She joined the East Anglian Specialist Registrar Rotation and, in 2002, was appointed Consultant Rheumatologist at the Norfolk and Norwich University Hospital, with some sessions at the James Paget. She has a special interest in the use of Ultrasound in Inflammatory Arthritis and has done research on Osteoporosis and Cardiovascular Disease. She is involved in teaching the Medical students in the Locomotion module.

Renal Physicians

David Hamilton

David Hamilton was appointed Consultant Renal Physician to the Norfolk and Norwich Hospital and oversaw the development of the Renal Dialysis Unit at the James Paget and was in charge of the Unit until Callum Ross took over.

Callum Ross

He was appointed Renal Physician to the Norfolk and Norwich with sessions at the James Paget and took over the running of the Renal Dialysis at the James Paget when David Hamilton retreated to Norwich.

Consultant Obstetricians and Gynaecologists

John Breeze

John Breeze was born in Sialkot, India, the son of missionary parents. He did his Medical training in Aberdeen, Scotland, and in Belfast, Northern Ireland, after which he spent a number of years in Gujarat State, India, working in a Mission Hospital as Obstetrician and Gynaecologist. On returning to the UK in 1967, he worked in Enniskillen, Northern

Ireland, as a Medical Assistant in Obstetrics and Gynaecology. He was appointed Consultant to the Great Yarmouth and Waveney Health Authority in 1968, at the age of 42.

With the opening of the new District General Hospital, he did most of his Gynaecology there, but Obstetrics continued to be based at the Northgate Hospital in Great Yarmouth until 1985. His special interests were Infertility, Colposcopy and Breech and Twin Delivery. Apart from teaching his junior medical staff, he examined for the Central Midwives Board. He retired in 1986, aged 60. A committed Christian, he continues to be active in his local church.

William Costley

Bill Costley trained at University College Hospital, London, and, after working in South Africa, he was appointed in 1972, at the age of 41, as Consultant Obstetrician and Gynaecologist to the Great Yarmouth and Waveney Health District. The following year, he was appointed Clinical Tutor and established the Postgraduate Medical Centre, which was known as the Coastal Medical Education Centre. He held this post until 1976, when he became Chairman of the Medical Staff. With the opening of the District General Hospital, most of his Gynaecology was done there, but the Obstetrics continued at Northgate Hospital, Great Yarmouth, until 1985. He introduced Laparoscopy to the District, which is an essential diagnostic and therapeutic procedure in Gynaecology.

He was a member of the Regional Manpower Committee from 1980 until 1989 and its Vice-Chairman from 1986 until 1989. He became Honorary President of Birthright, a Royal College of Obstetricians and Gynaecologists patient-run charity raising money for research into women's diseases and fertility problems, which later became known as Wellbeing. Between 1992 and 1997, he was the Royal College of Obstetricians and Gynaecologists Representative on the Council of Wellbeing. From 1995 until 1999, he was the President of the local British Medical Association and for many years was an Examiner for the Royal College of Midwives.

He retired from the National Health Service in 1996, at the age of 65, but continued to do some private work from the Coastal Clinic, in Park Road, Gorleston. He had set this up in 1978, originally in a rented bungalow in Albert Square, Great Yarmouth, and some years later he and a few of his colleagues bought a bungalow in Park Road. For many years, he continued to do locum work in South Africa and work as a ship's Doctor. He still does several sessions a week examining patients at the North Sea Medical Centre. His other interests include sailing, riding horses and listening to music.

John Graeme Murray McLean

Graeme McLean was born in Newcastle-Upon-Tyne and trained in Durham. He did his house jobs at the Royal Victoria Infirmary in Newcastle and held Registrar posts in Bath and Glasgow, before becoming Senior Registrar in Cardiff and Newport. He was appointed Consultant Obstetrician and Gynaecologist to the Great Yarmouth and Waveney Health Authority in 1977, at the age of 34, and transferred most of his Gynaecological sessions to the new District General Hospital when it opened. For several years, Obstetrics continued at the Northgate Hospital in Great Yarmouth. He had a special interest in Colposcopy.

He was Chairman of the Medical Staff Committee in 1983, Clinical Director of Obstetrics, Gynaecology and Paediatrics from 1991 to 1996 and Medical Risk Manager from 1996 to 1998. He became the second Medical Director to the Trust in 1998, holding the post until 2003, and was very keen in maintaining a strong clinical input into management.

He retired from full-time work in 2003, at the age of 60, but continued sessions in Obstetrics and Gynaecology and the Genito-Urinary Medicine Clinics until 2006. In addition, he became a Clinical Assessor for the National Clinical Assessment Service, examining the performance of doctors referred by Trusts, and a Clinical Advisor for the Healthcare Commission, providing advice on complaints that, following failure of local resolution, have been referred to the Commission.

He enjoys sailing his own boat, attending the opera and theatre and is doing an Open University Degree in Humanities.

Andrew Pozyczka

Andy Pozyczka was born in Newmarket, East Anglia, and trained at the Westminster Hospital, London. He was appointed Consultant Obstetrician and Gynaecologist at the James Paget Hospital in 1986, at the age of 38, and has had a special interest in Colposcopy and Oncology and Hysteroscopic Surgery. He has established an efficient Colposcopy Service and local Anaesthesia Surgery. He was Clinical Director then Divisional Director of the Women and Child Health Directorate.

He was Chairman of the Medical Staff Committee and has served on the Hospital at Night Committee and Project Board since 2004. He is on the Regional Obstetric and Gynaecology Advisor Group to the Strategic Health Authority. He is involved in teaching his juniors and the medical students.

He is keen on folk music, travel and used to roller skate.

Peter Greenwood

Peter Greenwood was born in Peterborough and did all his Medical training in Cambridge. He was Resident Medical Officer at Queen Charlotte's Hospital, London. Next, he was Senior House Officer and then Registrar in Obstetrics and Gynaecology at Nottingham City Hospital, before moving to Kings Mill Hospital, Mansfield. He held Senior Registrar posts in Edinburgh, before being appointed Consultant Obstetrician and Gynaecologist at the James Paget in 1990.

His special interests are in Subfertility and the application of ultrasound to Obstetrics and Gynaecology. He set up a specialised Infertility Clinic and has introduced a number of techniques such as GIFT (Gamete Intra-Fallopian Transfer) and Transport In Vitro Fertilisation. This was the first NHS programme in East Anglia and was one of the first in the country. He set up the Sperm Storage Bank at the James Paget and has obtained the licence not only for sperm storage but also for Donor Insemination. He has obtained the Advanced Diploma in Obstetric Ultrasound and is a Founder Member of the International Society for Ultrasound in Obstetrics and Gynaecology.

He has been Departmental Tutor, is an Examiner for the DRCOG and is a Level II Preceptor in Laparoscopic Surgery. He was an Honorary Senior Lecturer at St. Bartholomew's Hospital, London, in 1999.

He has been Departmental Lead for Audit and Clinical Guidelines, is Director of the Subfertility and Early Pregnancy Assessment Unit and is a member of several Trust Committees. He is a member of the Strategic Health Authority (SHA) NICE Subfertility Guidance Implementation Group and a member of the SHA Downs Screening Advisory Group.

He has written a number of publications on such topics as Fibroids, Epidural Analgesia in Labour, Pipelle Endometrial Sampling in a Dedicated Post-menopausal Bleeding Clinic, and book chapters on Fibroids and Transport IVF.

His outside interests are limited to playing golf badly, beating junior doctors at squash and gardening.

Ajay Rane

Ajay Rane was born and brought up in Stockport, Manchester, and did his Medical training at the B. J. Medical College in Poona, India. After qualifying, he did his specialty training at the Sassoon Hospitals. He did an MD on Caudal Epidurals and Moolgaoker Forceps, then spent a couple of years doing General Surgery and Urology to enhance his surgical skills. Next, he worked in Basingstoke with Mr. Moolgaoker, who has designed one of the first forceps with a mobile curve, hence making it one of the safest forceps in the world. He did his subspecialty training in Urogynaecology and Minimal Access Surgery in Liverpool and then trained as a Senior Registrar in Northern Ireland. He was appointed Consultant in Obstetrics and Gynaecology with a special interest in Urogynaecology in 1996 and started to develop this branch of Gynaecology, but moved to Australia in 1997.

He had an interest in bungee jumping, parachuting, white-water rafting and glacier climbing, but at the time of his appointment was more interested in mountain trekking, open-water diving and playing the saxophone.

Jane Preston

Jane Preston was born in Paisley, Scotland, and did her Medical training in Aberdeen, after she had obtained a Bachelor Degree in Medical Biology. Her initial Medical posts were held in Glasgow before joining the East Anglian Training Scheme for Obstetrics and Gynaecology, where she worked initially in Ipswich and later Norwich and did two years of research on Menorrhagia at Addenbrooke's Hospital, Cambridge. She was appointed Consultant Obstetrician and Gynaecologist to the James Paget in 1997, at the age of 36. Her special interests are Menstrual Disorders and Post-Menopausal Bleeding.

She introduced the Early Pregnancy Assessment Unit in 2000–2001. She introduced Thermal Balloon Ablation in 1998 as an alternative to Hysterectomy but, following an audit, replaced this by Microwave Endometrial Ablation in 2000. She introduced the Post-Menopausal Bleeding Clinic in line with cancer two-week wait requirements for Endometrial Carcinoma. She has introduced various guidelines and improvements for the safer delivery of babies.

She was Chairman of the Medical Staff Committee from 2004 until 2006, became Chairman of the Local Negotiating Committee in 2005 and was on the Consultant Contract Implementation Group from 2003 to 2005. She has been a member and Chairperson of many other hospital committees. She has been Secretary of the East Anglian Obstetrics and Gynaecology Society since 1999. She does College Accreditation Visits for the Royal College of Obstetricians and Gynaecologists and has been a member of the National Institute of Clinical Excellence Guideline Development Group for Heavy Menstrual Bleeding, which published its Guidelines in 2007. She was a member of the Norfolk Teenage Pregnancy Strategy Group (2000–2001) and the Sexual Health for Norfolk Working Group (Draft Report) from 2002. She was appointed an Instructor for the Advanced Life Support in Obstetrics in 2000.

She is very keen on teaching and is an Honorary Senior Lecturer of the University of East Anglia Medical School and is heavily involved in tutor work, examining and teaching. She was Associate Clinical Tutor (2002–2004) and District Tutor for Obstetrics and Gynaecology from 1999 to 2004. She continues to write papers and have them accepted in the main journals on a wide range of topics.

She was an accomplished sportsperson, having played lacrosse for Scotland and golf and tennis for her University, and was the President of the University Athletics Association. She occasionally manages to play golf and ride horses when she is not acting as taxi driver for her two children.

Andrew Simons

Andy Simons trained at St. Mary's Hospital Medical School, London, and, after SHO posts and a two-year research post, he joined the Registrar rotation in the North Thames Region. It was here that he developed his interest in Female Incontinence and increased his experience of Urogynaecology by spending a year in Sydney, Australia, as a Senior Fellow in Urogynaecology. He was appointed to the James Paget in August 1999 and set up weekly Urogynaecology Clinics and performed weekly Urodynamic investigations. Unfortunately, he left for a post in Chichester in 2001.

Nicholas Oligbo

Nicholas Oligbo was born in Ibadan, Nigeria and did his medical training at the University College Hospital in Ibadan. Two years after qualifying he came to England and held various training posts in the North East Thames Deanery before doing a locum Consultant post at Colchester General Hospital. He was appointed Consultant Obstetrician and Gynaecologist at the James Paget Hospital in 2001 with a special interest in Urogynaecology and minimal access surgery.

He has been a member of the Norfolk Continence Advisory Panel and the Great Yarmouth Integrated Continence Group. He was on the Department of Health Chlamydia Screening Steering Group in 2003 -2004 and was a member of the Hospital's Local Negotiating Committee. He was Lead Clinician for Maternity Services in 2005 and since then has been Clinical Director of Obstetrics and Gynaecology. He is a Recognised Teacher for the UEA medical students, is a UEA Midwifery College Lecturer and prepares OSCE courses for the Royal College of Obstetricians and Gynaecologists.

He introduced Laparoscopic Surgery for Ectopic Pregnancy to the Trust as well as Trans Obturator Tape Surgery for female incontinence. He has had articles published on Teenage Pregnancy, complications of vaginal tapes and its use after renal transplantation as well as other articles on obstetrics and gynaecology.

His interests outside medicine include swimming, keeping fit, animals and travelling.

Medhat Hassanaien

Medhat Hassanaien was born in London and trained at the Alexandria Medical School, Egypt. He was Senior Registrar at the Birmingham Women's Hospital before doing Locum Consultant posts at Southend Hospital and at the Whittington Hospital, London. He was appointed Consultant Obstetrician and Gynaecologist at the James Paget in 2003, at the age of 46.

His special interest is in Minimal Access Surgery, Pelvic Floor Surgery as well as Colposcopy. He is very keen on education and runs MRCOG courses in Obstetrics and Gynaecology at the James Paget Hospital and teaches on similar courses in London, Birmingham and Dubai. He is the College Tutor and a member of the East Anglia Training Committee for Obstetrics and Gynaecology. He is a member of the College's selecting panel for the overseas doctors' fellowship training.

He has had several publications on Minimal Invasive Surgery and has written several books. These include MRCOG Oral Assessment Examinations (2001) and MRCOG Part 2 Short Essay Book.

Outside Medicine, his main interests are swimming, travelling and computing.

Motas Rashid

Motas Rashid was born in Pakistan and trained at Punjab University. She did further training and research in Leeds. She was a Consultant in Obstetrics and Gynaecology in Saudi Arabia for four years before being appointed to the James Paget in December 2004. She has special interests in Urogynaecology, Menorrhagia and Colposcopy. She is involved in teaching at the University of East Anglia Medical School. She is continuing her research and has had recent papers published on Foetal Sex Ratio, Intra-partum Care and Female Genital Mutilation.

Consultant Oncologists

Walter Jackson

Walter Jackson had already been Consultant Radiotherapist at the Christie Hospital, Manchester, before being appointed at the Norfolk and Norwich in the 1970s. Initially, he held a clinic once a fortnight at the Yarmouth General Hospital. When the District General Hospital opened, he held a clinic every Friday. He was involved with the setting up of the Big 'C' Appeal in 1981 and was its Chairman for a number of years.

He retired in 1995. He has always had a passion for cycling and motorbikes and more often than not would come to the James Paget on his motorbike with the patients' notes either side of the rear wheel.

Maek Joseph Ostrowski

Joe Ostrowski trained at the University of Birmingham Medical School. He trained in Radiotherapy and Oncology at Queen Elizabeth Hospital, Birmingham, and Addenbrooke's Hospital, Cambridge, and was Visiting Radiation Oncologist at the Cancer Control Agency of British Columbia, Vancouver, Canada, for six months before he was appointed Consultant Radiotherapist at the Norfolk and Norwich Hospital in 1976. Since then, he has had sessions in the Coastal Hospitals. Initially, he held a clinic every fortnight at Lowestoft Hospital and has held weekly clinics at the James Paget since shortly after it was opened.

He has contributed to many national trials assessing the treatment of cancer and has contributed to the national audit of severe complications of radiotherapy of breast and cervix. He has initiated multi-centre trials on adjuvant chemotherapy in early breast cancer and the management of advanced disease.

He has been involved in many committees at the Norfolk and Norwich Hospital, e.g. Chairman of their Drug and Therapeutics Committee, Chairman of the Radiology Division, Lead Doctor for the Oncology Directorate and was involved in the Day Care Oncology Unit at the James Paget. He was Chairman of the NHS Healthy Norfolk 2000 Cancer Group and was a member of the Norfolk and Waveney Cancer Network Management Group, as well as Lead Consultant in Chemotherapy for the Cancer Network. He has been a member of numerous Regional groups and working parties dealing with Radiotherapy and Cancer.

He has been a member of the Faculty Board of Oncology of the Royal College of Radiologists, a Medical Adviser to the GMC Fitness to Practice Committee and has been External College Assessor on many Consultant Appointment Committees. He has been the principal or co-author of over 30 Peer Review publications and has contributed to chapters in five books.

William Miller Craig Martin

Craig Martin was born in Belfast, Northern Ireland, and did his Medical training at Queen's University, Belfast. Subsequently, he worked at the Middlesex Hospital and Mount Vernon in London before doing a PhD with the Clinical Research Council. He was appointed Consultant Radiotherapist in Belfast in 1981 and from 1984 to 1987 he was Professor at the Chinese University of Hong Kong. From 1987 until 1989, he was Consultant in Charge of Cancer in Papua, New Guinea, after which he became World Health Organisation Consultant from 1990 to 1993. Returning to the United Kingdom, he held a Locum Consultant post in Leeds in 1994, before being appointed Consultant Oncologist at the Norfolk and Norwich Hospital with sessions at the James Paget Hospital in 1995, at the age of 49.

His special interests are in Lung and Head and Neck Cancer as well as new techniques of using Radiotherapy. He was the Clinical Lead for Research for the Norfolk and Waveney Cancer Network and the Network Clinical Lead for Lung Cancer. He is a member of the Faculty Board of Clinical Oncology of the Royal College of Radiologists.

His interests are his Christian faith, playing the piano and tennis.

Andrew Bulman

Andrew Bulman was born in London and qualified at St. Thomas' Hospital, London. Joining the St. Thomas' surgical registrar circuit, he went on to complete a Mastership in Surgery on Breast Cancer Pathology. Moving to the Westminster Hospital, initially under Harold Ellis, he began training in Radiotherapy and Oncology, completing as Senior Registrar to the Yorkshire Regional Cancer Centre at Cookridge Hospital, Leeds, under Daniel Ash and Charles Joslin. After three years as Senior Medical Officer advising the Department of Health on the medical aspects of environmental radiation, he was appointed Consultant in Clinical Oncology at the Norfolk and Norwich University Hospital (NNUH) with sessions at the James Paget Hospital, at the age of 47, in 1995.Over the next 10 years, as a result of the Calman Cancer Plan for increasing oncology provision and site specialisation, the Oncology Department doubled in size and activity. Until 2003, he managed Chemo- and Radiotherapy for Cancers of the Breast and Colorectum. In 2004, the colorectal chemotherapy work at the James Paget was taken over by the appointment of the first full-time Consultant in Medical Oncology in Norfolk and in 2006 a videoconferencing link helped discussions at the Multi-Disciplinary

Team Meetings between the Norfolk and Norwich and the James Paget Hospitals. Patients with rectal cancer in increasing numbers have continued to travel to Norwich for consultations and the latest intensity modulated radiotherapy, usually given before surgery, thus improving their chances of complete excision and cure.

He has published 15 papers, mostly on single institution studies of breast, melanoma and gynaecological cancers and in later years has become a keen contributor to the multi-centre trials portfolio of the National Cancer Research Network. He was a Tutor to the UEA Medical School.

His main interests outside Medicine are climbing, sailing, gardening, wine and modern art.

Adrian Harnett

Adrian Harnett was born in London and trained at the Royal Free School of Medicine in London. He was Senior Registrar in Oncology at St. Bartholomew's Hospital, London, before being appointed Consultant in Radiotherapy and Oncology at Beatson Oncology Centre, Western Infirmary, Glasgow, in 1988. In addition, he was Honorary Clinical Senior Lecturer at the University of Glasgow. In 2002, he was appointed Consultant in Clinical Oncology at the Norfolk and Norwich University Hospital and the James Paget Hospital.

His special interests are in Breast Cancer, Urological Tumours, Ocular Tumours and Radiotherapy for Benign Eye Disease. He is the Clinical Oncology Representative for the Research and Development Committee and a member of the Data Monitoring Committee for Cambridge IMRT Trial. He has been Oncology Lead for Clinical Governance since 2004 and Clinical Lead for the Breast Cancer Network from 2005.

He has held many posts nationally and internationally. He was on the UKCCR ABC Steering Committee from 1994 to 2001 and on the National Cancer Research Institute Breast Clinical Studies Group from 2001. He was elected onto the Education Board of the Royal College of Radiologists from 1998 to 2002 and has been on the Training Accreditation Board of the Royal College of Radiologists from 1998. He was appointed Specialist Advisor to NICE's Interventional Procedures

Programme in 2004 and Clinical Lead for Early Breast Cancer for NCC-C/NICE in 2005 and Advisor for Technology Appraisal for Endocrine Treatment and Taxanes in Early Breast Cancer for NICE in 2006.

He is a Recognised Teacher and Student Advisor of the University of East Anglia and was Clinical Tutor for Specialist Registrars from 2002 to 2006, since when he has been Regional Postgraduate Education Advisor for Oncology.

His main research interests are in Breast and Prostatic Cancer. He has published over 50 papers, edited a book on *Megavoltage Radiotherapy 1937–1987* and written a book on *Case Studies in Breast Cancer* (2002) and another on *Case Studies in Urological Cancer* (2003). He has written chapters in several books and other publications.

His interests are church activities, participating in sport and playing the violin.

Daniel Epurescu

Daniel Epurescu was appointed as a Medical Oncologist to the Norfolk and Norwich University Hospital in 2003 and started sessions at the James Paget when Andrew Bulman gave up his sessions on the coast.

Ophthalmolgy

Peter Black

Peter Black was born in Wimbledon and trained at King's College and St. George's Hospital Medical School in London. Soon after qualifying, he joined the Royal Air Force and served in the Middle East and Germany. He was Consultant Ophthalmologist at RAF Hospital Wegberg, Germany, and then RAF Hospital Ely. In addition, he was an Honorary Consultant at Addenbrooke's Hospital, Cambridge, before his appointment to the James Paget in 1981, at the age of 37, to set up the Eye Department. Among the many committees he has served on he has been Chairman of the Surgical Division and Medical Staff Committee, Consultant Member of the Management Team and Representative to District and Regional Manpower Committees.

He was Chairman of the Regional Training Committee from 1993 to 2000. He has been very heavily involved with the Royal College of

Ophthalmologists, having been a College Inspector since 1992 and Regional Advisor and College Tutor to the James Paget. He examines for the College and is on their Examinations Committee. He was on College Council from 2000 until 2003, is a member of the Professional Standards Committee, the Equality and Diversity Group and the College Modernising Medical Careers Committee and is the Chairman of the Workforce Committee of the College. He has been an Assessor to the Health Committee of the General Medical Council since 1994 and an Expert Witness to its Fitness to Practice Committee since 2002. He is an Independent Clinical Review Assessor for the Joint Consultants Committee. He wrote some early papers on Ophthalmologic issues in Cerebral Palsy and Pancreatic Transplantation and, more recently, has published on Manpower issues and the European Working Directive.

He established the Eye Department at the James Paget and, together with Ali Amanat, has built up a first-class Unit. With David Wayne and Madeleine Borg, he set up a Diabetic Retinal Screening Service in 1987 which was one of the first in the country.

He enjoys dog walking, wildlife, the country, Norfolk and Suffolk in general and travel.

Ali Amanat

Ali Amanat was born in Bahrain and trained at King Edward Medical College, Lahore, Pakistan. He was Senior House Surgeon and Registrar at Addenbrooke's Hospital, Cambridge, before being Senior Registrar at the Western Infirmary in Glasgow. He was appointed Consultant Ophthalmologist at the James Paget in 1982, at the age of 34.

He has been Chairman of the Surgical Division and of the Medical Staff Committee, was Clinical Director of Surgical Specialties and served on the Capital Working Party. He is a member of the Regional Education Committee, College Tutor of the Royal College of Ophthalmologists and a Council member of the UK and Ireland Society of Cataract and Refractive Surgeons. He is a Recognised Teacher of the UEA Medical School and an Examiner for the MRCOphth and DO. He has written several articles on Lacrimal Scintigraphy.

Mr. A. M. Morgan

Mr. Morgan did his Medical training in Cambridge and at St. Thomas's Hospital in London. After pre-registration house posts at St. Thomas's and in Reading, he joined the Medical Branch of the RAF, eventually becoming an Ophthalmic Specialist serving in this country and overseas. On leaving the RAF in 1982, he became Warden and Chief Surgeon at St. John's Ophthalmic Hospital in Jerusalem for seven years, when he spent four years as a Consultant in Ophthalmology to the Ministry of Defence. He was appointed to the James Paget in 1993 as a long-term Locum and left in 1996.

He enjoyed playing squash and running.

Conall Hurley

Conall Hurley qualified at the Medical School, University College, Cork, and after holding SHO posts there went to the Royal Victoria Hospital, Dublin, where he became a Registrar. Next, he was Senior Lecturer in Ophthalmology at the College of Surgeons in Dublin and Registrar at the Royal Victoria Eye and Ear Hospital. From there, he joined the West Midland rotation as Senior Registrar and subsequently took a Fellowship in Oculoplastic Surgery and Ocular Oncology at the Institute of Ophthalmology in Glasgow. He was appointed Consultant Ophthalmologist at the James Paget in 1999, but returned to Ireland in 2001.

Nicholas Watson

Nick Watson was born in Cambridge and studied Medicine in Southampton. He developed an interest in Ophthalmology during his house jobs and held subsequent posts in Ipswich and Birmingham before moving to Aberdeen as Registrar and later Senior Registrar. He was appointed Consultant Ophthalmologist at the James Paget in1996.

His hobbies are sailing and cycle touring.

Kate Belfer

Kay Belfer joined the Department in 2001 and had a special interest in Retinal Surgery. She left in 2006.

Tom Butler

Tom Butler was born in Pembury, Kent, and trained at Leeds University School of Medicine. He did his early Medical jobs in Yorkshire before becoming Specialist Registrar in Ophthalmology at the Queen's Medical Centre, Nottingham, and Derbyshire Royal Infirmary, Derby, between 1999 and 2005. During this time, he spent 2003 as Clinical Fellow in Corneal and External Eye Disease at Sydney Eye Hospital in Australia. He was appointed Consultant Ophthalmologist to the James Paget in 2006, at the age of 34, and has special interests in Cornea and External Eye Disease, Cataract and Refractive Surgery.

He is in the process of developing the Corneal Services at the James Paget and plans greater engagement with the primary care ophthalmic services. He is involved with undergraduate and postgraduate teaching. He enjoys walking, camping, kayaking, cycling and music.

Miss Bridget Mulholland

Bridget Mulholland graduated from Sheffield University Medical School and trained in Ophthalmology at Moorfields Eye Hospital, London, and in Perth, Western Australia, where she developed her interest in Cataract, Oculoplastic and Lachrymal Surgery. She moved to East Anglia after being Consultant Ophthalmologist at the Royal Free Hospital, London, for two and a half years. She has a joint appointment between Norwich and the James Paget.

She enjoys playing music in amateur orchestras, sailing, kayaking and walking.

Dental and Facio-Maxillary Surgery

Geoff Cheney

Geoff Cheney qualified in Dentistry and then went on to qualify in Medicine. He was appointed Consultant Dental Surgeon and Oral and Maxillo-Facial Surgeon to the Norfolk and Norwich Hospital in the late 1970s and had some sessions at the James Paget. He became Regional Dean for Dental Studies and retired in the early 2000s.

Roger Rees

Roger Rees was born in Dyfed, South Wales, and trained as a Dentist at the Royal Dental Hospital in London. He then did his Medical training at St Bartholomew's Medical School in London, following which he was Dental Registrar at Guy's Hospital, London. As Senior Registrar in Facio-Maxillary Surgery, he worked at King's College Hospital, London, and Queen Victoria Hospital, East Grinstead, and spent part of the time as Technical Advisor in Oral and Maxillo-Facial Surgery for the Overseas Development Ministry for the Nigerian Military Government. He was appointed Consultant Dental Surgeon and Oral and Maxillo-Facial Surgeon at the Norfolk and Norwich Hospital with sessions for the Great Yarmouth and Waveney Health Authority in 1979, at the age of 35. He started work at the new District General Hospital when it opened. He has a special interest in Injuries to the Facial Skeleton and Head and Neck Cancer and was Head of his Department for many years.

He has developed a specialised service to the Great Yarmouth and Waveney Community by seeing and treating patients locally as appropriate and dealing with highly specialised surgery centrally within an integrated department between the James Paget and the Norfolk and Norwich Hospitals. He used to run an annual course for Dentists in Norwich on "Minor Oral Surgery for General Practitioners". Research interests included Endoscopic Reduction and Fixation of Fractures of the Mandibular Condyle and the Development of Instruments.

He retired in March 2005, at the age of 62, but since November, 2005 has been working at the James Paget doing one clinic and one day care list twice a month. He enjoys DIY and foreign travel.

Sharon Elizabeth Prince

Sharon Prince was born in Sheffield and trained at the University of Wales Dental School, Cardiff. Later, she did a Medical degree at Sheffield Medical School and became a Specialist Registrar in Oral and Maxillo-Facial Surgery at Queen Mary's University Hospital, Roehampton, before joining the Oxford and Anglian Rotation. She was appointed Consultant Oral and Maxillo-Facial Surgeon to the Norfolk and Norwich University Hospital with sessions at the James Paget Hospital in 2004and has a special interest in Facial Deformity. She is a member of the Local Dental Committee for Norfolk, the Oral Health Advisory Group and the Oral Surgery Waiting List Initiative Committee. She is a recognised Teacher for the University of East Anglia Medical School.

She has taken over as Lead Clinician from Roger Rees and co-ordinates the work of the Department, including the Maxillo-Facial Trauma Service. She has published a review of Carcinoma of the Tongue and Vascular Lesions of the Masseter.

Her outside interests include music, gardening and the ballet.

David Tewson

David Tewson was born in Newark, Nottinghamshire, and did his Dental training at Guy's Hospital Dental School, London, where he did his house jobs. He became Orthodontic Registrar at the Eastman Dental Hospital, London, and then Senior Registrar back at Guy's. He was appointed Consultant Orthodontist at the Norfolk and Norwich and James Paget Hospitals in 1988, at the age of 35. Since then, he has been Lead Clinician in the Specialty for the two Hospital Trusts and has developed a comprehensive hospital orthodontic service managing developmental anomalies of the jaws and teeth.

He has a special interest in Malocclusion of the Jaws and Teeth, Facial Deformity, Cleft Lip and Palate. Since 1998, he has been Chairman of the Norfolk Cleft Spoke Group during reconfiguration of cleft services and Chairman of the Norfolk Oral Health Advisory Group since 2003.

He was Specialty Advisor for the Royal College of Surgeons of England from 1994 to 1997 and Regional Advisor from 1997 to 2004. He has been Chairman of the East of England Cleft Forum since 2003 and is a member of the Consultant Orthodontist Committee of the British Orthodontic Society since 2004. He has been Dental Tutor since 1989 and has examined for the Membership in Orthodontics for the Royal College of Surgeons of Edinburgh since 1998 and since 2004 has been an Examiner for the Intercollegiate Fellowship. In 2007, he was appointed to the Examinations Board in Orthodontics of the Royal College of Surgeons of Edinburgh. His research interests are Cephalometric Assessment and Orthognathic Surgery Prediction and Outcomes.

Wendy Slaney

Wendy Slaney trained at the Royal Dental Hospital, London, and undertook hospital posts at the Royal and Guys before moving into the Community Dental Service in 1979.

In 1981, she attained the Diploma in Dental Public Health prior to moving to East Anglia. With the formation of the Great Yarmouth and Waveney Health Authority, she became District Dental Officer. With the creation of NHS Trusts, the role transferred to Anglian Harbours NHS Trust, where the emerging Clinical Director programme led to a Trust Board role as Director of Corporate Development (1992-1996). During this period she obtained an MBA with the Open University.

The services of Anglian Harbours transferred to the James Paget Healthcare NHS Trust in 1997 and Wendy undertook the role of Clinical Director for Surgical Specialities in 1999.

In 2003, she was appointed Medical Director and was interim Chief Executive from November 2006 until the appointment of Adrian Pennington in April 2007.

Orthopaedic Surgery

Tony Ashford Hodges

Tony Ashford Hodges was appointed Orthopaedic Surgeon to the Health District in the 1970s and moved to the new District General Hospital when it opened. He was always extremely cheerful and on at least one occasion when the operating theatre did not have the required instrument he went home to his workshop and came back with the necessary implement. He was very keen at DIY and built his own sailing boat, which he sailed to the Caribbean. He chose a steel hull, as a previous boat of his was wrecked off the coast of Australia. When he retired, he continued doing locums around the country for many years.

David Burgess

For 10 years after qualifying, David Burgess did General Surgery with some Plastic and Cardio-Thoracic Surgery at Charing Cross, St. Bartholomew's and St. George's Hospitals before going to Australia, where the job included some Orthopaedics. He then trained in Orthopaedics at Addenbrooke's, Charing Cross and the Royal National Orthopaedic Hospitals. He was appointed Consultant Surgeon in Orthopaedics and Trauma to the Health District in 1972, operating mainly at Gorleston Cottage Hospital, until the second phase of the James Paget was opened towards the end of 1984. He was Surgical Tutor for the Royal College of Surgeons of England for a time. He retired in 1993 and now lives in Horsham, West Sussex, but continues to do occasional medical litigation reports.

Ken Stewart

Ken Stewart had spent most of his working life as a Consultant Orthopaedic Surgeon in Africa before coming to East Anglia. He retired in 1987, but returned as a locum lto help reduce the number of patients waiting for hip replacements.

George Heyse Moore

George Heyse Moore was brought up in Exeter, where his father was Consultant Surgeon. He trained at the Middlesex Hospital Medical School, after which he specialised in Orthopaedic Surgery. He was Senior Orthopaedic Registrar in Exeter before being appointed Consultant at the James Paget in 1983. Tragically, his wife was drowned in a car accident soon after they moved to Norfolk, and he was faced with bringing up his two young children, Tom and Hannah. For a number of years he was Surgical Tutor for the Royal College of Surgeons of England and devised a course of weekly lectures for the surgical SHOs. His main interests were revision hip surgery and problems with the back. With Dr. Willy Notcutt, he set up a service which aimed to provide an urgent assessment of new back problems. In addition, he performed mini-discectomies using instruments which he had designed himself. He led a campaign to try and save the Gorleston Cottage Hospital, where Orthopaedics was done before the building of the second phase of the District General Hospital, but this seemed to hasten the arrival of the bulldozer. He always spoke his mind and he detested bureaucracy.

He had a way with words and wrote short stories and three novels. He was a craftsman, not only in the operating theatre, but also in his home and garden and he was an excellent cook.

On health grounds, he retired early in 2001 and died on 1st May 2007 after a long illness.

Robert Jones

Robert Jones did his Medical training at St. Thomas' Hospital, London. His house jobs were done there and in Herefordshire before he did SHO posts at St. Peter's Hospital, Chertsey, and in Essex. He was on the Orthopaedic Registrar Rotation at Oswestry before becoming Senior Orthopaedic Registrar in Exeter. Having done some Locum Consultant posts in the West Country, he was appointed Consultant Orthopaedic Surgeon at the James Paget in 1987. He arrived here in a blizzard, having taken seven hours to travel from Colchester.

His main interests are Hip Surgery and revising those hips which have gone wrong. For this purpose he set up the bone bank to fill up boney defects when doing hip revision operations. He has been Director of the Orthopaedic Department on several occasions and has been on the Medical Advisory Committee of Northgate Hospital and on the Infection Control Committee.

He has a passion for rugby and cricket and was President of the Broadland and the Great Yarmouth and Lowestoft Rugby Clubs. He is a great conversationalist and was the last Chairman of the Hall Quay Club.

"Raj" Nadarajan

"Raj" Nadarajan was born in India and trained at Tirunelveli Medical College. He was Tutor in Orthopaedics at Madras Medical College and later Orthopaedic Registrar and Senior Registrar in Sheffield, before being appointed Consultant Orthopaedic Surgeon at the James Paget in 1993, at the age of 42. He has a special interest in Surgery of the Shoulder and in Paediatric Orthopaedics and has developed both since he has been at the James Paget.

For relaxation, he enjoys wood carving, wood turning and water-colour painting.

Christopher Johnson-Nurse

Chris Johnson-Nurse was born in Cambridge and, after a commission in the Royal Air Force for three years, he did his Medical training at the Welsh National School of Medicine, where he was President of the Medical Students Union. After his house jobs in Cardiff, he held various Registrar posts in South Wales in Traumatic, Orthopaedic and Reconstructive Surgery, before joining the Cambridge Higher Surgical Training Programme in Orthopaedic Surgery. In 1985, he went to Australia as Director of Traumatic and Orthopaedic Surgery at Rockhampton Base Hospital, but after a year went into private practice. Between 1985 and 1987, he was Honorary Lecturer at the University of Queensland, before returning to Rockhampton. He was appointed Consultant Orthopaedic Surgeon to the James Paget in 1994.

He has been Chairman of the Surgical Division, a member of the Risk Management Steering Group and of the Implementation Group for Rehabilitation. He is a Recognised Teacher and Honorary Senior Lecturer of the University of East Anglia. He has written several papers on the Application of Flexible Carbon Fibres in Bone Fractures and Hernia Repairs as well as other papers on Orthopaedics.

Outside Medicine, his interests are golf, bridge and medieval history.

Gianfranco John Petri

John Petri was born in Naples, Italy, and did his Medical training at the University of Naples. He was Consultant Orthopaedic Surgeon at Centre Hospitalier de Macon in France, before being appointed Consultant Orthopaedic Consultant at the James Paget in August 1994, at the age of 39. His special interests are in Managing Trauma, Joint Replacements, Correction of Bone Deformities and Upper Limb Surgery.

Since being at the James Paget, he has modernised and improved the quality of Trauma Surgery and has conceived and then realised a system to improve the productivity of operating in Orthopaedics. This involves a team running two theatres so that, while one operation is taking place, the next patient is being prepared in the adjoining theatre. This system has almost tripled the number of operations he can perform on an operating list and resulted in the extinction of his Waiting List. He received a "Medical Futures Innovation Award" in November 2006 and has met the Prime Minister and Health Secretary Patricia Hewitt to discuss his increased productivity.

He has been Lead Clinician for Orthopaedics from 1998 to 2001 and from 2004 to 2007. He is involved in teaching Fracture Care at international level and has lectured in eight different countries and in four languages. He runs in-house Trauma Courses at the James Paget every year and also teaches Medical students from UEA. He has written a few papers, particularly on the Management of Trauma.

Unfortunately, he will be leaving the James Paget in July 2007, as he has been appointed Head of Orthopaedics at a Swiss hospital.

Erkki Venalainen

Erkki Venalainen was appointed Consultant Orthopaedic Surgeon in 2001, but left a year later.

Andrew Elliott

Andrew Elliott was born in Stellenbosch, South Africa, and did his Medical training at the University of Pretoria. After further training, he was Consultant Orthopaedic Surgeon to the local State Hospital and Cerebral Palsy School. He came to the James Paget as Locum Consultant Orthopaedic Surgeon and, fortunately for the hospital, he has decided to stay and has been appointed as Trust Consultant. He has a special interest in Anterior Cruciate Ligament Reconstruction in the Knee and is involved in new ways of working in Orthopaedics. He is Orthopaedic Clinical Tutor for the junior members of staff in his Department.

He is a keen bird watcher, plays golf and enjoys hiking, camping and music. He is a good spectator of cricket and rugby!

Harash Gupta

Harash Gupta held senior positions in South Africa and Australia before being appointed Consultant Orthopaedic Surgeon at the James Paget in 2005.

Alban Bowers

Alban Bowers did much of his Orthopaedic training at the Norfolk and Norwich Hospital after which he worked in Africa as a Consultant for ten years. He has been doing a long term locum at the James Paget since 2006.

Consultant Paediatricians

Eric Back

Eric Back had been educated at Cambridge University and commenced his Medical work at the London Hospital. He became a medical officer in the Royal Naval Reserve during the Second World War and later was invited to join Operation Tabarin in Antarctica, where he stayed for two years. After that, he went to the Falklands to work on weather reports and to give anaesthetics. On returning to the United Kingdom, he studied Paediatrics and subsequently he was appointed Senior Lecturer and later Professor of Paediatrics at the new medical school of the University of the West Indies in Jamaica. He was a visiting Professor in Paediatrics to a number of North American Medical Schools and was appointed Consultant Paediatrician to the Great Yarmouth and Waveney Health District in 1972, at the age of 51 years. He retired in 1985 and died on 22nd December 1992, at the age of 72 years. At his funeral, which was held in his village church of St. Mary and St. Margaret, Norton Subcourse, where he had been the churchwarden, there were many of his friends from his days in Cambridge and Antarctica.

Tony Edelsten

Tony Edelsten trained at St. Bartholomew's Hospital, London, and subsequently trained in Paediatrics in the West Country, Canada and South Africa. He was appointed Consultant Paediatrician in 1980 and initially worked at the Yarmouth General Hospital with Dr. Back until the move to the new District General Hospital in 1982. He was involved with the design of the new unit and has led the development of the Paediatric Department since Dr. Back retired. His special interest is Diabetes and he was instrumental in the introduction of the first ventilation facilities for neonates and in the provision of an Adolescent Unit.

He is an extremely keen tennis player and is President of the Norfolk Lawn Tennis Association. He also enjoys sailing and windsurfing.

Richard Stocks

Richard Stocks was born in Middlesex and trained at St. Bartholomew's Hospital, London. After various junior hospital posts, he was Paediatric Registrar in Southampton and Lecturer/Senior Registrar in Leicester. He was appointed Paediatric Consultant at the James Paget in 1985. His special interests are Cystic Fibrosis, Paediatric Oncology and Rheumatology.

He has been Chairman of the Medical Staff Committee, Clinical Director of Women and Child Health and Chairman of the Women and Child Health Clinical Governance Sub-Committee. He has been the Paediatric Speciality Tutor and was a member of the Trust Star Chamber and the Capital Working Party. He was Chairman of the Child Health Planning Forum and a member of the Norfolk Children and Young People's Group, among other committees. At present he is the Clinical Lead for Paediatrics, Chairman of the Children's Surgery Working Party and he has been the Trust's Clinical Lead for Cancer since 2001.

Regionally, he is a member of the Pan-Anglia Network Paediatric Oncology SSG, the Norfolk and Waveney Cancer Network Paediatric Oncology SSG, the Anglia Cancer Network Board, the East Anglia Paediatric Rheumatology Group, the Anglia Paediatric Gastroenterology Group and the Anglia Cystic Fibrosis Management Group.

He is a member of the Royal College of Paediatrics and Child Health Examinations Group. He examines for the College and has hosted the MRCPCH Examination at the James Paget.

Outside Medicine, his interests include walking/hiking, squash, golf, sailing, reading, music, local theatre and opera.

Murray Cresswell

Murray Cresswell had worked as a Consultant Paediatrician in Trent and North-West Thames Regions before being appointed at the James

Paget in 1992. He had also worked in the community and had taken a special interest in Cot Deaths and Infant Mortality. Other interests were Clinical Genetics and Neuro-developmental Problems and their Management.

His interests included music, swimming and sailing.

He left the Trust in 1998.

John Patrick Chapman

John Chapman was born in Bradford, West Yorkshire, and did his Medical training at Edinburgh University. Subsequently, he became a Specialist Registrar in the West of Scotland Deanery. He was appointed Consultant Paediatrician at the James Paget in 2000, at the age of 33, with special interests in Respiratory Problems, Allergy and Neonates. He has been Chairman of the Drugs and Therapeutics Committee since 2002 and Lead Clinician for Audit and Effectiveness since January 2006. He is an Honorary Senior Lecturer with the University of East Anglia Medical School. He has extended the use of hand-held computers into the practice of Paediatrics and outside Medicine his interests include information technology and cider making.

Rajeshwar Rao

Rajeshwar Rao was born in St. Mary's Hospital, Paddington, London, and grew up in New Delhi, India. After attending the University College of Medical Sciences, he did his house jobs and then started to train as a Paediatrician. In order to demonstrate a reasonable and stable income to his prospective parents-in-law, he joined the army for six years. He came to England in September 1989 and, after Registrar posts in Walsall and Ipswich, he did research on Asthma at Southampton University for three years. From there, he became Senior Registrar on the rotation in Wessex, before being appointed Consultant Paediatrician at the James Paget in December 1998. He had a special interest in Asthma, Allergy and Neonates. He left in 2000 for a job in Poole.

He is keen on listening to music and playing with his computer.

Ajit Verma

Ajit Verma was born in Patna, India, and did his Medical training there. He came to the United Kingdom in 1978 and did his first appointment in Neonatal Paediatrics near Glasgow. Subsequently, he worked in Durham, Manchester and Norwich. He obtained the MRCP and became Senior Registrar in Bath. He was appointed Consultant Community Paediatrician for the Great Yarmouth and Waveney area in 1991, but until recently had participated in the on-call rota with the Paediatricians at the James Paget, which has helped to develop the links between the hospital and the community.

He was the first Community Paediatrician in the area and since then has built up a team including two other Paediatricians who work from the Newberry Centre in Gorleston.

Stephen Nirmal

Stephen Nirmal was born in Nagercoil, India, and did his Medical training at Christian Medical College, Vellore, India. He did Specialist Registrar training in Paediatrics in Wales before doing a Locum Paediatric Consultant's post at Princess of Wales Hospital Bridgend in Wales in 2002. He was appointed Consultant Paediatrician at Moses Mathias Hospital in Nagercoil, India, where he stayed until January 2004. He returned to the United Kingdom to do a Locum Consultant post at Neville Hall Hospital, Abergavenny, in Wales, and was appointed Consultant Paediatrician at the James Paget in 2004, at the age of 40. He has a special interest in Epilepsy and Neurology and has started a Paediatric Epilepsy Clinic.

He is the Representative for the College for Paediatrics and is a member of the Hospital Education Committee. He has been a member of the Regional Training Committee for Paediatrics since March 2005 and a member of the East Anglian Paediatric Development Group Executive since August 2005. He has had papers published on Acute Tumour Lysis Syndrome in Hodgkin's Disease and the Immune Response of Infants to Fractional Doses of Poliovirus Vaccine. His interests outside Medicine are tennis and boating.

Sangeeta Garg

Sangeeta Garg was born in Delhi, India, and was trained at the Christian Medical College, Vellore, India. After being a Specialist Registrar in Johannesburg, South Africa, she was appointed Consultant Paediatrician. She then moved to Australia, where she became a Consultant in Brisbane. She was appointed Consultant Paediatrician at the James Paget in 2005 with a special interest in Diabetes, Endocrinology and Developmental Paediatrics. She is involved in the teaching of Medical students and the Paediatric junior medical staff. Outside Medicine, she looks after her children and enjoys cooking.

Vasanyaa Jayalal

Vasanyaa Jayalal was born in India and attended the Medical College at Trivandrum, India. He joined the Paediatric East Anglian Rotation as a Specialist Registrar and did a Fellowship in Neonatology in Sydney, Australia. His special interests are in Neonatology and Cystic Fibrosis. He is the Audit Lead for the Department and is on the Regional Neonatal Network Board.

He is a Problem-Based Learning Tutor and an OSCE Assessor for the UEA Medical students. He is a Neonatal Life Support Course Instructor.

Pathology

Norman John Ball

John Ball was born in 1928 in Worsley, Lancashire, and did his Medical training at Trinity College, Dublin, and his MD in 1956. After various house appointments in Dublin, he was Medical Registrar at Dr. Stevens Hospital, Dublin, before being awarded the John Dunne Fellowship in Histopathology at Queen's University Belfast from 1957 to 1962. He was Registrar in Clinical Pathology at the Royal Victoria Hospital, Belfast, in 1962, before becoming Lecturer in Pathology at Trinity College, Dublin. Between 1963 and 1970, he was Pathologist to the General Hospital, Edmonton, Alberta, in Canada, and also Histopathologist and Haematologist to Hansen's Laboratory in Edmonton. In 1970, he was appointed Pathologist to the Royal Jubilee Hospital, Victoria, on

Vancouver Island. He was appointed Director of the Northgate Hospital Laboratory in Great Yarmouth in 1972, at the age of 44, as a single-handed Consultant and over the years built up a large and highly efficient Department with subspecialties of Histopathology, Haematology, Biochemistry and Microbiology.

He was Chairman of the Medical Staff Committee, Consultant Representative on the District Health Authority and was a member of the James Paget Directors Committee, which consisted of the Heads of Departments. He was Chairman of the Regional Medical Advisory Committee, a member of the Regional Expensive Pathology Equipment Committee and the Norfolk Representative of the Consultants and Specialists Association.

He retired in 1993, at the age of 65, but continued doing some Pathology locums around the country for another five years. He is keen on fishing, golf and sailing.

David Harrison

David Harrison did his medical training in Manchester and was appointed Consultant Histopathologist in 1974. For many years he was the Home Office Pathologist. He retired in 2001.

Terry Mitchell

Terry Mitchell trained at Charing Cross Hospital Medical School and, after house jobs there and in Wembley, he became Senior House Officer and subsequently Registrar in Pathology at Charing Cross. Later, he became Senior Registrar/ Honorary Lecturer in Haematology at Fulham Hospital. After a year's Governors Research Fellowship at Charing Cross, he was appointed Senior Lecturer and Honorary Consultant Haematologist at Charing Cross in 1973. He was appointed Consultant Haematologist to the Great Yarmouth and Waveney Health District in 1981. He started Haematological Clinics and expanded clinical input by having beds, first on the medical wards, and then he gradually took over the beds on Ward 17, which was set up as the Infectious Disease Unit. He worked with the Oncologists in the management of lymphomas, etc., and with Addenbrooke's for bone marrow transplants. In addition, he was Clinical Tutor for nearly five years.

He was Director of Clinical Services for five years and was a member of the Unit Management Team, the Capital Working Party and Hospital Manpower Committee. He was the Chairman of the Sandra Chapman and the Second Scanners Appeal and was Chairman of the Regioinal Haematology Committee.

He was Associate Dean of the University of Cambridge Clinical School of Medicine and Chairman of the Eastern Region Postgraduate Medical and Dental Education Executive and Committee. He was a member of the Regional Task Force and Manpower/Training Committee, as well as the East Anglian Joint Pre-Registration Committee. He was Chairman of the Anglia Pathology Continuing Medical Education Committee and was College Tutor of the Royal College of Pathologists for 13 years. He was Chairman of the Clinical Admissions Interview Committee. He was an Inspector for Clinical Pathology Accreditation (UK) Ltd. and Vice-President of the Leukaemia Care Society.

He wrote Multiple Choice Questions in Haematology, An Introduction to the Pre-Registration Year and a chapter on treatment of blood disorders in renal disease. He wrote many papers on such topics as Myeloma, Platelet Dysfunction with Eosinophilia, Auto-transfusion for Elective Aortic Surgery, as well as many others.

He first started seeing patients with chronic fatigue problems in 1985, initially seeing them at 7 am before his haematology clinics. In 1996, he managed to obtain funding for this work and for the services of an occupational therapist from the Norfolk and Suffolk Health Authorities. He retired from haematological practice in 2000 and since then has been building up services in East Anglia to help people and their families with chronic fatigue problems and he is one of 14 Consultants in England who form a collaborative team responsible for effecting the new services.

Among his interests outside Medicine he has a passion for moths.

Anne Gerken

Anne Gerken held various junior Medical posts in London after qualifying. She then became Registrar in Medical Microbiology at Fulham Hospital, then Lecturer and Honorary Senior Registrar in

Medical Microbiology at Charing Cross Hospital. In 1973, she was appointed Consultant Microbiologist and Honorary Senior Lecturer at Charing Cross. She was appointed Consultant Microbiologist at the James Paget in 1981 and ran a single-handed service until she retired in 2001. She was originally laboratory-based at Northgate Hospital until her Department moved to the James Paget, with the opening of the second phase in 1984. She expanded the laboratory services and developed the clinical services by doing ward rounds, having an input into specialist units and by giving antibiotic advice. She established the district antibiotic policy. She expanded the Infection Control Team and played an energetic role in its activities.

She was Clinical Tutor and Chairman of the District Medical Education Committee for over three years and was Medical Careers Tutor for 10 years. She was Chairman of the Local Working Party on Junior Doctors' Hours and Chairman of the Hospital Manpower Committee. She was Lead Clinician for Clinical Audit for eight years and was an Examiner for the Part II Final Examination in Microbiology.

She was a member of the East Norfolk Health Authority Communicable Disease and Environmental Advisory Committee and their Immunisation Advisory Committee. She was Chairman of the Pathology Quality Group. She was Chairman of the East Anglian Medical Microbiology Development Group and was an Inspector in Medical Microbiology for Clinical Pathology Accreditation (UK) Ltd. She was a member of the Standing Advisory Committee in Microbiology and the Academic Activities Committee of the Royal College of Pathologists.

She had a number of papers published on such topics as Bacterial Impurity of Dairy Cream Samples in London, Microbiological Aspects of Cytotoxic Drug Therapy, Intra-operative Auto-transfusion for Elective Aortic Surgery, Infection in Homosexuals and on an Outbreak of Cryptosporidiosis in Great Yarmouth.

After retiring as Microbiologist at the James Paget, she did various locums in that speciality for three years at Addenbrooke's and Norfolk and Norwich University Hospitals. Since 2004, she has been working as a Consultant, helping her husband, Terry Mitchell, run the Chronic Fatigue Service for East Anglia.

Steve Absalom

Steve Absalom trained at Sheffield University Medical School, where he was President of the Sheffield Medical Group, and, after house jobs, joined the Senior House Officer Pathology Rotation at the Northern General Hospital in Sheffield, before becoming Registrar in Chemical Pathology at St. George's Hospital, London. Next, he was Lecturer and Honorary Senior Registrar in Chemical Pathology at Charing Cross and Westminster Medical School in London, before becoming Senior Registrar in Chemical Pathology at Leicester Royal Infirmary. He was appointed Consultant Chemical Pathologist at the James Paget in 1992, at the age of 37.

Apart from his clinical commitments and the task of overseeing his own Department, he has spent much of his time at the James Paget in management. He became Clinical Director of the Clinical Services Directorate in 1998 until April 2004, when he was appointed Divisional Director of Core Clinical Services. Throughout this time, he has been heavily involved in many major committees and working parties concerning the development of the Trust, such as Resource Allocation Working Party, Capital Working Party, Accommodation Review Group and the Medical Manpower Committee. Recently, he was elected to the Southern Regional Council of the Association for Clinical Biochemistry.

He was District Clinical Tutor for four years from 1994, when he became Associate Clinical Tutor and Careers Counselling Tutor. He has been involved in planning part of the curriculum for the Medical School and regularly teaches the Medical students.

He has an interest in Hyperlipidaemia and set up a Lipid Clinic in 1992. In addition, he has developed an open access service for dynamic endocrine tests. He set up a Pathology Audit Group in his Department and has overseen many audit projects.

He is married to Sharon Rhodes, Consultant Anaesthetist at the James Paget, and together they enjoy films and the theatre.

Mark Wilkinson

Mark Wilkinson qualified from Birmingham University and spent six years as Lecturer in Pathology in Nottingham, before being appointed Consultant Histopathologist at the James Paget in 1993. He has a great passion for teaching and when a post came up at the Norfolk and Norwich Hospital in 2002, he applied for it and was appointed.

Jane Braithwaite

Jane Braithwaite was born in Hertfordshire and did her Medical training at Girton College, Cambridge, and St George' Hospital, London. After house jobs, she held a variety of junior Medical posts in London, before becoming a part-time Senior Registrar in Haematology based at St. George's Hospital, while she was having three babies. In June 1988, she was appointed part-time Senior Registrar in Haematology at James Paget Hospital and two years later she was made Consultant, at the age of 38. She resigned in December 1996 and became a GP Registrar in Bungay for a year before doing some GP locums with some Haematology for six months. For the following two years, she held various Consultant Haematology appointments, interspersed with some GP locums in Bungay. She was appointed Consultant Haematologist to Calderdale and Huddersfield NHS Trust in 2001, but after nearly two years, decided to return to the James Paget as Haematologist in 2003.

She has been a member of the Ethics, Transfusion and Thromboprophylaxis Committees. She was Royal College of Physicians College Tutor for two years from 1995 and she participates in teaching the Medical students.

She jointly wrote Multiple Choice Questions in Haematology and has had articles published on Infant Chlamydia Pneumonia and Chemotherapy for Non-Hodgkin's Lymphoma.

She enjoys coast walking near her cottage on the North Norfolk coast, cycling, skiing and playing bridge.

Helena Daly

After leaving her Consultant Haematology post in the West Country, she was appointed Consultant Haematologist at the James Paget in 1997. She retired on health grounds less than a year later.

Talal Jeha

Talal Jeha was born in Syria and did his Medical training at Damascus University. His first job was in Beirut, Lebanon, and then he held various posts in Haematology in Bath and Dorset. Subsequently, he worked in Dubai, Riyadh and at the Fred Hutchinson Institute in Seattle. He was appointed Consultant Haematologist in 1996 and left in 2003 for another post abroad.

Wayne Kinsey

Wayne Kinsey was appointed Consultant Histopathologist in 1996, but moved to Norfolk and Norwich University Hospital in 2003. For a time he was Lead Histopathologist.

He was an expert on the Hammer horror films.

Shalal Sadullah

Shalal Sadullah was born in Karachi, Pakistan, and trained at the Dow Medical College, Karachi. He came to the United Kingdom in 1984 and, after several locum posts, held various junior Medical posts in Bournemouth, before becoming Registrar in Haematology at King's College Hospital, London. After two years as Leukemia Research Fellow at the Tenovus Laboratory, Southampton, and Royal Bournemouth Hospital, he became Senior Registrar in Haematology in Dundee for four years. He was Consultant Haematologist at the Borders General Hospital in Melrose, Scotland, from 1997 until 2000, before being appointed at the James Paget in 2000. His special interests are Haemato-oncology and Lymphoma.

He was Lead for the Audit and Effectiveness Committee from 2000 to 2004 and has served on the Clinical Governance, Research and Development and Blood Transfusion Committees. He was appointed Lead Clinician for Haematology in April 2001 and developed a Fast-Track Deep-Vein Thrombosis Service, as well as Nurse-led anticoagulant Clinics with radical changes to the delivery of anticoagulant services. He established a combined Lymphoma Clinic with Haematologists and Oncologists. These various works have enabled Haematology in the James Paget to establish itself as one of the front-line units within the Region.

From 2002, he has been Haematology Lead for the Norfolk and Waveney Cancer Network. He has been the Regional Representative for East Anglia for the British Society of Haematology since 2003 and from June 2007 will be the Trust's Divisional Director for Core Clinical Services.

His research involved treating patients with Follicular Lymphoma with Chimaeric Monoclonal Antibodies and assessing the response clinically and by molecular methods for the detection of minimal residual disease. He has published several papers on this, as well as other topics.

His outside interests include sport in general (he played cricket for the Pakistan under-19 team in zonal matches) and music.

Geoffrey Waters

Geoffrey Waters was born in Grahamstown, South Africa, and trained at the University of Cape Town. He was a Consultant Pathologist in South Africa for many years, before being appointed Consultant Histopathologist at the James Paget in 2002. His special interest is in Lung, Gastro-intestinal and Skin Pathology. He was appointed at a time when increasing specialisation was threatening the existence of having an independent Histopathology in every District General Hospital. He played an important and active role on the Project Board, which saw the amalgamation of Histopathology at the Norfolk and Norwich University and James Paget Hospitals onto a new site in Norwich in July 2005.

His interests include boating of all types, photography and music.

Marius Vander Walt

Marius Vander Walt came as a locum from South Africa and was appointed in August 2004. He resigned in June 2005 to return to South Africa. He is a very keen photographer and donated some of his photographs to the Mortuary, and they now hang in the waiting area for relatives.

Joseph Murphy

Joe Murphy was appointed jointly to the Norfolk and Norwich University and to the James Paget Hospitals in August 2004. His main interest is in Breast Histopathology and he was based at the James Paget until the Department moved to Norwich in July 2005.

Henrik Hellquist

Henrik Hellquist was appointed in September 2003 and moved to Norwich with the Department in July 2005.

Ngozi Elumogo

Ngozi Elumogo trained at the Benin City Medical School in Nigeria and, after various house jobs and general practice, she started training in microbiology at the University College Hospital, Ibadan. She became Research Registrar at the Public Health Laboratory in Newcastle, where she studied Mycobacterium Tuberculosis, and then moved to south-east Scotland as Specialist Registrar. Following this, she became Clinical Lecturer and Honorary Specialist Registrar at the University of Edinburgh Medical School. She was appointed Consultant Microbiologist in 2002 and, since 2006, has been the Director of Infection Prevention and Control.

Tony Hegarty

Tony Hegarty was born in Cork, Ireland, and trained at the Medical School in Cork. He worked in a Mission Hospital in Zambia from 1972 to 1975, before returning to Ireland, where he held various training posts in Dublin, Galway and then moved to Birmingham. He was appointed Consultant Microbiologist at Queen Elizabeth Hospital, Kings Lynn, Norfolk, in 1984 and worked there until he was appointed to the James Paget as Consultant Microbiologist in 2003, at the age of 56.

Cesar Gomez

Cesar Gomez comes from Valencia in Spain and, after qualifying, he worked as family doctor before moving to a Consultant post in the Accident and Emergency Department in Valencia. He then decided to train as a Haematologist and was appointed as Consultant Haematologist at the James Paget in July 2006.

He enjoys music and plays the classical Spanish guitar.

Consultant Radiologists

Alleyn O'Malley

Alleyn O'Malley trained at the London Hospital Medical School and was appointed Consultant Radiologist to the Great Yarmouth and Waveney Health District in 1975 and for a number of years he and Ifor Williams were the only two Radiologists in the District. Soon after the move to the new District General Hospital, he led the highly successful appeal to provide a CT Scanner. For many years he worked with Dr. Chris Brookings at the Mammography Unit at the North Sea Medical Centre and, when the James Paget had its own Unit, he worked with Dr. Holly Archer there. He retired in 2000, but continued doing locum work in the X-ray Department for many years.

Ifor Williams

Ifor Williams received his medical training in Cambridge and at the Westminster Hospital, London. He was appointed Consultant Radiologist to Newmarket Hospital and then went to Stanford in California for a year. On his return, he was appointed to Northwick Park Hospital, Harrow where, apart from his clinical work, he was involved in research on the colon. He moved back to East Anglia in the 1970s working mainly at Yarmouth General and Lowestoft Hospitals. With the opening of the new hospital in 1981, he transferred there and retired in 1984. His garden and computer keep him physically and mentally active.

Vinod Kumar

Vinod Kumar was born in Delhi, India, and trained at the Government Medical College in Patiala, India. He was Registrar and Senior Registrar in Radiology in Nottingham and other hospitals in the Trent Region, before being appointed Consultant Radiologist at the James Paget in 1982, at the age of 33. His special interests are in Imaging the Gastro-intestinal Tract, Biliary Work and in the use of Ultrasound. He helped Stuart Hishon establish the ERCP service in the hospital. He was Chairman of the Medical Staff Committee in 1987, but regards himself as not a committee person.

Philip Lawrence

Philip Lawrence was born in London and trained at the London Hospital Medical College and did his Radiology training in the Nottingham hospitals. He was appointed Consultant Radiologist at the James Paget in 1984, at the age of 34. He has a special interest in the use of Ultrasound and has been the James Paget Representative on the Regional Health Authority Radiology Advisory Committee. He wrote a case report on the Sonographic Appearances in Neonates with Generalised Meconium Peritonitis, calling it the Snowstorm Sign in 1984 and has played a part in teaching Radiographers to perform barium enemas, inject for intravenous urograms and report plain films.

He has an amateur radio licence, holds a private pilot's licence and is the local medical examiner for people wishing to maintain their pilot's licence.

Mike Webber

Mike Webber did his Radiological training in the Nottingham hospitals before being appointed Consultant Radiologist at the James Paget in 1985. He has been Director of the Department and has overseen the introduction of PACS. Although he retired in 2003, he continues to do locum work in the Department two days a week.

Antonio Martinez

Antonio Martinez did his early Medical training in Bilbao, Spain. He was Senior Registrar in Radiology at King's College, London, and he had worked at St. Mary's, Hammersmith, Central Middlesex and Northwick Park Hospitals in London. He joined the hospital as Consultant Radiologist in October 1994. He expanded Interventional Radiology, especially Angiography, in the hospital and it was a sad day for the hospital when he accepted a university post back in Spain in 1997.

Frances Holly Archer

Frances Holly Archer trained at the Welsh National School of Medicine in Cardiff and was Registrar and Senior Registrar in Radiology at Addenbrooke's Hospital, Cambridge. She became Assistant Director of

Diagnostic Imaging at the Princess Alexandra Hospital in Brisbane, Australia, and then Director of the Central Queensland Breast Screening Service in Rockhampton.

She was appointed Consultant Radiologist with a special interest in Mammography at the James Paget Hospital in 1994 and has built up a highly successful Mammography Unit and Breast Screening Service. She has been a member of the Local Negotiating Committee and has served on the Risk Management, Clinical Governance and Audit Committees. She has been a member of the Norfolk Orthopaedic Collaborative and the Regional Radiology Directors Group. She is an Honorary Senior Lecturer of the University of East Anglia Medical School and is heavily involved with teaching there.

Eryl Thomas

Eryl Thomas was born in Essex but left at the age of six weeks to spend her childhood in Wales. She trained at the University of Bristol. Her junior Medical posts were held in the south-west of England and she became Senior Registrar in Radiology in Bristol and Plymouth. She was appointed Consultant Radiologist at Broadgreen Hospital, Liverpool, in 1992, after working there for a year as Locum Consultant. When her husband was appointed to a Consultant post in Norwich, she held Locum Consultant posts in East Anglia before being appointed Consultant Radiologist at the James Paget in 1996.

Since being at the James Paget, she has played a big part in developing Ultrasound Imaging and MR Scanning. She is extremely active in most of the Multi-disciplinary Meetings which have evolved over recent years. She is Radiology Lead for the Imaging Site Specific Group of the Cancer Network, Lead Radiologist for CT Scanning, Radiology Trainer for Specialist Registrars on the Radiology Academy Rotation, Senior Lecturer for UEA and a member of the Clinical Ethics Advisory Group.

She has had several papers published on the value of Ultrasound in Diagnosis and Management. Among others are papers on Liquid Crystal Thermography and C-reactive Protein in the Detection of Deep-vein Thrombosis and the Accuracy of Digital Subtraction Angiography for the Quantification of Atherosclerosis.

She is a member of the Norwich Philharmonic Choir and used to play the oboe in the North Wales Youth Orchestra and the Bristol University Symphony Orchestra. Other activities include sailing and looking after her two children.

Sinan Hamid

Sinan Hamid was appointed Consultant Radiologist in 1999 and left in 2002.

Ahmad Al-Mari

Ahmad Al-Mari was appointed Consultant Radiologist in 2000, but stayed for less than a year.

Bruce Smith

Bruce Smith came from South Africa to do a long-term Locum in Radiology in 2003 and stayed until 2006. He was extremely accomplished in all aspects of Radiology, but particularly in CT and MR Scanning. He was always willing to help out and loved explaining what he was doing.

Brian Evans

Brian Evans was Consultant Radiologist in Ipswich with a special interest in Mammography and at one time had been the Regional Lead for this service. After retiring early, he started in 2000 a long-term locum, two to three days a week, at the James Paget in the Breast Imaging Unit. With his calm ways and great experience, he helped Frances Holly Archer build up a very successful unit. He retired in 2006.

Alfred Kruger

Alfred Kruger was born in South Africa and trained at Pretoria University and the University of the Free State, South Africa. After further study, he went into private practice Radiology at Nelspruit, a city near the Kruger National Park, for 16 years. He worked at the William Harvey Hospital in Kent in 2003 and 2004. In 2005, he became a Locum

Consultant Radiologist at the James Paget and now has a permanent post. He has taken on part of the work in the Breast Imaging Department and has another special interest in Interventional Radiology.

Dr. K. Ashraf

Dr. Ashraf was appointed Consultant Radiologist in 2006.

Dr. Suri

Dr. Suri was appointed Consultant Radiologist in 2006.

Consultant Thoracic Surgeons

Findley Kerr

Findley Kerr was Thoracic Surgeon at the Norfolk and Norwich Hospital and did out patient sessions at the James Paget once a month when it first opened. He operated at the Norfolk and Norwich and at Kelling Hospital in North Norfolk.

Barry Ross

Barry Ross trained as a Thoracic Surgeon under Lord Brock at Guy's Hospital, London, and moved to the Norfolk and Norwich Hospital as Consultant in the 1970s, where he built up the Norfolk and Norwich Institute of Medical Education. For many years he did Outpatient Clinics at the James Paget and was always available for advice on Thoracic problems.

Roger Vaughan

Roger Vaughan did outpatient sessions at the James Paget Hospital in the 1980s and then moved to Yorkshire. He is now working in Birmingham

Deirdre Watson

Deidre Watson was born in Kent and trained at Guy's. She was Consultant Thoracic Surgeon at the Birmingham Heartlands Hospital and Birmingham Children's Hospital from 1980 until she moved to

Norfolk, where she was Consultant Thoracic Surgeon at the Norfolk and Norwich, with sessions at the James Paget. She retired in 2002.

She was on the Council of the Royal College of Surgeons of England, the Council of the British Thoracic Society, the Council of the European Association for Cardiothoracic Surgery and Honorary Secretary of the Society of Cardiothoracic Surgeons of Great Britain and Ireland. She was Consultant Advisor to the Chief Medical Officer from 1994 to 2000 and was on the Department of Health Standing Committee on Lung Cancer. She examined for the FRCS for the Royal College of Surgeons of Edinburgh.

She wrote many publications on a wide range of topics in Cardiothoracic Surgery, as well as writing several book chapters and contributing to a number of Government and other national reports.

Wynn Parry

Wynn Parry is Consultant Thoracic Surgeon at the Norfolk and Norwich University Hospital and for a time did weekly clinics at the James Paget

Mr. van Leuven

Mr. van Leuven is Consultant Thoracic Surgeon at the Norfolk and Norwich University Hospital and followed on from Wynn Parry in running the outpatient clinics.

Consultant Neurologists

John Pilling

John Pilling has been coming to do outpatient clinics from the Norfolk and Norwich Hospital for most of the time that the James Paget has been opened. Although he has retired he has come back as a locum. When he has finished his clinics he is often seen seeing patients on the wards who have been referred to him.

David Dick

David Dick was appointed to the Norfolk and Norwich Hospital in the 1990s and does Outpatient sessions at the James Paget.

Public Health Doctors

Roger Newberry

Roger Newberry was appointed Great Yarmouth Medical Officer of Health in 1968. He had trained at St. Bartholomew's Hospital in London and later became Assistant Medical Officer of Health for South Essex. He was very much involved in the planning of the new hospital. He retired soon after it opened and subsequently the Community Paediatric Centre in Lowestoft Road, Gorleston was named after him.

Ann Brown

Ann Brown succeeded Roger Newberry staying here for about five years. During that time she was the secretary of the highly successful CT Scanner Appeal

Wulfram Forsythe-Yorke

Dr. Wulf Forsythe-Yorke was born in Grantham, Lincolnshire, and did his Medical training in Cambridge and the Middlesex Hospital Medical School. After house appointments, he did his National Service and was commissioned into the Royal Army Medical Corps. Subsequently, he served in Kenya, Northern Ireland, Nepal, Germany and the United Kingdom, where he ended up as Brigadier and Commanding Officer of the Queen Elizabeth Military Hospital, London. He retired from the Services in 1991 and was appointed Director of Public Health for the Great Yarmouth and Waveney Health Authority.

During that time, he chaired or co-chaired 15 health committees, was involved in Sizewell B contingency planning and coastal flood emergency measures. In 1993, he was appointed Trainer in Public Health and member of the Faculty of Public Health Consultant Approval Panel. In 1994, the Health Authority was abolished and he was transferred to the East Norfolk Health Commission and made redundant. The same year he was appointed Independent Medical Advisor to the Benefits Agency and later to the Department of Works and Pensions; a job which he continues to do part-time. He was County Commander of St. John Ambulance 1991–1999. He has held many honorary posts and at present is President of the Norfolk branch of the RAMC Association, President of St. John Division, Belton, Great Yarmouth, and is a Governor of the James Paget University Hospitals NHS Foundation Trust. He has been awarded many foreign decorations, is a Knight of the Order of St. John and holds the OBE.

When he was in Nepal, he did some research into snake bites. He has published papers on Florence Nightingale and Medical Victoria Cross Holders and, when in Kenya, translated the First Aid Handbook into Swahili.

His main interests are the classical arts, travelling and languages, making pseudo-antique furniture and he is developing an interest in sailing.

Nurse Consultants

Katharine Kite

Katharine Kite trained as a Nurse at University College Hospital, London, where she became a Staff Nurse. After a year's Orthopaedic course at the Orthopaedic Hospital, Oswestry, she worked as Staff Nurse at the Major Injuries Unit, Birmingham Accident Hospital. She then moved to Norwich, where she was Night Charge Nurse for Orthopaedics. Following a spell in the West Norwich Intensive and High Dependency Care Unit at the West Norwich, she attended an Intensive Care Nursing course in Peterborough before returning to Intensive Care in Norwich. She took her B.Sc. in Nursing Studies in 1994 and obtained her PhD in 1998 on "Learning to doubt: the professional development of nurses in one intensive therapy unit". In July 2001, she was appointed the first Nurse Consultant at the James Paget and has been attached to the Critical Care Directorate since then.

Since 1996, she has been part-time Lecturer to Ed.D and PhD students at the School of Education and Professional Development, UEA, and part-time Lecturer to B.Sc. students at the School of Health, UEA. She has been Visiting Fellow at the School of Education and Life-long Learning, UEA, since 1998. In the past, she has been Research Associate and Evaluation Consultant for various nursing projects. She has written a number of papers on Mouth Care in Intensive Care, the Professional Development of Nurses in Intensive Care, the experience and meanings of post-take ward rounds for the learning of pre-registration house officers, as well as several others. She has been overseeing the development of the "Outreach Team", which is based in the ITU, and helps in the management of ill patients on the wards.

Jan Austin

Jan Austin trained as a Nurse at the Chelmsford and Essex Hospital and worked at the Yarmouth General Hospital, before becoming Sister-in-Charge of the Central Treatment Suite, when the District General Hospital opened. It was here that Dr. Turner and Dr. Notcutt held their Pain Clinics and where she developed her interest in the subject. She was appointed Clinical Nurse Specialist in Pain Management in 1990, did a Diploma in Theory and Practice of Aromatherapy and then obtained her B.Sc. in Nursing Practice. Next, she did an M.Sc. in Pain Management and became Consultant Nurse in Pain Management in December 2005. Her responsibilities include managing an interdisciplinary team of 15 staff, providing nurse-led clinical services to both in-patients and outpatients across the Trust, developing and delivering education programmes and undertaking research and audit of practice.

~ 8 ~

Voluntary Organisations

Hospital Volunteers

This is a group of men and women, numbering over a hundred who man reception desks, help in clinics, deliver paper work and specimens and do innumerable tasks to help the efficient running of the hospital.

The Trust is most fortunate in having a large group of volunteers who give unstinting assistance to the hospital. Some help by raising money within the hospital, some act as receptionists or deliver information around the hospital, others supply services such as the WRVS and League of Friends Shop, the Rainbow stall, a trolley service to the wards and clinics or a mobile library. Others have formed patient groups to help others with similar problems. All of these people help out willingly with good humour and kindness and, in the majority of cases, they are also raising money for the hospital. The hospital is indeed fortunate to have the services of this dedicated group of people.

Patient and Public Involvement (PPI) Forums

By Patrick Thompson, Chairman

Patient Forums became operational on 1st December 2003 when Community Health Councils came to an end. One was created for every NHS Acute Trust, Foundation Trust and Primary Care Trust. They are associated with, but totally independent of, NHS Trusts. They are often referred to as a 'critical friend' of the Trusts. There are currently around

550 Forums involving 4,500 people. All Forum members are volunteers, organise their meetings and elect their own chairs.

All Forum members are appointed and managed by the Commission for Patient and Public Involvement (CPPIH), which was established as a non-departmental public body to oversee PPIFs. One of the main functions of CPPIH is to advise the Secretary of State on arrangements for public involvement in, and consultation on, matters relating to the health service.

PPI Forums have statutory powers conferred by CPPIH. These powers enable Forums to make a difference by providing a voice for patients and members of the public on services provided by specific NHS Trusts. Specifically, Forums have the power to:

- Collect information relevant to its function from particular NHS organisations and other authorities within 20 working days from the initial request.
- Refer any health matters relevant to the Forum's function to local authority overview and scrutiny committees, CPPIH, or any other authority the Forum thinks appropriate.
- Enter and inspect premises owned or controlled by the Trust.
- Appoint a committee (which could include non-Forum members) to help the Forum meet its responsibilities.
- Form a joint committee with other Forums to help with joint pieces of work.

The local Forum works in association with the James Paget University Hospitals NHS Foundation Trust and aims to ensure the local community has its say in influencing the delivery of Healthcare services by the Trust. It achieves this aim by reviewing healthcare services provided by JPUH on behalf of patients and the public.

The present Forum is made up of 15 dedicated members from the Great Yarmouth and Waveney area who meet regularly, both informally and in public. Forum activities support their agreed work plan and each member gets involved in activities that reflects their interest and suits their availability.

The Forum has established an excellent and mutually respectful working relationship with the JPUH Trust which actively encourages Forum involvement in all aspects of its service delivery. The Chair of the Forum regularly meets with the Chief Executive Officer and Chairman of the Trust, sits on the Trust Board as an observer and is able to take forward any issues on behalf of the Forum. There is also Forum member representation on a number of groups and committees throughout the Trust and a variety of other organizations, including those in the voluntary sector and local government.

Past achievements include:

- Participation in National Food Watch and Care Watch Surveys.
- Inspection of Accident and Emergency Department, Oulton Unit, Emergency Assessment and Discharge Unit and Catering Department at James Paget Hospital.
- A patient transport survey with Great Yarmouth and Waveney PCT PPI Forum.
- Patient and public representation at the Governors' and Trust Board meetings.
- Patient and public representation on a variety of committees and groups; for example: Cleft Lip and Palate, Diabetic, Physiotherapy, Maternity Liaison Group, and many more.

The Forum is currently focusing on a number of issues, including:

- The review of Healthcare services provided by the Acute Trusts within the East of England Strategic Health Authority.
- The transition of the PPI Forums into Local Involvement Networks (LINks).
- The Turnaround Plans for the Norfolk and Great Yarmouth and Waveney Primary Care Trusts.
- National Care Watch Campaign – surveying patients on issues of dignity and level of care.
- Responding to the Department of Health on the Trust achievements and compliance of Quality Standards set down by the Healthcare Commission.
- Revision of the Out of Hours service.
- Infection Control and Cleanliness inspection visits.
- Planning and development of the new Palliative Care East Centre.

Patient Groups

BRAS

The BeReAssured Scheme was founded in 1985 after Hugh Sturzaker had spoken to a number of his patients who had breast cancer. This disease is extremely common and is one of the most feared and he felt that it would be helpful to have a group of ladies who had experienced the disease who would meet up with those who had been newly diagnosed. This group of ladies would know better than anyone else what it felt like to be told they had breast cancer and, hopefully, they could give advice and support to these patients and their partners. Thus, in March 1985, he convened a meeting with Dr. Ann Brown, District Medical Officer, to which 10 of his patients and Dr. Roy Vining, a Lowestoft GP, were invited.

As a result of the meeting, the group was established. It decided to call itself BRAS and Dr. Brown agreed to donate £50 from District Funds to help with initial expenses. Later, leaflets were designed and produced giving details about the group and contact telephone numbers. The plan was that each week two of the group would attend an outpatient clinic and any patient newly diagnosed with breast cancer would be given the opportunity of meeting them. Some patients were so upset that they wanted to get home straight away, but each one was given a leaflet and many took the opportunity to telephone one of the BRAS ladies later on. The motto on the leaflet was "Don't be alone, pick up the phone". In addition, two members of the group would visit patients on the wards who were about to have breast surgery or were recovering from it. They describe themselves as "basically ordinary, caring, compassionate ladies who have faced breast cancer and, most importantly, have survived". Each makes a point that on attending a clinic or the ward that they are immaculately dressed and look as though they have just been to the hairdressers.

Joan Johnson was the first secretary and, after a short time, Anne Davis succeeded her and continues in the post. The first chairperson was Mrs Rene Burgess, who was an inspiration to all. Even in her nineties, her memory and wit were as sharp as ever and she would still wear one of her late husband's trilby hats. She said that as a youngster she ate fish twice a day and this might have been a factor in her having such a wonderful memory. She was very proud to have been nominated and to have received Maundy Money from the Queen in Norwich Cathedral. Afterwards, being interviewed on television, she was asked for her views about the occasion, to which she replied that the Queen was just like any other elderly lady! Her successor is Mrs Pat Clifford, and four of the original 10 – Anne Davis, Pat Goose, Sheila Thompson and Rita Middleton – still play an active part in BRAS.

Apart from the original £50 grant, the group has been self-funding, raising money from among themselves on a regular basis. It has also received donations from various organisations that have wished to support it and has raised money at the Annual Hospital Fete with cake and bottle stalls. The money has been used to fund, among other items, two electrically controlled beds – the first on the general wards – and more recently a liposuction machine to help in breast reconstruction.

The BRAS were established many years before Breast Care Nurses came into being and the group was involved in the selection of the hospital's first Breast Care Nurse Specialist, Mrs Wendy Dwornik. Over the years, the number of these Specialist Nurses has increased to three and it might be asked whether there was still the need for the BRAS. The answer lies in the appreciation shown by many patients who have been helped by these ladies over the years. They have had no specialised training nor passed any examinations in breast disease, but they have had the experience of being diagnosed with and treated for breast cancer and have survived. Above all, they show understanding and compassion and are willing to listen to and support the newly diagnosed patient and her family.

The BRAS ladies meet at the hospital every seven to eight weeks to draw up rotas for visits, to discuss any particular problems and at the same time the Breast Care Nurses usually attend. This gives all of them the opportunity to exchange information and learn from each other. The highlight of the year is the Annual Dinner, which is usually held at the Burlington Hotel in Great Yarmouth, to which the Breast Care Nurse Specialists, Chris Tom (the Orthotic Manager) and the Breast Surgeons and their spouses are invited. It is an opportunity for everyone to get together socially and to congratulate each other for a job well done.

The BRAS ladies have worked together for over 22 years bringing help, comfort and support to many patients and their relatives. They have also been a support to the Breast Care Nurse Specialists, the nurses in the clinics and on the wards, as well as to the Breast Surgeons. Deservedly, their contribution was recognised when the Breast Service was awarded its Charter Mark.

Breast Friends

Breast Friends is a support group for persons who have had breast cancer and was started about seven years ago. It meets in the Burrage Centre at 7.30pm on the first Thursday in every month. Attendance varies from 12-20. There are occasional speakers and the group meets to help each other. It is self financing and, in addition, raises money for breast related projects. There is no membership fee and the group is always delighted to welcome new members.

Heartcare

Rosemary Pinter was the Founder and President of Heartcare, which was launched in November 1992 as a result of a meeting between Dr. Grabau, Consultant Cardiologist, Colin Jarvis, a patient who had heart attacks and coronary artery bypass surgery, and Rosemary Pinter, who was the Occupational Therapist on the Cardiac Rehabilitation Programme. Colin Jarvis was the first of many volunteers who visit patients recently suffering from a heart attack and other heart diseases which led to an emergency admission to hospital and he continued this for five years.

Great Yarmouth and Waveney Breathe Easy

This is one of about 140 Breathe Easy groups in the United Kingdom which are part of the British Lung Foundation. The British Lung Foundation represents all of the many lung conditions and the Breathe Easy Group aims to advise, inform and support sufferers, their families, friends and carers.

The Group works with Respiratory Nurse Specialists and Physiotherapists and meets on the last Wednesday of every month – except December – in the Hopton Village Hall. At the meetings there is a guest speaker, refreshments, raffle and some input from a Medical Advisor. There is a free, regular newsletter for the members; events and outings are organised and the group arranges fund-raising for lung disease research and respiratory related equipment for the hospital and local surgeries. The group advises and informs members about what assistance is available to help them cope with everyday living and members can telephone for help and advice.

The Head and Neck Tracheostomy/Laryngectomy Support Group

Based on an article by Denise Smith

The Head and Neck Tracheostomy/Laryngectomy Support Group first met in 1994, having identified a need for the local population by patients affected by head and neck cancer. The group is affiliated to NALC (the National Association of Laryngectomy Clubs) and therefore has links with similar clubs that serve this special patient group. The Group is also featured on the CANCER BACUP site and is often approached by patients from other areas, seeking support or access to information. The meetings are held in the Burrage Centre, at least three times a year, and at the meetings the patients and families have the opportunity to discuss issues pertaining to their needs and seek support from others who have experienced the same or similar head and neck cancer. There are occasional guest speakers and there is the opportunity to discuss future fundraising activities. The Group relies to a degree on monies from grateful patients or their families/friends to assist in purchasing specialist equipment for community patients. It raises funds to support head and neck cancer research locally, specifically as head and neck cancer is seen as a rare disease and so helps to raise the profile of this cancer type.

The most recent development has been the formation of the "Patient buddies". These are a group of six patients that regularly assist the Nurse Specialist in supporting new head and neck cancer patients. They also attend the monthly Specialist Cancer Clinics at the hospital and talk to patients in the waiting area to help support them at a time when they might be concerned about their consultation. The Group has found, through its patient surveys that this is what patients relate to, because they are talking to people who have experienced the same or similar cancer and the "Patient Buddies" are able to shed some of the myths attached to cancer treatments.

Ten to twelve patients regularly attend the social meetings and there are a number of helpers who may not attend the meetings but give support in many other ways. This contribution from the members is seen as crucial to the Nursing Support Team that cares for these patients, who often remain life-long patients to the service.

Ostomy Support Group

The Ostomy Support Group was founded on 27th October 1989 to provide a regular meeting place for patients with colostomies, ileostomies and ileal conduits. The Group meets every three months in the Celebration Suite of the Burrage Centre, when one hundred or more of them and their families meet for a social evening. There is often a speaker and money raised has provided for *in vitro* fertilisation for one of its members, special pneumatic cushions for the wards and patients at home, equipment for the hospital and, frequently, contributions are made to members who might need some financial assistance.

The first Chairman was Mr. A Leedham and his successor was Mr. Eddie Symonds, who still holds that post.

~ 9 ~

Voluntary and Fund Raising Organisations

The Arts Committee

The Arts Committee was founded in 1985 and was chaired initially by Dr. David Turner, Consultant Anaesthetist. The original Committee consisted of Madeleine Borg, Pam Higginbottom, Brian Callan, Edna Fletcher, Elayne Guest, Peter Black, Julian Macey and Margaret Carver. All the Committee members worked in the hospital, except for Julian Macey and Margaret Carver, who are well-known local artists and have been the backbone of the Committee until they retired from it in 2006 after 21 years' devoted service.

The Committee decided that its first task was to ascertain from a broad section of staff, patients and visitors to the hospital what they wanted by way of the arts. Thus, a survey was carried out in November 1985 and 363 questionnaires were returned out of 565 handed out. The survey showed that there was a real interest in promoting art exhibitions and art works in the wards and corridors.

The first art exhibition was held in February 1986 using borrowed screens and pictures from the Great Yarmouth Society of Artists. Over a thousand people attended the exhibition and 13 pictures were sold for £1,670, of which 15% commission went to the hospital. Many artists were amazed at the thought of staging an exhibition in the corner of a hospital corridor, but it was a great success and was repeated annually. More recently, the exhibitions have been held in the Boardroom. Artists started to save their best works for display at these exhibitions. There was also enthusiastic support from Mr. Andrew Butcher, the General Manager of the hospital, and Mr. Noel Johnson, Chairman of the Great Yarmouth and Waveney Health Authority. Subsequently, a staff art exhibition was introduced and is held annually.

Elayne Guest succeeded David Turner as Chairperson and remained a driving force on the Committee until her retirement in 2006, when Ian Walker, Senior Operating Department Assistant and Chairman of the Great Yarmouth Guild of Artists, became Chairman of the Committee. However, over the years the vast majority of the work has been done by Margaret Carver and Julian Macey. They combed Norfolk and Suffolk for quality artists to exhibit, reaching from Brancaster in north Norfolk to Sudbury in Suffolk. Many of the artists were of international standard and the art exhibitions were highly regarded. The works exhibited were always subject to selection from invited artists.

On many occasions, Margaret Carver gave demonstrations of pastel painting. Visitors tried their hand by adding trees, bushes or clouds to the picture and members of staff would check each day to see how their picture was progressing. As a result of the exhibitions, works were given to be displayed around the hospital. Some artists loaned pictures for the same purpose. The Arts Committee commissioned a mural for a corridor from John Dashwood, several paintings for the children's ward, as well as a sculpture by a local artist. It also paid for the brickwork notice, hedging and lighting displaying the name of the hospital to the left of the hospital entrance.

Other activities it became involved in were:

- A competition for the logo of the hospital.
- A hospital tie.
- An annual Christmas card.
- Displays of artwork from the local schools and colleges.
- Instituting the Staff Photography Competition, which is organised by Madeleine Borg.
- Donations to the Intensive Care Unit and Rehabilitation.
- Purchasing of music equipment.

Hospital Christmas cards are chosen from competitions and local societies are invited to take part. Usually, four cards are selected and the most popular are of local scenes. In the first year, 10,000 cards were sold, with a 50% mark-up, which gave a good profit. Cards were sold in packs of four for £1. Although some are sold in businesses in the local towns, the majority have been sold by Julian Macey and a small team of volunteers who spent many days standing just beyond the foyer of the hospital. One year, whilst selling Christmas cards, Julian Macey was subconsciously tapping on the wall behind him. A doctor from the clinic next door came and said that they could not make out what the unusual tapping was that they could hear in their stethoscopes. The peak of sales in a year was 20,000 cards.

Display cases were purchased to show the work of local artists, with 20% commission on sales going to the Arts Committee. The cases were hired by the artists for a three-month period and sometimes they were used for displaying work by local schools and colleges. In the first three years, the commission on sales of paintings was over £2,000.

Photographic competitions were held and the winning photographs were enlarged and displayed in the corridors behind Lexan, a special, transparent Perspex material. In addition, in the early days, Craft Fairs were held. It was also hoped to provide a Stress Relief Centre in the hospital to include pictures, music and literature. At that time, the Committee had £10,000 in the bank and it was its intention to apply for Lottery Funding, which could have amounted to £100,000. Unfortunately, at that time, the hospital had other projects of greater priority and the opportunity was lost. At present there is £30,000 in the kitty and Margaret Carver hopes that some of this could go to funding such a facility in the near future. She says that "our aim was to introduce quality art into the hospital, recognising the therapeutic value of art and to humanise the hospital for patients, staff and visitors. Many encouraging letters were received, including one from a holidaymaker who was in intensive care and the sight of a painting on the wall gave him hope to recover. Many people also commented on the pictures in the hospital and are lifted from their immediate concerns and trouble by the art works on display."

Over the years, many works of art have been acquired by the hospital in various ways. Some were given outright; others were given on long loan, while others were given for specific areas or purposes. Many were purchased or commissioned by the Arts Committee. The Committee is attempting to make a complete inventory of all these paintings and so far the following have been listed:

- Bruer Tidman: 3 oil paintings.
- Colin Burns: 2 prints.
- Colin Grapes: oil painting.
- Oulton Broad Group: oil mural.
- Peter Metcalf: 3 watercolours.
- David Dane: print.
- Geoffrey Chatten: 3 oil paintings and 3 prints.
- Margaret Carver: oil painting and pastel.
- Peter Agapu: watercolour.
- John Dashwood: mural.
- David Balder: oil.
- Wilfred Sutton: oil.
- Sam Capps: 2 watercolours.
- Gordon Goodman: watercolour.
- Ian Kent: watercolour.
- Vivienne Robinson: watercolour.
- John Applegate: oil.
- Clifford John: 2 oils.
- Don Rose: watercolour.
- Rowland Fisher: 2 oils.
- Helen Daniels: watercolour.
- Norman Harper: oil.

Over the years there have been many funny incidents and here are a few:

A man came into an exhibition and bought seven pictures, claiming he was a visiting surgeon. However, when he did not return, checks were made and it was found that there was no-one of that name and he was a patient at the psychiatric unit.

During one of the Craft Fairs, a raffle was held and a ticket was bought by a patient who wrote down his name and the ward he was on. He won a cuddly toy in the draw, but when Margaret Carver took it to the ward she was told that he would not need it where he was gone as he was dead.

With another raffle, Margaret Carver and Julian Macey went home thinking that the other person had the money from the raffle. Realising their mistake, they made a mad dash back to the hospital to retrieve the lost money from a black sack that had been put out as rubbish with the used tickets.

In an attempt to attract an international artist to exhibit his work in an exhibition, he was told that "one million people came to this hospital last year". His response was merely, "Yes, but how many came out?"

The Arts Committee has more than achieved its aims of bringing art of high quality into the hospital for the benefit of patients, staff and visitors. Much of this has been achieved by the hard work and devotion of a small group of people, but particularly of Margaret Carver and Julian Macey. They have spent endless hours organising art exhibitions, craft fairs, selling Christmas cards, etc., and the hospital has benefited greatly in many ways. Hopefully, a place within the hospital can be found to have an area where patients, staff and visitors can go and relax, surrounded by great art, some literature and where small recitals might be performed.

League of Friends

From information supplied by Heather Cave, Mary Morris and Joyce Mowbray

The League of Friends was formed in 1982. Before then it was hoped that the League of Friends of Lowestoft and those of Great Yarmouth would combine to form the Friends of the new hospital, but it was not to be. On each occasion a meeting was arranged, it was attended by a contingent from either Great Yarmouth or from Lowestoft, but the two sides never attended together. As a result, it was decided to form a new Friends and the first Chairman was William Smith. The original membership was 17 and this rose to 29 by the end of the first year, when £8,000 had been raised. Initially, there were requests to the local councils for donations and much of the earlier fundraising was through 'Interest' evenings, games evenings, bingo sessions and small informal gatherings, often accompanied by raffles.

Mary Morris and Joyce Mowbray are two of the longest-serving members and are still active members. Mary Morris remembers the Young League being formed in 1985 with Vickie Cunnane as their leader. It was the "fun squad" and they held keep fit evenings at the Ocean Rooms and a bed-push each year from Northgate Hospital to the Pleasure Beach and back.

Initially, there was no hospital shop and a fortnightly stall was set up in the hospital foyer. The gifts sold were goods donated by the public. Regular Scrabble evenings were another source of revenue. In 1990, the Friends had stalls on Yarmouth Market and at the Bygone Village. Raffle tickets were sold in the hospital foyer and plants were sold which had been grown by the Occupational Therapy Department in the greenhouse supplied by the Friends. A model railway exhibition was held in the Burrage Centre.

In 1991, Brackley Brass Band gave a performance in Trinity Church, Lowestoft; there were several coffee mornings; and a wheelchair marathon from Cromer to the Pier Hotel in Gorleston by Dave Percival raised £3,000.

In 1992, the Friends took over the organisation of the Hospital Fete from the Hospital Social Club and raised £7,500. They continued to organise the Fete over the next 10 years. Many jumble sales were organised.

In 1993, the Friends had its own shop in the hospital foyer and it is through here that most of its income is now generated. They also receive donations, large and small, from members of the public.

Over the years there have been hardly any departments or wards in the hospital which have not benefited from money raised by the Friends. The list of equipment and facilities donated would be too large to mention, but a sample of those donations include:

- Greenhouse for Occupational Therapy and Rehabilitation.
- Cancer treatment equipment of many and various kinds.
- Cancer counselling facilities.
- Conservatory Room for patient comfort (Ward 6).
- Patient Discharge Lounge and reclining leather chairs (Ward 4).
- Patient Waiting Rooms and furniture (Ward 8).
- Relatives Room at the Mortuary completely refurbished, with access to the garden.
- Large donations to all Public Appeals.
- Substantial funding to Sandra Chapman Centre and Ward 17.

- Blood cleansing apparatus for theatres for use in transfusion services.
- Ultrasound equipment.
- Special furniture for the larger patients.
- Low beds.
- Numerous hoists for movement of patients.
- New curtains for the Oulton Unit.
- Numerous smaller items.

Over the years, over £900,000 has been collected and used to purchase items for the benefit of patients and staff. This is an enormous achievement from a small group of very dedicated individuals.

At present there are 28 active members but, as they say, they "are an ageing group". New members are needed and it would be marvellous if the Young League could be re-launched.

Women's Royal Volunteer Service

From information supplied by Andrea Allen

The keys to the WRVS shop in the foyer were handed over by Peter Harrison, the Commissioning Officer, on 21st December 1981, the first day the hospital opened to patients. It was more of a kiosk and was where the League of Friends now has its shop. The new shop was opened in 1993 and is on the opposite side of the foyer from where it used to be and by this time the WRVS had raised £165,000.

The WRVS has over 70 volunteers. Some prefer to work in the shop; others like to go round the wards with either the paper trolley or sweet trolley.

In 1984, the WRVS made its first gift to the hospital. It was for £12,295 and was for furnishing the new Endoscopy Suite at the end of the Day and Emergency Ward. Many gifts, totalling over £317,000, have been made over the years and a decision is awaited to see whether the present shop will be extended or refurbished. In either case, the WRVS will be using some of its funds to facilitate this.

Among the gifts and facilities it has help to provide are:

- Various endoscopes.
- Conservatory and greenhouse.

- Various beds and pressure-relieving mattresses.
- Different types of monitoring equipment.
- Donations to many appeals.
- ECG machines.
- Defibrillator.
- Bladder scanner.
- Patient information booklets.
- Spectrophotometer for Microbiology Department.
- Centrifuge for Haematology Department.
- Microscope for Cytology Screening.
- Headlight to aid surgery.
- Video diagnostic and treatment equipment.
- Various hoists.
- Arthroscopic surgery sets for Orthopaedics.

Rainbow Days

Rainbow Days has been going for five years and is run by Jill Jacobs and Dave Hughes. They man a stall in the hospital foyer four days a week and attend fetes in the local area to raise money for the hospital. For the last few years they have organised the annual hospital fete. In the last five years they have raised nearly £90,000 and £29,000 of this went to the ITU Appeal. Now they are raising money for the Palliative Care Unit Appeal.

PIGGY

People in Gorleston and Great Yarmouth (PIGGY) was founded in 1975 by Aideen Wayne to raise money on alternate years for the hospitals and the community. It was based around an annual charity football match between the Dennis Waterman XI and a local team. Among the equipment bought was the first cardiac pacemaker in the area, and the first mobile infant incubator so that babies could be transported more safely to Norwich, Cambridge or Great Ormond Street Hospital in London. Sadly, Aideen died and in her memory a pig was made by local sculpture, Barry Sutton, which now resides in the foyer of the hospital.

Facilities Provided by Public Appeals

Over the years the hospital has benefited from the great generosity of the local population and the local papers have played a big part in this by publishing lists of contributors and photographs of various presentations and activities which people have got up to in aid of fundraising.

CT Scanner

Only Addenbrooke's and Ipswich had a CT Scanner in East Anglia when the appeal was launched for £370,000, and £500,000 was raised in just over six months. It had been thought that it would take at least two years to raise the money and there was no budget for the revenue for the running costs until then. Some of the money raised enabled the Scanner to be used for the first 18 months by paying for the revenue costs. In spite of stopping the appeal, money still came in and, by the time it was necessary to replace the CT Scanner and install an MRI Scanner, there was already one million pounds in the fund.

Renal Unit

Dr. Wayne set up this appeal before the hospital had been built. £350,000 was raised over 15 years and provided a new building with six beds for renal dialysis. It was opened on 1st July 1991.

Sandra Chapman Unit

£500,000 was raised by a public appeal. The campaign was spearheaded by Dr. Terry Mitchell, Consultant Haematologist. It is an extension to Ward 17 which provides outpatient facilities and a lounge for patients receiving oncology and haematology treatment. The idea was suggested by Sandra Chapman, Deaconess for Hopton and Corton, while she was undergoing chemotherapy. It was opened in January 1992 by the Bishop of Norwich.

Conservatory for Wards 15 and 16

This was constructed in 1993 and cost £30,000. The WRVS gave £10,000, the League of Friends £3,000 and £570 came from the Pharmacy from the sale of Christmas badges. The Staff of Wards 15 and 16 raised the rest of the money by organising various functions. It was constructed alongside the existing Day Room and provides extra space and facilities for the elderly patients and their visitors.

Endoscopy Appeals

The WRVS paid for the equipping of the first proper Endoscopic Suite in the James Paget in 1984.

In 1991, an appeal was launched to raise money for new endoscopes. Prior to this, the image was transferred up the endoscopes by fibreoptic bundles and it was seen by looking into the end of the instrument. Alternatively, and more commonly, a television camera was attached to the endoscope and the pictures were seen on a TV screen. The new endoscopes had a little microchip at the distal end of the instrument which picked up the image and transferred it by wires to a computer which analysed it and displayed it on the TV screen. Much of the money for this came from a legacy of an old patient of the hospital.

Breast Care Unit Appeal

This was launched on 9th May 1993 and raised £150,000 in the next year so that the unit was able to open on 1st April 1994. It provided on-site mammography facilities and became the centre for organising Breast Screening for the District.

Scanner Appeal

The appeal was started on 10th April 1995 to raise £500,000 to replace the old CT Scanner and to obtain an MRI Scanner. This was added to the £1,000,000 which was remaining from the original appeal.

Mammography Screening Van

This cost £110,000 and was bought by Big 'C' with a contribution from the James Paget Healthcare NHS Trust. Big 'C' gave £75,000 and a group of volunteers was formed in November 1997, under the Chairmanship of John Wells, to raise money locally to pay back Big 'C'. The group did this in less than two years and continues to raise money for Big 'C'.

ITU Appeal

The appeal was launched in May 2000 to raise £600,000 for equipment for the Unit which was being built inside the old Ward 22, or Day and Emergency Ward, which it was called originally. Among the various activities organised to raise the money were antique fairs, fetes, a summer ball, fashion shows, football matches and a charity stall in the hospital foyer. The appeal reached its target the day John Wells retired on 31st October, with a cheque for £10,000 from the hospital's WRVS shop. The total bill for the project was £1,800,000.

Local Big 'C' Fundraising Committee

This was formed in November 1997 under the Chairmanship of John Wells. Since then it has raised £150,000 for Big C.

The Palliative Care East Centre Appeal

This is the current hospital appeal for which the aim is to raise £1.5m to build a centre in the grounds of the James Paget University Hospital which will provide a much-needed care base for patients and their families in the Great Yarmouth and Waveney area.

Palliative Care supports patients and their families whose lives are affected by cancer and other life-threatening illnesses. It is about making the end of life worth living by helping patients and families to come to terms with the situation and to live out the time that remains as fully as possible. Palliative Care offers a holistic approach to care, including not only physical assessment and effective pain management but also emotional, psychological and practical support.

First-class clinical care will go hand-in-hand with skilful and compassionate listening and include complementary therapies as well as exposure to art, music and a beautiful garden. Professionals and volunteers will be working together under the same roof as Macmillan Nurses and Palliative Care Specialist Doctors who will see patients for clinical assessment and effective management of their symptoms as well as support their emotional needs and answer questions about illness, treatment and the way ahead.

Physiotherapy and occupational therapy will be at hand to help with issues of mobility and physical rehabilitation. Where families need help with social care, financial shortfalls and benefits, the Family Support Worker will provide advice and practical support.

Well-trained volunteers will give time and space to patients and their loved ones and allow them to share their journey and express feelings and concerns, hopes and dreams. Complementary Therapy Practitioners will offer acupuncture, reflexology and aromatherapy, as well as explore art and music therapy.

~ 10 ~

Twenty-Five Years of Change

In the last 25 years the Health Service has changed out of all recognition. This has been the result of the changes affecting diseases, the way they are investigated and treated and the way that the Health Service is managed. Many of these changes have been mentioned earlier, but here these changes are brought together.

Diseases

Diseases have altered in their presentation and in their incidence over the years. Lung cancer in men is on the decline, probably due to fewer people smoking; yet the incidence in women continues to rise. The incidence of cancer of the mouth and larynx – also smoking-related – is also declining. Tuberculosis reached an all-time low in the 1970s, but started to increase in some areas of the UK where there was a high immigrant population and now more cases are being seen in Great Yarmouth and Waveney. Duodenal ulcer is seen much less commonly in hospitals nowadays, probably due to the availability of effective drugs, and then it usually presents as a complication with bleeding or perforation of the ulcer as a consequence of taking non-steroidal anti-inflammatory drugs, which have been given to the elderly with arthritis.

Gastric cancer now occurs more frequently in the upper part of the stomach, whereas 25 years ago it occurred more frequently in the lower stomach; and the incidence of oesophageal cancer increases each year. Is this something to do with the diet? The incidence of cancer of the breast, bowel and prostate has not changed greatly, but the National Breast Screening Programme has resulted in many tumours being detected at an earlier stage, which means that there is a greater chance of more conservative treatment as well as the prospect of a better chance of a cure. A screening programme for bowel cancer has recently started following trials, conducted by Jack Hardcastle and his team in Nottingham, which showed that screening resulted in tumours being detected earlier and lives being saved.

Pancreatitis, which is an inflammation of the pancreas, occurs much more frequently. It is mainly associated with gall stones and alcohol. By contrast, the incidence of infectious diseases in children has declined, due to immunisations and better living conditions. However, Acquired Immunodeficiency Syndrome (AIDs) was not discovered until 1981 in America. Since then, it, and the human immunodeficiency virus (HIV) which causes it, have spread throughout the world and the incidence in East Anglia, although low compared with many parts of the UK, continues to rise.

As the population ages, the diseases of old age, such as arthritis and cataract, increase. In addition, obesity is becoming much more common, which leads to diabetes, hypertension, heart attacks and strokes, as well as increased damage to the joints. A recent study also suggests it predisposes to cancer.

This small review of a number of diseases shows how incidences can change quite markedly in just a few years. This makes it difficult to plan for the future, but one point is clear. Many of these diseases and conditions are preventable. Stopping smoking, improving the diet and taking more exercise would be extremely beneficial to the individual and to the public at large. Also, a reduction in promiscuity and more sensible attitudes towards sexual intercourse would lower the incidence of teenage pregnancies and reverse the spiralling rise in sexually transmitted diseases. Money spent on campaigns to improve lifestyle could prevent suffering, reduce the bills for drugs, operations, radiotherapy, sick pay and social services and dramatically improve the nation's health. Individuals need to be more responsible for their own health rather than relying upon and expecting the NHS to provide all the solutions. It seems wrong that money and facilities to unblock a lady's fallopian tube or to provide her with IVF - where here failure to conceive is the result of

STI blocking her tubes due to her promiscuous way of life - may be diverted from providing cancer treating drugs or helping prevent a person going blind.

Investigations

The CT and MRI Scanners have revolutionised the investigation of patients. They produce much better pictures than the more traditional X-rays and, as far as cancer is concerned, will show how far the tumour has spread locally and whether it has spread further. This has made an enormous difference in planning the treatment of a patient. The scans also help to assess how well the patient is doing after the initial treatment. These scans have replaced more invasive investigations. An MRI scan will accurately show whether a disc, bone or tumour is pressing on the spinal cord or a nerve and has made the myelogram obsolete. This investigation involved inserting a needle into the patient's back and injecting a liquid, which would show up on X-ray, into fluid around the spinal cord and its main nerves. A high-quality CT Scan can demonstrate blood vessels, so avoiding many angiograms, which are invasive X-rays involving the injection of liquids into arteries or veins.

In the past, X-ray images were recorded on films and one person might have a large number, which was heavy and cumbersome to transport around the hospital. It was also difficult to find the right films among a large collection. Picture Archiving Communication System (PACS) has changed all that. The image is recorded digitally and transferred to a central computer, so allowing the image to be seen anywhere that there is an appropriate screen connected to the computer. It also enables the images to be manipulated – enlarging part of an image or going through a whole sequence of images – and for them to be transferred easily and instantly to another hospital which has the same system.

Investigations performed on blood are important in assessing most diseases. Once the sample of blood has been taken, the tests can be performed anywhere there is the appropriate machinery. These analysers are very expensive, so it makes financial sense to centralise them, providing there is an efficient and cheap means of transport between the hospital and the laboratory. Some years ago, blood samples from some of the London clinics were sent to America via Concorde each evening and the results were available the next morning. Fortunately, 99.4% of blood tests are carried out at the James Paget, and this is important when results are required urgently. Having the tests performed on site makes it possible for clinicians and laboratory staff to communicate much more easily.

By contrast, the histopathological services have moved to Norwich and communication has to rely on teleconferencing and the telephone. Direct contact with the Pathologist and discussion over the specimen is no longer possible. The move was necessitated by the increasing need for pathologists to become more specialised and due to the shortage of histopathologists. At the same time, the laboratory at the new Norfolk and Norwich University Hospital was inadequate and the opportunity was taken to take over an empty building on the University Science Park and amalgamate the two departments.

Thus, there have been many technical advances in the methods by which patients are investigated, but the machines are increasingly expensive and this may lead to further amalgamation and centralisation.

Treatment

There have been dramatic changes in treatment. Forty years ago, most hospitals frequently performed operations on patients whose peptic ulcers were resistant to treatment. The operations involved removing a large amount of the stomach or cutting nerves to it. Unfortunately, although this cured most ulcers, many people had side effects from the operations. These operations were still done when the hospital was opened but, with the discovery of the bacterium helicobacter pylori and the development of more effective drugs, the only need nowadays for operating on the stomach is for cancer or for complications such as bleeding from or perforation of an ulcer. As these operations are performed so infrequently, the average surgeon now has little experience of doing these types of operations, hence the move to try and centralise such surgery in specialised centres.

Drugs have also reduced the need for other operations. For example, alpha blockers can improve a man's urinary flow and reduce or delay the need for him to have his prostate removed. However, these drugs are not

cheap and the cost of treatment for one or two years would probabl
cover the price of the operation. The way an operation is performed ha
also changed. Most prostate glands which are causing difficulty i
passing urine are dealt with by means of a transurethral resection of th
prostate (TURP). This involves passing a telescope up the urethra an
cutting away strips of the prostate with a wire connected to an electri
current. Alternatively, an 'open' procedure may be done through a
incision in the lower part of the abdomen, allowing the prostate to b
removed in one or two pieces. When the hospital was opened, all fou
general surgeons performed these operations and, although the majorit
were performed as TURPs, many were still performed as open proce
dures. Nowadays, all urological operations are performed by Urologist
and an open prostatectomy is rarely done. Now, a patient goes hom
within one to three days of having a TURP, whereas he would spend fiv
to six days in hospital after an open procedure.

This shorter stay applies to all forms of surgery and is the result o
newer operations, new ways of doing them, better anaesthetics and th
realisation that a patient does not need to stay in hospital for a long tim
after an operation. Forty years ago, many patients stayed in hospital fo
up to three weeks after a hernia repair.

Cataract surgery is a prime example of a shortened stay. For the firs
10 years that the hospital was open most patients had a general anaes
thetic and stayed in hospital for a week. With newer operation tech
niques, and by performing the operation under local anaesthetic, almos
all patients are done as day cases and beds have been replaced b
comfortable armchairs. The newer techniques can be done much
quicker, so double the number of cataract operations can be done on a
operating list.

Since 1991, laparoscopy has had a major impact on surgery. Befor
then, removal of the gall bladder required an incision in the uppe
abdomen and most patients remained in hospital for three to five days
Laparoscopic cholecystectomy is performed through four tiny incisions
so the cosmetic result is far better and the pain is much less. Many
patients are dealt with as day cases and the majority of the rest go home
the next day. The laparoscopic approach has been extended to repairin
hernias, removing the spleen, kidneys and parts of the bowel as well a
many other operations. Gynaecologists used laparoscopic method

before the general surgeons for doing such procedures as sterilisation, oophorectomy and, more recently, hysterectomy. However, for many years the uterus has been removed through operations performed through the vagina. More recently, procedures have been devised to either remove the lining of the uterus with cautery (rather like a TURP) or by destroying the lining with a technique known as endometrial ablation. In both cases, the uterus remains and the procedures are carried out by passing instruments into the uterus through the vagina. These operations cause minimal disturbance to the patient and are done either as day cases or in the outpatient clinic.

Endoscopy is very valuable for aiding diagnosis and is also used for treatment, e.g. inserting feeding tubes into the stomach (PEGs), removing polyps from the colon and rectum and procedures can be done to prevent gastro-oesophageal reflux or to deal with pharyngeal pouches. Previously, all these were open procedures requiring at least several days in hospital.

Over the last 25 years, anaesthetics have improved, so aiding the patient's recovery with fewer side effects. Spinal and epidural anaesthetics are used much more frequently, along with blocks of nerves with local anaesthetic. These techniques may be combined with some sedation, so that the patient is not aware of what is going on in theatre. The problem with these anaesthetics is that it may take much longer to prepare the patient for the operating theatre, with the result that the surgeon is not operating for much of the time. This is especially the case in orthopaedic operations, when it takes a considerable length of time to place the patient in a particular position before the operation can start. Mr. John Petri overcame this problem by using two theatres, so that while he was operating in one the following patient was being prepared next door. This worked very well and by also increasing the length of his operating time he was able to operate on many more patients. This has led to the abolishment of his waiting list. Unfortunately, this system is expensive in terms of theatres and staff used, so dual anaesthetists are being tried out. This involves only one theatre and anaesthetic room and while an operation is being finished in the theatre another anaesthetic team is preparing the next patient in the anaesthetic room.

Post-operative pain is one of the serious side effects of an operation and this has been greatly helped by the use of Patient-Controlled Analgesia (PCA). The James Paget was one of the first hospitals in the country to use this technique. It has improved post-operative pain relief and has saved many hours of nurses' time which were spent assessing the patient's needs for pain relief, drawing up the drugs, having them checked and then giving them to the patient.

Many of the above techniques have increased the numbers of patients having day case surgery and now about 80% of elective procedures are done this way. However, it requires that the patient desires it and that arrangements are in hand to overcome any subsequent problems.

Hormones have been used for treating certain types of breast and prostate cancer for many years and, more recently, newer and more effective ones have become available. Chemotherapy is given much more frequently than in the past and, with newer agents, it is more effective. There are, also, better ways of dealing with the side effects. Measuring certain substances in the blood, such as carcino-embryonic antigen after colorectal surgery, can also help to assess the efficacy of the treatment.

Radiotherapy is given much more accurately now, due to the benefit of computer planning of the treatment. This has resulted in fewer side effects. Most radiotherapy is given in Norwich but for a year or two before the move to the new Norfolk and Norwich University Hospital there were some prolonged delays in people starting their radiotherapy. Some patients overcame this delay by receiving their radiotherapy in Ipswich. At present there are trials to assess the value of giving radiotherapy in the operating theatre after the tumour has been removed from the breast. If the effectiveness of the early results of this trial is confirmed, it means that the patient will not have to undergo several weeks of radiotherapy when they have recovered from the operation. The only problem is that there are no facilities for delivering radiotherapy at the James Paget, although the possibility was looked at some years ago. Perhaps this issue should be looked at again.

Multi-Disciplinary Team meetings have been one of the big developments in managing patients with cancer in the last 10 years. There is a team for each body site, e.g. breast, colorectal, lung, urology, gynaecology, etc. Usually, these meetings are held weekly when surgeons, physicians, radiologists, oncologists, histopathologists and nurse care specialists gather to discuss all patients newly diagnosed and those for whom further results are available or for people who have developed another tumour. These meetings bring together the local specialists, along with the results, so helping to make the right decision about the further management of each patient. Unfortunately, the move of the Histopathology Department to Norwich has meant that communication is by teleconferencing. In some meetings, the oncologists also communicate by this means, rather than being present at the James Paget. After the meeting, the patients are brought up to the hospital to explain what plans have been suggested.

The introduction of the Specialist Care Nurse has been a great advance in the last 10 to 15 years. They have the knowledge, the time and the sensitivity to spend more time with the patient and relatives to explain what is going on. They run their own clinics and their introduction has greatly benefited patients with, e.g., stomas, incontinence, asthma, tracheotomies and diabetes.

Over the years, there has been an increasing emphasis on quality. More time is given to explaining to patients and their relatives what is happening and what is to be done. This has been helped by giving them leaflets or booklets about their condition and details about the procedures planned. In the past, consent to a procedure involved the patient signing a piece of paper. Now, emphasis is very much on <u>informed</u> consent. The sheets of paper are very much larger, an explanation of the possible complications has to be given and the patient has a copy of the consent. All of this is very time-consuming, but is necessary. However, with the way that this is going it will probably be necessary to have a written consent before a doctor may talk to a patient!

Increasingly, it is appreciated that privacy and dignity for patients is important and ways of achieving this are being sought. There are signs on curtains around the beds indicating that the patient is not to be disturbed at certain times and it is unusual to have both males and females in the same bay, except in the Emeregency Assessment and Discharge Unit. Unfortunately, it is not possible to increase the number of toilets and bathrooms on each ward without a major refurbishment and, although this is planned, it will take up to two years to modernise all the wards.

Management of Health Service

The management of the Health Service has changed many times over the years. Centrally, there is the Department of Health and when the hospital was built the cascade of command was via the Regional Health Authority to the Area Health Authority (AHA) and then to the Great Yarmouth and Waveney Health District. On 1st April 1982, the AHA was abolished, giving more power to the newly formed Great Yarmouth and Waveney Health Authority. Initially, most of the management was housed at the Great Yarmouth and Waveney Health Authority Headquarters at Havenbridge House, Great Yarmouth. For the first year, the two managers in the hospital were Sally Cockrell, as Senior Nursing Officer, and Peter Harrison, as Administrator. A year later, the team was Sally Cockrell, Tony Wilson, as Unit Manager, and Consultant Surgeon John Corson. This continued until 1984, when Arthur Lawn, Unit Estates Manager, joined the Unit Management Team. The following year, Andrew Butcher was appointed as Unit Manager and the number of Managers started to increase. On 1st April 1993, the hospital achieved more independence by becoming an NHS Trust and with it more clinicians were brought into management roles.

A few years later, the East Anglian Regional Health Authority merged with Oxford and Bedfordshire to form a banana-shaped region stretching across most of England and necessitating moving the various headquarters to a new one at Milton Keynes. No sooner was this accomplished, than Regional Health Authorities were replaced by Strategic Health Authorities (SHAs) and the western part of the banana was amputated and the Eastern SHA was formed by taking in areas south down to London. On 1st August 2006, the James Paget became a Foundation Trust. This gave it even more independence. No longer was it responsible to the SHA, but it now reports to Monitor in London and when all Trusts become Foundation Trusts the SHAs will cease to exist.

This is a shortened account of the changes in health management and indicates the disruption that this must have caused to all concerned in the various upheavals. Each change meant that large numbers of people had to reapply for their jobs. It was all supposed to be more efficient and to reduce the number of managerial and administrative jobs. However, this was not done without great expense in providing new headquarters, relocation expenses and redundancy packages. Nevertheless, it did bring many of the decisions and responsibilities down to the grass roots with a corresponding increase in the number of managers in the individual Trusts.

Margaret Thatcher and the Conservative Government introduced the 'Internal Market' in the 1980s, thinking that competition would improve efficiency. In 1992, the Government, under John Major, set targets to reduce Coronary Heart Disease and Strokes, Cancer, HIV/AIDS and Sexual Health, Mental Disease and Accidents. However, the Internal Market tended to be rather divisive and the system was dismantled by the incoming Labour Government in 1997. It poured a great deal of extra money into the Health Service, much of which went on increased salaries, but with it the James Paget obtained two new CT Scanners and a new MRI Scanner, as well as money for modernising the Accident and Emergency Unit, among other improvements. The Government introduced increasingly stringent targets to reduce waiting times for patients with suspected cancer to be seen and for those with cancer to start treatment within 31 days of being informed of the diagnosis. The waiting time for patients to be seen in outpatient clinics was up to a year or more when the hospital was first opened. Now it is less than thirteen weeks. Twenty five years ago patients were waiting one to two years for treatment yet now the majority are treated in less than three months and no one is waiting more than six months. By the end of next year it is expected that everyone will be treated within eighteen weeks of being referred by their GP. In addition, people attending Accident and Emergency Departments had to be admitted or be discharged within four hours.

The Government transferred the power of how to spend the money to Primary Care Trusts and, of course, they needed offices and large numbers of managers. The Government also brought back competition in the form of Independent Treatment Centres, the use of established private hospitals for NHS patients, paying for patients to receive treatment abroad and for the patient to choose from a number of hospitals where they would like to be treated. Initially, the Independent Treatment Centres could not be staffed by Consultants working for the Health Service, so many of the operations were done by foreign staff with variable ability. They are heavily subsidised by the Government, with income guaranteed for five years, irrespective of the number of patients treated. They have the potential to take away the 'bread and butter' operations from the local Trust and reduce the opportunities for learning by the junior Medical staff. Fortunately, there is no Independent Treatment Centre near the James Paget, but the Strategic Health Authority is discussing setting up three near Norwich, Newmarket and Peterborough. It is planned that each would do ten million pounds worth of work annually and it is thought that this would take away two million pounds of revenue from the James Paget each year.

Other changes in the last 25 years have been the increased numbers of Consultants, Nurses and Managers. Consultant numbers have doubled at the James Paget, and this has been the case throughout the country. As a result, there has been a shortage of applicants for posts in the last 10 years and the Trust has had to resort to advertising abroad for many of the posts. It is interesting that many of these doctors have moved to other jobs after a few years. However, it is encouraging that recently there have been many more applicants for the posts advertised and their quality seems much better.

Just under 10 years ago there was a shortage of nurses and expeditions were made to Australia, the Philippines, India and Spain to recruit. Ironically, now the Trust is having difficulty in placing all the nurses it has trained. The Government is constantly producing new targets and an increasing number of managers and staff are required to record, monitor and produce the figures and oversee ways of trying to keep within targets. Many of these managers are nurses but an increasing number of senior managers have come up the NHS management ladder having started off in junior management positions. In every Trust there is an increasing number of clinicians who are spending a substantial amount of their time in management. Although this takes them away from many of their clinical duties it does mean that their opinions are heard at the highest level.

With the reduction in hours that junior doctors are permitted to work it has become difficult to maintain medical cover 24 hours a day. The ENT Surgeons have overcome this difficulty by closing down the ENT Department at the James Paget over the weekends, with emergencies being referred to Norwich. Increasingly, nurses are being trained to take on more duties which were done by doctors. Already this has happened in the Accident and Emergency Department, the Intensive Treatment Unit and the Emergency Assessment and Discharge Unit. Such changes in the ways in which work is done will be essential in making the 'Hospital at Night' concept work.

This brief review of some aspects of the Health Service has indicated that changes are continually occurring throughout all aspects of the service. This makes it extremely difficult to plan for the future. What is certain is that it is essential that all ideas and schemes should be adaptable and flexible so that the hospital can meet the challenges of the future.

Achievements and Successes

How do you measure achievement and success? Achievement involves accomplishing or carrying out a feat or task or attaining a desired level of performance. Similarly, success involves the accomplishment of an aim. By any standard, the Trust has been very successful. It has had three stars in three of the last four years; it became a Foundation Trust last year and is now a University Hospital. It has met almost all the targets set for it by the Department of Health and has remained in financial balance since it became a NHS Trust in 1993. All these achievements have been made over a very long period.

This success results from a combination of good management, good clinical work, commitment to education and the wonderful support of the local population. Above all, it has depended on the dedication of all the staff working in the hospital. These different aspects will be looked at separately.

The managers of the hospital have had the good fortune of working well with the clinicians, other health professionals and other staff. Initially, when the hospital was new, there were few managers and most of the Consultants were young and enthusiastic to produce the best service available. The hospital was successful in attracting two first rate chief executives who, between them, held the post for over 12 years. Nationally, a NHS Trust Chief Executive stays in post for an average of less than three years. This gave the Trust stability and was backed up by John Wells, who was Chairman for over 10 years – a national record.

There has not been too much of 'them and us', although there have been the odd jibes about 'carpet city' which refers to the old and cheap carpet on the floor between the senior managers' offices. Since Adrian Pennington started on 1st April 2007, he has encouraged dialogue with the staff, has weekly sessions which any member of staff can attend and frequently he is seen walking around the hospital getting to know the staff and see any problems at first hand. This augurs well for the future.

Clinically, the hospital has frequently been a leader. It was the first in East Anglia to provide a Stoma Care Service and Gail Hunting, the first Sister in that Department, gave advice to and visited all hospitals in East Anglia during the early years of her appointment. The James Paget was one of a few hospitals to pioneer Patient-Controlled Analgesia (PCA) and at one time had more PCA pumps than any other hospital in the country, thanks to the generosity of the local population. For many years the James Paget was the only hospital in East Anglia to provide mammograms for its NHS patients, as a result of an agreement with the North Sea Medical Centre, which was paid for by money raised by the local population. The Pain Relief Clinic has a national and international reputation and the Retinal Screening Programme for diabetic patients was years ahead of its time when it was set up in 1987.

The Audiology Department was one of only a few centres to assess digital hearing aids and subsequently was involved in assessing children's hearing services. More recently, it has been one of a number of centres participating in universal neonatal hearing screening. This is a great achievement for a Department which, when the hospital opened, was run from Norwich and the only permanent member of staff was the student audiologist, Jenette Powell, who now runs the Department.

The Critical Care Score was pioneered at the James Paget. This is calculated from a number of observations which are routinely recorded on a patient. It warns if a patient is deteriorating and so can trigger action by the nursing and medical staff. It is a simple system and has been taken up by many other hospitals.

The hospital had a big struggle to provide its own Breast Care Unit and Breast Screening Service, but in recent years its results bring it into the top three in the whole of the Eastern Region. Mr. Jerome Pereira was the first Breast Surgeon in a District General Hospital in East Anglia to offer breast reconstruction. Prior to this, most reconstruction was performed by Plastic Surgeons many months after the original Surgery. Mr. Pereira offered reconstruction at the time of the original surgery. He audited his results, encouraged other hospitals to participate in the audit, and now there is a national audit of breast reconstruction of which he is the Lead Clinician.

The Orthotics Department was the first to trial Lycra gloves for children with cerebral palsy and is trialling the use of Lycra leggings in patients who have had strokes. It is also involved in pioneering work with the use of Botox injections in children with cerebral palsy.

Charter Marks were introduced by John Major's Government to reward excellent service and these have been awarded to the Tracheostomy Support Service, the Breast Nursing Service, the Children's Ward, the Day Case Eye Service and the Sandra Chapman Unit, among others.

Success can come out of tragedy and this seems to be the case with the recent outbreak of Clostridium difficile, which hit the headlines at the end of March 2007. Well before this time, the hospital was aware that there was a problem and traced it to a virulent strain of Clostridium. It instituted new methods of cleaning, isolation and reducing the number of beds in certain bays from six to four. These measures quickly brought the outbreak to an end and at the time of writing the Trust probably has the lowest incidence of this disease in the country. So impressed are the Strategic Health Authority and the Department of Health, that the latter is to publish a booklet, written by the Trust, about how the outbreak was tackled and giving advice to other Trusts in how to deal with similar outbreaks and, more importantly, how to prevent them occurring.

Many members of staff have sat on the Councils or been officers of their regulatory body or college, which is recognition of the work they have done for their speciality and enables them to exert an influence nationally. Increasingly, hospital Trusts are cutting down on allowing their staff to fulfil these functions. This is unfortunate for the national organisations, but it prevents the Trusts exerting their influence nationally. Clearly, a person must not neglect his or her duties to their patients and the Trust, but there is much to be gained by this involvement for all concerned.

The Trust's commitment to education has increased over the years, but has taken off with the development of the Medical School at the University of East Anglia. The education facilities in the centre of the hospital and in the Burrage Centre became insufficient and the new Education and Training Unit has been an overdue addition. Many departments help in the teaching of students in their own speciality and even more are involved in teaching the Medical students.

Throughout its existence, the hospital has been most fortunate in the support it has had from the local population. The people regard it as 'our' hospital and have supported all its appeals for equipment, departments and new buildings with great enthusiasm. It might be asked why they should pay for health service improvements when already they pay their taxes. The consequences are that this hospital has many facilities which other hospitals do not have and these have been provided by the generosity of people living nearby. The additional benefit is that the process of raising the money can be fun and generates many new friendships. In addition, many do voluntary work for the hospital either through the Friends of the Hospital, the WRVS, Rainbow Days or work as volunteers at reception, in clinics or anywhere else they can be helpful. It is interesting that so many of the developments over the last 20 years have resulted from voluntary appeals, e.g. mammography and the breast unit, retinal screening for diabetics, the CT and MR Scanners, the ITU appeal, the endoscopy appeals, etc.

Patients also help by participating in patient-help groups such as the BRAS, Heartcare, Ostomy Support Group, Breatheasy, Tracheostomy Support Group, etc. Patients who have had an illness or a cancer know what it is like to be told the diagnosis and to go through a course of treatment. Therefore, they are in a privileged position to help patients who have been newly diagnosed with the condition. These groups not only give support; most also arrange social activities and raise money for the cause.

Central to the success of any organisation is its staff and national annual staff satisfaction surveys show that the James Paget comes in the top 10% in the country and the satisfaction rating continues to improve. Similarly, national surveys among patients show that the majority of patients rate the service provided by the hospital as very good or good.

This section demonstrates that the hospital has good managers working with a motivated and innovative workforce which are providing a very good service for its patients and which is appreciated by them. Nevertheless, it is important not to be complacent and the Trust must continue in its efforts to make this a first class hospital.

~ 11 ~

The Future

The last 25 years have been a success story for the James Paget Hospital, but what does the future hold? There has been increasing specialisation, shorter working hours for junior Medical staff, increasing costs for drugs and equipment and now there is patient choice and the introduction of independent treatment centres. Added to this is the fact that the hospital is over 25 years old, with a life expectancy of 40 years when it was built. Each of these topics will be discussed in turn.

Increasing specialisation has been mentioned several times throughout this book. It affects most specialities. Mr. McDonald started work in Great Yarmouth in 1945. Not only did he do all the general surgery on the chest, abdomen, head and neck and limbs, he did much of the gynaecology as well as the post mortems. Operations on the chest are done by thoracic surgeons and elective operations on the chest have not been done at the James Paget for over 10 years. Now, general surgery has been subdivided into vascular, breast, colorectal, upper gastro-intestinal surgery and, although the older surgeons could deal very well with all aspects, the modern surgeon will have been trained in only one of these branches. Already, vascular surgery has been centralised in Norwich and only operations on varicose veins are performed at the James Paget. Most operations on the stomach are now for malignancy and it is likely in the not-too-distant future these operations will also be done in Norwich. Similarly, when Mr. Studley retires, operations on the pancreas will be centralised in one or two hospitals in East Anglia. At present, the designated ones are Addenbrooke's, Ipswich and Norwich, but if national guidelines are to be followed, it will eventually come down to only one of these hospitals. Already, operations on the liver are restricted to just Addenbrooke's and Norwich.

There is a great deal of expertise in breast surgery at the James Paget, particularly in breast reconstruction. One of the latest developments is sentinel node biopsy, which involves removing one or two nodes from the armpit (axilla) after they have been localised by the injection of a radioactive substance or a dye into the breast. At present, it requires patients going to Norwich to receive the injection as there is no radioactive laboratory at the James Paget. Unfortunately, most patients are reluctant to do this journey and are deciding to have the traditional operation on their axilla, while some have elected to go to Norwich for the operation. Although the results of localisation with only dye are nearly as good as with a radioactive injection, it is important to have this facility in the hospital and negotiations need to be made to have a nuclear medicine laboratory at the James Paget. This would be important if intra-operative radiotherapy is advocated after removal of breast tumours.

There is a big work-load with colorectal surgery with excellent support from the colorectal nurse specialists and the imaging department. Unfortunately, there has been no pouch surgery performed since Hugh Sturzaker's retirement and this operation is now performed in Norwich. The development of laparoscopic colorectal surgery has progressed little since Kevin Murray retired, but his successor, who starts in September, should carry this forward.

As far as Gynaecology is concerned, most operations for malignancy have been centralised in Norwich and are performed by oncological gynaecologists. The same is happening in Urology and, before long, all major surgery for malignancy affecting the kidneys, bladder and prostate will be done in Norwich. For some years now, Mr. Premachandra has performed most of the operations he does for head and neck cancer in Norwich.

In Orthopaedics, the majority of work involves replacement of worn-out hips and knees and this work will continue here. Operations on the back were done mainly by Mr. Heyse Moore and when he retired most of these were done in Norwich. However, in the last year, two Norwich surgeons do regular clinics and operating lists for back problems here. This has reversed the drift of surgery westwards. However, there is increasing specialisation in certain aspects of orthopaedics, such as hand surgery. With more hand problems in an ageing population, perhaps it would be worthwhile considering the appointment of a surgeon to deal with this aspect of surgery, although he or she will need the backup of specialised physiotherapists.

Most eye surgery deals with cataracts and there is little likelihood that this will not continue, although some of the very highly specialised surgery which is performed infrequently will continue to be referred elsewhere.

Peter Forster is being replaced by two rheumatologists and one has already been appointed, so it is likely that the work in this Department will be expanded.

At present, it seems unlikely that there is any threat to Dermatology, Gastro-enterology and Endoscopy. All have excellent Consultants and new Departments which are well run. Paediatrics continues to have specialists in most of its fields and liaises well with Norwich and other centres. Paediatric Surgery continues giving a good service for the simpler and more common paediatric operations.

The Pain Relief Service is well recognised nationally and it is unlikely that there will be any change in that in the immediate future. With the retirement of Wolf Grabau – although he will be returning to do outpatient clinics – Dr. Jesudason will be the sole Cardiologist, apart from a locum, but new appointments are expected. Since the hospital started, permanent cardiac pacemakers have been fitted in Norwich and, in recent years, cardiology has become much more invasive, necessitating patients going to Papworth and more recently to Norwich for angiography, angioplasty and stenting. It is unlikely that this service would be offered at the James Paget.

Oncology services are based in Norwich and the number of Consultant sessions held at the James Paget has quadrupled since the hospital opened. Most chemotherapy, which involves injections or infusions, is given on an outpatient basis in the Sandra Chapman Unit. A small proportion of treatments need to be given on an in-patient basis and as there is no oncological cover at the James Paget it has to be administered in Norwich. Agreement was made last year for the Trust to appoint an Oncologist who would be based at the James Paget and have some sessions in Norwich. This would give greater continuity of cover and would enable in-patient chemotherapy to be given here, provided there are the necessary oncologically trained nurses.

The hours that junior doctors are allowed to work has decreased in recent years and is due to reduce further within two years. This will produce extra strains on providing full cover over the 24 hours and the Eye Department feels that it will only be able to maintain its emergency service by coming to some arrangement with its colleagues in Norwich. The introduction of 'The Hospital at Night Project' will certainly help other departments to maintain cover.

The Medical School has been a great success and the James Paget has played a big part in this. It should ensure good quality junior Medical staff for the future and, hopefully, will add to the quality of the GPs and Medical Consultants in the years ahead. The research being done by the hospital staff is also increasing.

The future of the building also needs to be considered. When it was built, it had a life expectancy of 25, 40 or even 60 years, depending on who you spoke to. The roof at the Queen Elizabeth Hospital, Kings Lynn, is collapsing and there are plans to rebuild the hospital. The James Paget is built to the same design and, although it has been well maintained, it is not efficient in energy conservation and the layout of the wards leaves much to be desired. There are plans to improve this, but is it worthwhile spending millions of pounds on a structure which has a limited life? Would it be better to 'bite the bullet' and rebuild? If so, should this be done on adjacent land or somewhere else in co-operation with the local authorities of Great Yarmouth and Lowestoft, who are considering new buildings? If this were done it would be at least five to seven years before this could be completed and the present wards could not be left as they are. This is particularly so when patients can choose which hospitals they wish to be treated in. It is also a shame, considering all the work and money which has gone into developing the many departments and buildings over the years. These are difficult decisions, but the various options are already being looked at and a decision is expected by the Autumn.

When this story started, the Health Service provision for the people in the area was said to be the worst in the country. When the hospital opened, it had the longest waiting lists and although there have been a number of threats to its future, caused by the transfer of certain services to larger and more specialised hospitals, the James Paget has been a leader and innovator in many fields in the past and the Medical School has been a great success. The people of Great Yarmouth and Waveney have a hospital that by all standards is one of the best in the country and it has the good fortune to have a most supportive population which has given it so much. This success is reminiscent of James Paget, who grew up in Great Yarmouth and, in spite of his father's financial problems which interrupted his education, went on to become one of the most famous medical men in the country.

The people of Great Yarmouth and Waveney can be proud of the part they have played in the success of the James Paget University Hospital and let us hope that it can continue to build on the success of the last 25 years. As the great physician, Sir William Osler said; "The best preparation for tomorrow is to do today's work superbly well"

Bibliography

Birch, C.A. *Names We Remember,* Ravenswood Publications, 1979.

Buchanan W.W. Sir James Paget (1814–99): Surgical Osler? *Proc. R Coll. Physicians Edinb.* 1996; **26:** 91–114.

Crisp N. *Creating a patient-led NHS.* London: DoH, 2005.

Davies, P.P. *History of Medicine in Great Yarmouth. Hospitals anc Doctor.* Paul, P. Davies, 2003.

Edwards A. *The Way We Saw It. 125 years of the Great Yarmoutl Mercury 1880-2005.* Archant Regional Newspapers, 2006.

Ham C. Does the district general hospital have a future? *BMJ* 2005 **331**:1331–3.

Hedges A.A.C., Boon M, Meeres F. *Yarmouth is an ancient Town* Blackall Books, 2001.

Ministry of Health. *A hospital plan for England and Wales.* London HMSO, 1962.

Paget J. On the Disease of the Mammary Areola preceding Cancer o the Mammary Gland. St Bartholomew's Hospital Reports 1984 **10:** 87–89.

Petri DJ, Banerjee T.S. Dual Operating – An Old Innovation. *Ann R Col Surg Engl (Suppl)* 2006; **88:** 208–210.

Sturzaker H.G. Survival of the Fittest? *BMJ* 1979; **2:** 374–375.

Sturzaker H.G. Beds, bugs and bureaucracy. *Hospital Doctor* 6 Octobe 2005: 26–29.

DGH News 1-5 Commissioning Team of Great Yarmouth and Waveney Health District 1980–1981.

James Paget Hospital NHS Trust Annual Reports 1993–1997

James Paget Healthcare NHS Trust Annual Reports 1998–2006

James Paget University Hospitals NHS Foundation Trust Annual report 2006–2007

Making Waves, The Quarterly magazine from James Paget Hospital, December 1991–March 1993; The James Paget NHS Trust, June

1993–June1997; The James Paget Healthcare NHS Trust, September 1997–April 2006; James Paget University Hospitals NHS Foundation Trust, September 2006- March 2007.

Yarmouth Mercury and Great Yarmouth Mercury 1975–2007 Hicks, N.

Index

A

B

C

E

I

J

K

L

M

N

O

P

R

S

U

Y

Z